RARE
BIRDS
YEARBOOK
2009

www.rarebirdsyearbook.com

First published in UK in 2008 by
MagDig Media Limited

ISBN 978-0-9552607-5-9

Editor
Erik Hirschfeld

Design & technical production
Ingvar Ronde

BirdLife International
Jez Bird, Stuart Butchart (Science Coordination),
Martin Fowlie, Adrian Long (General Coordination),
Jim Lawrence, Gina Pfaff, John Sherwell

Features
Juan Ignacios (Nacho) Areta
Alejandro Bodrati, Kristina Cockle
Martin Davies, Erik Hirschfeld
Nick Langley , Blake Matheson
Don Roberson

Front cover photo
Blue-crowned Laughingthrush © Gregory Guida

Inside cover photo
Chatham Albatross © Alan Tate

Maps
All maps have been prepared
using Google Earth Pro and are based on shapefiles
provided by BirdLife International

MagDig Media Limited
1 Brassey Road
Old Potts Way, Shrewsbury
Shropshire SY3 7FA
ENGLAND

E-mail: editor@rarebirdsyearbook.com
www.rarebirdsyearbook.com

CONTENTS

FOREWORD

Each of us came to an awareness of birds in a different way – Margaret early in life, as she grew up in northern Quebec, among biologists; Graeme later, through a focusing of his childhood interest in nature, acquired in Muskoka and the Kawartha Lakes regions of Ontario. We agreed to become the Honorary Presidents of BirdLife International's Rare Bird Club because we are both convinced of the crucial importance, for world conservation efforts, of the detailed, highly informed, and effective work done by the BirdLife International Partnership.

In these times of environmental crisis, birds are the canaries in the coal mine: they are excellent indicators of the health and wealth of any given habitat, and when a species dwindles or disappears, it's a serious danger sign. If Nature were left to its own devices, it's true some species would become extinct, or would evolve into other species; but the natural rate of extinction or change would be one species every hundred years. Birds had been on Planet Earth for over two hundred million years by the time human beings arrived. They were superbly adapted to their living spaces, until we started altering those spaces. However, human actions – usually unintentional, but lethal all the same – are now causing an extinction rate that is 50 times the natural one. That is an enormous challenge to face and overcome, but the work of reversing extinction must be undertaken, for once a species is gone, it's gone forever.

In this respect, the BirdLife Partnership's tracking of bird species is essential, for how do you know whether a species is flourishing or fading unless you keep track? Through many years of dedicated and expert research, the BirdLife Partnership has assessed the status of every bird species in the world.

In addition, the Partnership's studies of the factors affecting the welfare of a species, and the implementation of effective recovery plans where necessary, have been instrumental in the recovery of some Critically Endangered birds. Just as human actions can cause extinctions, human actions can reverse them.
This edition of the Rare Birds Yearbook contains more than alerts and warnings; there is encouraging news as well.

The good-news story we know best (and warmly welcome) is a significant improvement in the Grenada Dove's chances for survival. This change is due to a very co-operative relationship that eventually developed amongst Dove researchers, the Project builders, the Government of Grenada, and BirdLife's Caribbean program. The major improvements include:

- A newly defined national park that looks stronger and more robust than the previous one at Mt Hartman.

- Significant modifications to the initial project design.

- Because the Four Seasons development will result in the habitat loss of four territorial male doves - the Grenada

Government is working hard to designate other critical habitat as a national park.

- It has been generally agreed on the need for an informed and authoritative Dove Trust, with the mandate and responsibility to allow for the Grenada Dove to increase its population. Negotiations on the establishment of this critical initiative continue.

Success stories such as this are examples of what the BirdLife Partnership can do, given sufficient resources. But those resources are not yet sufficient. Unfortunately, of the money donated to charity, ninety-seven percent goes to human-related causes, and, of the remaining three percent, half goes to our pets. That leaves one and a half percent for wild nature – all wild nature. It's time for us to alter that ratio. Companies, institutions, and individuals can all play a part.

We sincerely trust that the publication of the Rare Birds Yearbook will not only demonstrate the gravity of their situation for those birds on the brink of extinction, but will also inspire faith in their future. Many species have been brought back from the edge of death; many more can be. In almost all human cultures, birds have been a symbol of hope, and it is hope – and the action it generates – that we need for them now.

MARGARET ATWOOD   GRAEME GIBSON

HONORARY PRESIDENTS
RARE BIRD CLUB

INTRODUCTION

A year has passed since the first edition of Rare Birds Yearbook was published and the total number of Critically Endangered birds has increased to 190. Nothing is static in this world. The good news is that some birds have left the list, but it is unfortunate that one more species has been added to the total. Read the good news about those that have left on page 13 and keep your fingers crossed, as I do, that more species from this edition will join them when the 2010 edition is published. Another piece of good news which I am very happy about is that the Rare Birds Yearbook itself has become a Species Champion (see pp. 18-21). It is very satisfying for me to know that the birds featured in this book actually get

a financial return from it, which is made possible by you as a buyer of Rare Birds Yearbook. On behalf of the birds, I wish to thank everyone who buys this book and thereby helps the birds that feature in it. And, of course, I wish to thank everyone who has contributed to this book in different ways such as submitting photos and patiently replying to my many questions.

I hope that those of you who buy the 2009 edition and are also fortunate to own the 2008 edition will find that these two books differ so much from each other that it is definitely worth having them both. My personal challenge, which has kept me busy over the year that has passed, was to update as many facts as possible in the species accounts and to present completely new material relating to conservation in the features. Not to mention photos, the one important part of this book that I have not had full control over myself; I do not take pictures of birds, I just enjoy looking at them.

In some cases with the species covered here not much has happened since last time. Hooded Seedeater, for example, has not been recorded since the last edition. Consequently, rather than repeating what was said about that species in the 2008 edition, I have devoted more space to other species and features. The majority of photos (over 130 new photos in the accounts) have also been replaced thanks to the many, amateur and professional, photographers around the world who have responded to the call of the photo competition.

The brand new features this year cover varied topics such as the Californian Condor, philosophical conservation issues, the Preventing Extinctions initiative, an exciting encounter with one of the world's rarest birds of prey, the story of the world's largest bird fair, interactions between man and birds and the specialisation of bamboo-dependent species, such as Purple-winged Ground Dove. But we must not forget that there are a large number of birds that are not Critically Endangered, but still very rare and quite threatened. Therefore, I made my own, very subjective, selection of a number of these and present them in a special feature. Let us hope that you will never again read about them in Rare Birds Yearbook!

Finally, we must remember those diligent people who are working practically with bird conservation, often unpaid in unglamorous circumstances and driven by not much more than their own enthusiasm and love of birds. Many of them are organised in the BirdLife partnership, and a snapshot of eleven partner organisations and what occupies their minds is given on pages 234-245.

When I now see the final proofs and layouts after 2,200 emails and a six month-long production process, I feel confident I have met my goals in renewing the book.

The contacts with readers from all over the world has been very inspiring and I have made several changes in response to the feed-back. For example, the information on threats has been incorporated into the species' accounts rather than listed separately at the end, which has made more space available for updates and given greater clarity for readers.

Finally, I hope you will enjoy reading this book as much as I have enjoyed producing it and am looking forward to hearing from readers with views, news, suggestions, ideas for future features and general comments.

Malmö, Sweden, October 2008

ERIK HIRSCHFELD
EDITOR RARE BIRDS YEARBOOK
editor@rarebirdsyearbook.com

Acknowledgements

The following people have, in various ways, helped with producing Rare Birds Yearbook 2009 and are sincerely thanked.

Sue Abbott, Fredrik Ahlström, Ciro Albano, Per Alström, Fred Amidon, Dave Anderson, Tim Appleton, Pep Arcos, René de Roland Lily Arison, Nick Askew, Steve Beissinger, PG Bentz, Lainie Berry, Ulf Björnholm-Ottosson, David Blockstein, Andres Bosso, Chris Bowden, Nick Brickle, Rachel Bristol, Sam Bromley, Dr. Michael Brooke, Don Buden, Fiona Burns, Hernan Casañas, Nancy Chepkorir, Willliam S. Clarke, Tom Clements, Sheila Conant, Alex L. Cortes, Hans Cronert, Martin Davies, Nik Devasar/Delhibirds, Pedro Devely, Godefridus Dijkman, Paul Donald, Niels Poul Dreyer, Will Duckworth, Marc Duquet/Ornithos, Alec Earnshaw, James Eaton/BirdTour Asia, Johan Elmberg, Richard Erickson, Birgit Fessl, Jon Fjeldså, Hans Flyman, Damien Fouillot, Sávio Freire Bruno, Sue Friscia, Laura Gardner/Leeds Castle, Lucy Garrett, Dimiter Georgiev, Thomas Ghestemme, Kris Gillam, Mwangi Githiru, Jaqueline Goerck, Esteban Gomez, Gerard Gorman, Pamela Gubanits, Ivonne Guzman, Adrian Hailey, Markus Handschuh, Gerald Roger Hau, H. Ross Hawkins, Floyd Hayes, Jan-Uwe Heckel, Janos Hennicke, Geoff Hilton, Peter Hodum, Paquita Hoeck, Steve Holmer, John & Jemi Holmes, Jiri Horacek, Jon Hornbuckle, Josep del Hoyo, Rob Hutchinson/BirdTour Asia, Kate Huyvaert, Elena Ilyashenko, M Jeri Imansyah, Mochamed Indrawan, Olaf Jahn, David James, Marie James, Jack Jeffrey, Anthony Jeremiah, Gustavo Jiminez, Åke Johansson, Robert Jönsson, Omaliss Keo, Dylan Kesler, Abolghasem Khaleghisadeh, Lloyd Kiff, Niels Poul Krabbe, Markus Lagerkvist, Frank Lambert, Lucia Lastimoze, Miguel Lentino, Hugh Lewis Wright, Lars Lindell, Andre de Luca, Tomas Lundquist, Peter Luscomb, Melanie Luyt, Michael Macek, Gwen Maggs, Jenny Magnusson, Pauline van Mechelen, Charlie Marsh, Annie Marshall, Juan Martinez-Gomes, Paul Matiku, Matthew Mattiessen, Viktoria Maurer/Swarovski, Pete McClelland, J. D. McCracken, Prachi Mehta, Stephen Mendes, Veronica Mendez, Craig Millar, Colin Miskelly, Ricardo Monteiro, Forest Morning, Hanna Mounce, Sue Murray/Yellow-eyed Penguin Trust, Dave Murray, Petr Mückstein, Markus Nipkow, Diego S. Olivera, Lasse Olsson, Ron Orenstein, Stefan Oscarsson, Kiyoaki Ozaki, Charlotte Packman, Lisa Marie Paguntalan, Dan Palmer, Kees de Pater, Pedro Paz, Mark Pearman, Marcos Pérsio, Dirk Petzold, René Pop, Doug H. Pratt, John Puschok, Hugo Rainey, Sharon Reilly, Robin Restall, Michelle Reynolds, Magnus Robb, Herb Roberts, Bonnie Rusk, Lars Rydgren, Lars Råberg, Sadegh Sadeghi Zadegan, Paul Salaman, Marc Salamolard, Paul Scofield, Alex L. Scott, Elaine Secord, Iréne Senften, Gianluca Serra, Rob Sheldon, Jevgeni Shergalin, Hadoram Shirihai, Luís Fábio Silveira, Ed Smith, Brent Stephenson/Wrybill Birding Tours, Margaret Suman/Yellow-eyed Penguin Trust, Jennifer Sutfin, Blas Tabaranza, Johannes Tallroth, Markus Tallroth, Vikash Tatayah, Graeme Taylor, JoãoTeixeira da Costa, Jean Marc Thiollay, Vince Thompson, Anne Tieber, Carl Christian Tofte, Marifel Torre Moyano, Magnus Ullman, PierreUnge, Jonas Waldenström, Jack van Hal, Ross Wanless, Ryan Watson, Henri Weimarskirch, Ana Venturini, Thomas White, Peter Widman, Lukáš Viktora, Roger Wilkinson/Chester Zoo, Bayu Wirayudha, Anders Wirdheim, Roland Wirth, Lance Woolaver, Glyn Young, Victor Yue and Adam Riley/Rockjumper Tours.

ACKNOWLEDGEMENTS

The following photographers or artists are gratefully acknowledged:

Sue Abbott, Roger Ahlman, Ciro Albano, Achmad Ariefiandy, J. J. Arieta, David Bakewell, Stefan Behrens, Daniel Bengtsson, P-G Bentz, Lainie Berry, Melinda Bitting, Jeff Blincow, Leo Boon, Nik Borrow, Chris Bowden, Joseph Brandt, James H Breeden Jr., Philip Briggs, Sávio Freire Bruno, Andy Bunting, Hilary Burn, Joe Burnett, Dante Buzzetti, Tom Callens, Chaiwat Chinuparawat, Ryan Choi, Soon-Kyoo Choi, Valère Claverie, Kristina Cockle, Tomasz Cofta, Chris Collins, F X Couzi, Alan Crawford, Robert L. Curry, Martin Davies, M Debarba, Jim Denny, Paschalis Dougalis, Nils Poul Dreyer, Eddie Duff, Jonathan Eames, James Eaton, Jens & Hanne Eriksen, Birgit Fessl, Daniel Fitter, Simon Fordham, Kim Franklin, Fundacion ProAves, Leif Gabrielsen, Adriano Gambarini, Lucy Garrett, Dimiter Georgiev, Thomas Ghestemme, Kris Gillam, Mike Gillam, Robert Gillmor, Roberto Güller, Gregory Guida, Roy de Haas, Jack van Hal, Catrin Hammer, Sven Hammer, Samuel Hansson, Ruben Heleno, Jose Oswaldo Cortes Herrera, Geoff Hilton, Peter Hodum, Ron Hoff, John & Jemi Holmes, Jon Hornbuckle, Andrew Howe, Miloslav Hromádko, Simon Hum, Rob Hutchinson, Marvin Hyett, Dean Ingwersen, Jack Jeffrey, Dick Jenkin, Anthony Jeremiah, Zheng Jianping, Mery Juiña, Omaliss Keo, Anne King, Jon King, Maxim Koshkin, Shelley Kremer, Kulojyoti Lahkar, Javier Lascurain, Greg Lasley, Jim Lawrence, Marcus Lawson, Miguel Lentino, Tasso Leventis, Chie-Te Liang, Chen Lin, Rich Lindie, Juan Pablo Lopez, James C. Lowen, Andre De Luca, Mark Alexander MacDonald, Alejo P Manaloto, Luiz Claudio Marigo, Juan Martinez, Newton Maxwell-Hassis, Ian R. McHenry, Ian Merrill, Colin Miskelly, Dave Monley, Pedro Monteiro, Jonathan M. Morel, Michael J Morel, Pete Morris, Gulam Rasool Mughal, Dhritiman Mukherjee, Petr Mückstein, Dwight Nadig, Kerrie T. Naranjit, Tseveenmyadag Natsagdorj, Ken Norris, Lasse Olsson, Tun Pin Ong, Ronald Orenstein, Stefan Oscarsson, Tony Palliser, Denis Paterson, Vitor de Q. Piacentini, René Pop, Giovanni Alberto Chaves Portilla, M K Poulsen, Douglas H. Pratt, Duncan Pritchard, Alonso Quevedo, Houssein Rayaleh, Markus Rehnberg, J-B Requier, Ron Ridout, Jon Riley, Don Roberson, Rafael Rodriguez, Lily Arison Réne de Roland, Jonathan Rossouw, Paddy Ryan, Petr Saj, Santosh Saligram, Amano Samarpan, Fabrice Schmitt, Alex L. Scott, Gianluca Serra, Hadoram Shirihai, Chen Shuihua, M. Silvosa, Durgesh Kumar Singh, Brent Stephenson, Anette Strand, Andrea K Suardo, Christer Sundström, Tom Svensson, Andy & Gill Swash, Alejandro Tabini, Markus Tallroth, Alan Tate, Graeme Taylor, F. Théron, Kai-Michael Thomsen, Ray Tipper, Robert Tizard, Joe Tobias, Carl Christian Tofte, Chris Tzaros, Thomas Valqui, Munir Virani/The Perergrine Fund, Eric van der Vlist, Nigel Voaden, Ross Wanless, Dick Watling, Merlijn van Weerd, Emily Weiser, Lyn Wells, Tony Wilson, Jan van der Winden and Edwin Winkel.

Conservation works!

Since last year, Marquesan Imperial-pigeon has been downlisted from Critically Endangered to Endangered

Photo: © Pete Morris / BirdQuest

SPECIES CAN BE BROUGHT BACK from the edge of extinction. A year after the launch of The BirdLife Preventing Extinctions Programme, we are already seeing positive results – but the search is on to find more Species Champions to fund the work.

In the year 2000, Marquesan Imperial-pigeon *Ducula galeata* was known only from a rapidly declining population on the island of Nuku Hiva, French Polynesia. Illegal hunting, predation by rats, habitat degradation by livestock and proposals for roads and tunnels threatened the remaining birds.

Following an awareness raising campaign by Manu (BirdLife in French Polynesia), the threat of poaching has been reduced. Livestock numbers are decreasing, and thanks to lobbying by Manu, the new road and tunnel project was cancelled. At the same time, a second population was established on the rat-free island of Ua Huka where five birds were released in April/May 2000, and five more in 2003. This translocated population is growing, and is expected to reach 50 individuals by 2010.

So when BirdLife International published its 2008 IUCN Red List assessments for birds, Marquesan Imperial-pigeon was downlisted from Critically Endangered to Endangered. It joined 17 other birds downlisted from Critically Endangered to lower categories of threat in recent years, as a result of successful conservation action.

Some of these birds feature on another list, drawn from a study which estimated that of species qualifying as Critically Endangered in 1994, 16 would have gone extinct in the subsequent decade if conservation work had stopped.

Seychelles Magpie-robin *Copsychus sechellarum* is a classic example of a species once reduced to tiny numbers (12-15 in 1965) which was saved from extinction by timely conservation action. In 2000, Seychelles Magpie-robin qualified for downlisting from Critically Endangered to Endangered as a result of work led by Nature Seychelles (BirdLife in Seychelles), which included controlling invasive alien predators such as cats and rats, restoring habitat, and supplementary feeding to increase reproductive rate and the survival of young birds.

From one declining population on Frégate island, Seychelles Magpie-robin was introduced to three other islands. Three of these populations have reached carrying capacity and further island reintroductions are planned, although at least one bird has made its own unaided way to a new island.

But local and international determination to save the Seychelles Magpie-robin might not have been effective without the backing of sound science, adequate resources and political will.

The 2008 IUCN Red List

In total, eight species were newly uplisted to Critically Endangered on the 2008 IUCN Red List; Tristan Albatross *Diomedea dabbenena*, Spoon-billed Sandpiper *Eurynorhynchus pygmeus*, Tachira Antpitta *Grallaria chthonia*, Reunion Cuckooshrike *Coracina newtoni*, Mariana Crow *Corvus kubaryi*, Floreana Mockingbird *Nesomimus trifasciatus*, Akekee *Loxops caeruleirostris* and Gough Bunting *Rowettia goughensis*.

At the same time, six were downlisted from Critically Endangered to Endangered; Gorgeted Wood-quail *Odontophorus strophium*, Marquesan Imperial Pigeon *Ducula galeata*, Purple-backed Sunbeam *Aglaeactis aliciae* and Gurney's Pitta *Pitta gurneyi* or Vulnerable; Rondonia Bushbird *Clytoctantes atrogularis* and Somali Thrush *Turdus ludoviciae*. Guadaloupe Junco *Junco insularis* went from Critically Endangered to Not Recognised.

On the face of it, this sounds as if conservationists are winning almost as many battles as they are losing. However, with the exception of Marquesan Imperial-pigeon, the downlistings are due to improved knowledge -such as the rediscovery of a population of Gurney's Pitta in Myanmar. In other words, the situation of five of these species was not as "critical" as the data available to the assessors prior to 2004 indicated.

But of the "uplisted" species, six have been categorised as Critically Endangered because of a genuine deterioration in their status since 2004. Two-thirds of Critically Endangered species (66%) have declining populations, while just 5% are stable/fluctuating, and 6% increasing owing to conservation efforts.

Agriculture, logging and invasive species are the most severe threats, affecting 87%, 55% and 51% of globally threatened bird species respectively.

But a total of 24 Critically Endangered species are threatened by climate change and associated severe weather. This is a trend that looks set to increase in the near future, as species face shifts in range, loss of habitat to rising sea levels, storms, droughts, and changes in the marine ecosystem.
BirdLife's Chief Executive, Dr Michael Rands warns: "In the long term, human-induced climate change may be the most serious stress of all".

Species Guardians take the lead in conserving globally threatened species

Recent rapid declines in the population of Kittlitz's Murrelet *Brachyramphus brevirostris* have been linked to glacial recession resulting from climate change. Polynesian Ground-dove *Gallicolumba erythroptera* occurs on a handful of low-lying Pacific atolls in French Polynesia, and an increase in frequency of storm surges as a result of climate change is predicted to impact this species.

Prolonged heavy rains have already caused nesting failure and massive mortality among fledgling and juvenile Akekee, endemic to Kaua`i in the Hawaiian Islands. However, a more insidious threat due to climate change comes from avian pox and malaria, carried by introduced mosquitoes. Akekee is mostly found in mountain forests above 1,100 metres, while until recently mosquitoes were commonest below 900 metres. But there is evidence that the disease-bearing insects may now be breeding at 1,200 metres, and it is predicted that a small increase in temperature will eliminate much of the mosquito-free zone on Kaua`i.

Spoon-billed Sandpiper *Eurynorhynchus pygmeus* has been uplisted from Endangered to Critically Endangered because of accelerating population declines, driven partly by habitat loss and degradation in its migratory and wintering ranges. But climate change and associated habitat shifts are expected to have an increasing impact on this species and others dependent on tundra for breeding. Modelling indicates that 57% of the Spoon-billed Sandpiper's breeding habitat could be lost by 2070.

For further information on the science behind the Preventing Extinctions Programme, and the state of Critically Endangered birds, the pressures on them and the actions needed, see BirdLife's new report *Critically Endangered birds: a global audit* downloadable from **http://tinyurl.com/4w3sqo** This draws on material in *State of the world's birds 2008* available at **www.birdlife.org/sowb** To find out more about Preventing Extinctions Programme and how to become a Champion, see **www.birdlife.org/extinction**

The population of Spoon-billed Sandpiper is declining rapidly

Photo: © Zhang Jianping

PREVENTING EXTINCTIONS

BirdLife's Preventing Extinctions Programme

BirdLife has identified the priority conservation actions needed for Spoon-billed Sandpiper, Akekee and all the other Critically Endangered species. Most species require a combination of activities, but the most important are protection and management of Important Bird Areas (47% and 36% of species respectively), followed by awareness-raising and communications activities (34%), and control of invasive species (22%).

Over 77% of species require research on their population size, trends and distribution, while 35% need ecological research and 19% research on the threats that impact them. For 35%, monitoring of population trends is a priority. For 16% there is currently no known population (often because there have been no recent searches). Another 15 lost species (8%) are considered Possibly Extinct or Possibly Extinct in the Wild.

Since 2004, 167 Critically Endangered bird species have been receiving targeted conservation action. BirdLife's Partners, alongside other organisations, agencies and governments, are heavily involved in carrying out actions for 51% of these species.

The great news is that at least 117 species are benefiting from targeted conservation through reduced threats, leading to slower population declines, and even population increases.

The last four years have seen a substantial expansion of BirdLife International's focus on Critically Endangered species, and the implementation of conservation action for them.

"We all have a responsibility to act now to prevent the ongoing extinction crisis," explained Michael Rands. "Governments, non-governmental organisations, academic institutions, individuals and the corporate business sector have a role to play. In recognition of the urgency, BirdLife has launched the Preventing Extinctions Programme."

Central to the programme is the development of two new communities: BirdLife Species Guardians, experts who will take the lead in conserving threatened species in their country, and BirdLife Species Champions, companies, organisations or individuals who will raise awareness of and fund the vital conservation that is so urgently required.

The Guardians' role is to take and encourage greater conservation action for their species, working with national and local governments, concerned individuals, NGOs and local communities. Guardians are monitoring the status of their species, implementing effective conservation action and reporting back to BirdLife International each year. In return, BirdLife provides Guardians with technical support, training, and funds for conservation action based on mutually-agreed project plans, and Birdlife's regional programme offices and in-country Partners help with liaison with decision-makers and governments, and media relations.

BirdLife Species Champions demonstrate their commitment to protecting the planet's natural heritage by funding the work undertaken by the Species Guardians. "Saving threatened birds from extinction is inevitably expensive and always takes time," says Jim Lawrence, BirdLife's Preventing Extinctions Programme Development Manager. "The average cost for each project is over £20,000 a year. We need to raise £19 million over the next five years. Preventing extinction requires sustained investment, which is why we are asking all of our Species Champions to make a three-year commitment."

As well as providing funding, Species Champions help publicise the urgent need for action by drawing attention to the plight of the species they support, and all the other threatened species the BirdLife Preventing Extinction Programme embraces.

Rare Birds Yearbook has been a BirdLife Species Champion since January 2008.

"As a dedicated amateur birder and lister, it is very important for me to be a Species Champion. In my opinion, everyone who has the least interest in seeing a diversity of species should also act to maintain this diversity. Consequently, all purchasers of the Rare Birds Yearbook take their first step towards this by just buying the book and automatically giving £4 to the BirdLife Preventing Extinctions Programme" says Erik Hirschfeld, Editor of Rare Birds Yearbook.

The BirdLife Preventing Extinctions Programme is already delivering results

White-shouldered Ibis *Pseudibis davisoni*, which occurs in Cambodia, Vietnam, Laos and East Kalimantan, Indonesia, is described as the most threatened large waterbird in South-East Asia. It has a severely fragmented population of fewer than 250 mature individuals.

in focus (the optical retailer) is a Species Champion for White-shouldered Ibis. The Species Guardian is developing a proposal to establish a Protected Forest in Western Siem Pang, Cambodia, the most important site for the species, where 108 birds were recorded in November 2006. The Cambodian government has made a commitment in principle to designate the area a Protected Forest, but it is currently threatened by plans for a plantation concession.

The Guardian, Kry Masphal, is lobbying the government to complete the notification process. Large information boards have been placed in five key villages within the IBA to inform local people about development plans and threats to their land from proposed concessions. A Local Conservation Group at Western Siem Pang has been supported since August 2007. The group, including former hunters, conducts monthly patrols record key species and any illegal activities. In September–November 2007, 40 chainsaws were confiscated and one illegal logger sent to court as a result of information provided by the patrol team.

Research and monitoring continues to be carried out, examining the influence of traditional land management practices on the foraging and breeding ecology of White-shouldered Ibis.

Azores Bullfinch *Pyrrhula murina* is endemic to the

but underwent a steep decline and is now restricted to extremely small range because of widespread clearance of native forest for forestry plantations and agriculture. Alien invasive plant species have overrun the

Photo: © Ciro Albano

Araripe Manakin

remaining patches of natural vegetation, suppressing the natural fruit, seed and buds the bullfinch feeds on. At the latest count, 370 individuals remain.

Birdwatch Magazine is a Species Champion for Azores Bullfinch. The Species Guardian is SPEA (Birdlife in Portugal). Habitat is being managed to improve conditions for the species, by creating fruit tree orchards to improve food availability at the end of the winter, and clearing alien plants and planting native species. Research and monitoring of the population size, distribution and habitat quality is being carried out.

Public awareness about the bullfinch – locally known as Priolo – is being raised through a website, CD-ROM, brochures and school kits, and collaboration with the regional Ministry of Tourism on nature trails and tourist information. An analysis of the economic benefits of the work to protect the Priolo, and the ecosystem services offered by the protected area, showed that the project provides the equivalent of full-time employment for 25 people per year, and adds €335,000 per year to the regional GDP.

Photo: © Ruben Heleno

Azores Bullfinch Azores, Portugal, where it is confined to native forest in the east of the island of São Miguel. It was locally abundant in the nineteenth century,

Belding's Yellowthroat *Geothlypis beldingi* is already receiving conservation actions within its range in Baja California, Mexico by ProNatura Noroeste, the Species Guardian. The British Birdwatching Fair is a Species Champion for Belding's Yellowthroat. Owing to its specialised habitat requirements the species is highly susceptible to drainage and disturbance of wetlands. While it is not uncommon at the sites where it still occurs, the total area of suitable habitat at those sites is not thought to exceed 10 km², and the total population is probably between 1,000 and 2,500 individuals.

An action plan has been developed identifying key threats and outlining a conservation strategy for Belding's Yellowthroat, and research and monitoring is being carried out. Local bird guides are being trained, to help to raise the birds' profile and provide links between livelihoods and the bird's conservation.

Along with the Critically Endangered São Tomé Fiscal and São Tomé Grosbeak, Dwarf Olive Ibis *Bostrychia bocagei* is endemic to São Tomé. The Peter Smith Trust is a Species Champion for Dwarf Olive Ibis, while Associação dos Biólogos Santomenses (ABS) is the Species Guardian for all three species. ABS is campaigning for designation of protected areas, proposing suitable boundaries and raising awareness to safeguard the ibis from hunting.

Djibouti Francolin *Francolinus ochropectus* is largely restricted to Forêt du Day, Djibouti. The British Birdwatching Fair is a Species Champion for Djibouti Francolin. Houssein Rayaleh (Djibouti Nature), the Species Guardian, is working in collaboration with the World Pheasant Association. Djibouti Nature is advocating for Protected Area status, setting up a community-run juniper nursery, and developing a Site Support Group.

Restinga Antwren *Formicivora littoralis* has a very small range at Restinga de Maçambaba, Brazil. Dr Urs-Peter Stäuble is a Species Champion for Restinga Antwren. SAVE Brasil (BirdLife in Brazil), has appointed a local NGO at the site, Pingo D'Agua, as the Species Guardian. It is carrying out biological surveys, assessing the complicated land ownership situation, launching an environmental awareness and education campaign, and promoting the establishment of a protected area.

RioTinto Alcan has been recruited as a BirdLife Species Champion for Kakapo *Strigops habroptilus*. RioTinto has been working in partnership with the New Zealand Government Department of Conservation (DOC) and Forest & Bird (BirdLife in New Zealand) to protect and nurture the tiny remnant population since 1990. By 1995 there were only 51 individuals left, but the population has now grown to at least 86, and there is cautious optimism that the species has a future. With a particular emphasis on scientific research, the Kakapo recovery programme is designed to increase breeding frequency and productivity, and to determine why Kakapo breed so infrequently.

Belding's Yellowthroat

Photo: © Javier Lascurain

Sir David Attenborough, the greatest wildlife communicator of our age, chose the occasion of this year's British Birdwatching Fair to announce that he was becoming a Species Champion for Araripe Manakin *Antilophia bokermanni*. A survey in 2006 led to an estimate of only 800 individuals, all confined to an area of moist forest less than 28 km2 in extent on the north-eastern slope of the Chapada do Araripe, south Ceará, Brazil.

The Species Guardian for Araripe Manakin is the Brazilian conservation organisation Aquasis. "We believe that if we can convince the one million nearby city dwellers that their water supply will be guaranteed if they preserve the moist forest, we will save the Araripe Manakin," explained Aquasis Director Alberto Campos.

So as well as the work of protecting and restoring the forest, Sir David will be supporting a campaign to reach rural communities, local government officials with the power to grant or refuse development licences, and city schoolchildren.

Dwarf Olive-ibis

Photo: © Tasso Leventis

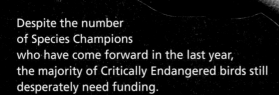

Despite the number
of Species Champions
who have come forward in the last year,
the majority of Critically Endangered birds still
desperately need funding.

"The harsh reality is that Species Champions
are unlikely to step forward for every threatened
bird in time," says Jim Lawrence. "Accordingly, a
small percentage of every Champion's contribution is
collectively pooled to help fund the protection of these
species."

Any contribution to the Preventing Extinctions Programme, whatever
size, makes a very real difference. You have already contributed £4 by
buying this copy of Rare Birds Yearbook. "Together, the many small donations
we are already receiving from generous donors are collectively funding species
recovery right now," says Lawrence.

But he adds that recruiting more BirdLife Species Champions is imperative. "Many
Critically Endangered species will simply not be with us after the next few years if
conservation is not put in place for them soon."

To find out more about how to become a BirdLife Species
Champion or Preventing Extinctions Programme supporter
please contact BirdLife International today.
Send an email to: species.champions@birdlife.org
Call us on: +44 (0)1223 277318
Write to us at: BirdLife Species Champions, BirdLife International,
Wellbrook Court, Girton Road, Cambridge CB3 0NA
United Kingdom
You can keep up with our progress on our website at
www.birdlife.org/extinction

Waved Albatross, Photo: Andy & Gill Swash

BirdLife
INTERNATIONAL

BirdLife International Partnership

Andorra
Associació per a la Defensa
de la Natura
Apartado de Correus Espanyols No 96
Andora La Vella
Tel: + 376 84 3248
Fax: + 376 84 3868
Email: adn@andorra.ad
Web: www.adn-andorra.org

Argentina
Aves Argentinas/AOP
Matheu 1246/8
(C1249AAB) Buenos Aires
Tel: + 54 11 4943 7216
Fax: + 54 11 4943 7216
Email: info@avesargentinas.org.ar
Web: www.avesargentinas.org.ar

Armenia
Armenian Society
for the Protection of Birds
Garegin Njdeh 27,10
Yerevan 0026
Tel: +374 10 22 65 41
Fax: +374 10 22 65 41
Email: armbirds@yahoo.com
Web: www.aspbirds.org

Australia
Birds Australia
Suite 2-05
60 Leicester Street
Carlton, Victoria 3053
Tel: +61 3 9347 0757
Fax: +61 3 9347 9323
Email: g.hamilton@birdsautralia.com.au
Web: www.birdsaustralia.com.au

Austria
BirdLife Austria
Museumsplatz 1/10/8
1070 WIEN
Tel: +43 1 523 4651
Fax: +43 1 524 7040
Email: office@birdlife.at
Web: www.birdlife.at

Azerbaijan
Azerbaijan Ornithological Society
Mukhtarov str. 13, apt.16
AZ1001 Baku
Tel: +994 12 437 9087
Email: info@aos.az
Web: www.aos.az

Bahamas
Bahamas National Trust
PO Box 4105
Nassau
Tel: +242 393 1317
Fax: +242 393 4978
Email: bnt@bnt.bs
Web: www.bnt.bs

Bahrain
Bahrain Natural History Society
PO Box 1858
Manama
Tel: +973 17 710 868
Fax: +973 17 710 678
Email: saeed@alreem.com
Web: bahrainwildlife.com

Belarus
Akhova Ptushak Belarusi
PO Box 306
Minsk
220050
Tel: +375 17 263 0130
Fax: +375 17 263 0613
Email: apb@tut.by
Web: www.ptushki.org

Belgium
BirdLife Belgium
Coxiestraat 11
2800 Mechelen
Tel: +32 15 297 249
Fax: +32 15 424 921
Email:
wim.vandenbossche@natuurpunt.be
Web: www.natuurpunt.be
& www.rnob.be

Belize
Belize Audubon Society
PO Box 1001
12 Fort Street
Belize City
Tel: +501 22 35004
Fax: +501 22 34985
Email:
executivedirector@belizeaudubon.org
Web: www.belizeaudubon.org

Bolivia
Asociación Civil Armonía
400 Avenidad Lomas de Arena Avenue
Casilla 3566
Santa Cruz
Tel: +591 3 356 8808
Fax: +591 3 356 8808
Email: armonia@armonia-bo.org
Web: www.armonia-bo.org

Botswana
BirdLife Botswana
Private Bag 003
Suite 348
Mogoditshane
Gaborone
Tel: +267 31 90 540
Fax: +267 31 90 540
Email: blb@birdlifebotswana.org.bw
Web: www.birdlifebotswana.org.bw

Brazil
SAVE Brasil
Rua Fernão Dias
219 cj 2 Pinheiros
São Paulo SP 05427-010
Tel: +55 11 3815 2862
Fax: +55 11 3815 0343
Email:
jaqueline.goerck@savebrasil.org.br
Web: www.savebrasil.org.br

Bulgaria
Bulgarian Society
for the Protection of Birds
PO Box 50
1111 Sofia
Tel: +359 2 979 9500
Fax: +359 2 979 9501
Email: bspb_hq@bspb.org
Web: www.bspb.org.

Burkina Faso
Fondation des Amis de la Nature
(NATURAMA)
01 BP 6133
Ouagadougou 01
Tel: +226 50 37 32 40
Fax: +226 50 37 28 86
Email: naturama@fasonet.bf

Burundi
Association Burundaise
pour la Protection des Oiseaux
Avenue de la Victoire n° 25
PO Box 7069
Bujumbura
Tel: +257 24 9470
Fax: +257 24 9471
Email: aboburundi@yahoo.fr

Cameroon
Cameroon Biodiversity
Conservation Society
PO Box 3055
Messa, Yaoundé
Tel: +237 220 2645
Fax: +237 220 2645
Email: gdzikouk@yahoo.fr

Canada
Bird Studies Canada
PO Box 160
Port Rowan
Ontario N0E 1M0
Tel: +1 519 586 3531
Fax: +1 519 586 3532
Email: generalinfo@bsc-eoc.org
Web: www.bsc-eoc.org

Canada
Nature Canada
85 Albert Street, Suite 900
Ottawa
Ontario K1P 6A4
Tel: +1 613 562 3447
Fax: +1 613 562 3371
Email: info@naturecanada.ca
Web: www.naturecanada.ca

Chile
Comité Nacional Pro Defensa
de la Flora y Fauna
Ernesto Reyes 035
Providencia
Santiago
Tel: +56 2 777 25 34
Email: secretaria@codeff.cl

Cook Islands
Te Ipakurea Society
PO Box 3063
Rarotonga
Tel: +682 21 144
Fax: +682 23 513
Email: 2tis@oyster.net.ck

Cuba
Centro Nacional de Areas Protegidas
Calle 18a # 4114 e/ 41 y 47 Playa
Ciudad Habana
Tel: +53 7 202 7970
Fax: +53 7 204 0798
Email: cnap@snap.co.cu
Web: www.snap.co.cu

Cyprus
BirdLife Cyprus
PO Box 28076
2090 Lefkosia
Tel: +357 2 245 5072
Fax: +357 2 245 5073
Email: melis@cytanet.com.cy

Czech Republic
Czech Society for Ornithology
Na Belidle 252/34
150 00 Prague 5
Tel: +420 274 866 700
Fax: +420 274 866 700
Email: cso@birdlife.cz
Web: www.birdlife.cz

Denmark
Dansk Ornitologisk Forening
Vesterbrogade 138-140
1620 Copenhagen V
Tel: +45 33 28 3800
Fax: +45 3331 2435
Email: dof@dof.dk
Web: www.dof.dk

Dominican Republic
Grupo Jaragua
Calle El Vergel # 33
El Vergel, Santo Domingo
Tel: +1 809 472 1036
Fax: +1 809 412 1667
Email: jaragua@tricom.net

Ecuador
Aves y Conservacion
Joaquín Tinajero
E3-05 y Jorge Drom
Quito
Tel: +593 2 22 49 968
Fax: +593 2 22 49 968
Email:
aves_direccion@avesconservacion.org
Web: www.cecia.org

Egypt
Nature Conservation Eqypt
Wadi Holdings building
10 Managem Wa Mahager St.
Mohandeseen
Giza
Tel: +202 33 045 140
Fax: +202 33 031 584
Email: info@ncegypt.org
Web: www.ncegypt.org

El Salvador
SalvaNATURA
33 Avenida Sur # 640
Colonia Flor Blanca San Salvador
Tel: +503 279 1515
Fax: +503 279 0220
Email: jmalvarez@saltel.net
Web: www.salvanatura.org

Estonia
Eesti Ornitiliigiaühing (EOÜ)
PO Box 227
Vesti Str. 4
50002 Tartu
Tel: +372 7 422 195
Fax: +372 7 422 180
Email: Andres.Kalamees@eoy.ee

Ethiopia
Ethiopian Wildlife
and Natural History Society
PO Box 13303
Addis Ababa
Tel: +251 11 663 6792 main
Fax: +251 11 618 6879
Email: ewnhs.ble@ethionet.et

Falkland Islands
Falklands Conservation
PO Box 26
Stanley
Tel: +500 22247
Fax: +500 22288
Email: info@conservation.org.fk
Web: www.falklandsconservation.com

Faroe Islands
Føroya Fuglafødifelag
(Faroese Orginithological Society)
Postsmoga 1230
110 Tórshavn
Faroe Islands
Denmark
Tel: +298 352 309
Fax: +298 352 301
Email: ffff@kallnet.fo

Finland
BirdLife SUOMI-FINLAND
Annankatu 29A
PO Box 1285
00101 Helsinki
Tel: +358 9 4135 3300
Fax: +358 9 4135 3322
Email: office@birdlife.fi
Web: www.birdlife.fi

France
Ligue Pour La Protection des Oiseaux
La Corderie Royale
BP 90263
17305 Rochefort Cedex
Tel: +33 546 82 12 55
Fax: +33 546 82 12 50
Email: lpo@lpo.fr
Web: www.lpo-birdlife.asso.fr

French Polynesia
Société d'Ornithologie
de Polynésie "Manu"
BP 21098
98713 Papeete
Tahiti
Tel: +689 52 11 00
Fax: +689 52 11 00
Email: sop@manu.pf
Web: www.manu.pf

Georgia
Georgian Centre
for the Conservation of Wildlife
PO Box 56
Tbilisi 0160
Tel: +995 32 32 64 96
Fax: +995 32 53 74 78
Email: office@gccw.org
Web: www.gccw.org

Germany
NABU
Nature and Biodiversity
Conservation Union
Herbert-Rabius-Str. 26
53225 Bonn
Tel: +49 228 40 36 0
Fax: +49 228 40 36 200
Email: first name.name@NABU.de
Web: www.NABU.de

Ghana
Ghana Wildlife Society
PO Box 13252
Accra
Tel: +233 21 663 500
Fax: +233 21 670 610
Email: wildsoc@ighmail.com
Web: www.ghanawildlifesociety.org

Gibraltar
Gibraltar Ornithological
and Natural History Society
The Gibraltar Natural
History Field Centre
Jews Gate
Upper Rock Natural Reserve
PO Box 843
Tel: +350 72639
Fax: +350 74022
Email: gonhs@gibnet.gi
Web: www.gonhs.org

Greece
Hellenic Ornithological Society
Vas. Irakleiou 24
10682 Athens
Tel: +30 210 822 7937
Fax: +30 210 822 7937
Email: info@ornithologiki.gr
Web: www.ornithologiki.gr

Hong Kong
Hong Kong Bird Watching Society
GPO Box 12460
Hong Kong
Tel: +85 2377 4387
Fax: +852 2314 3687
Email: hkbws@hkbws.org.hk
Web: www.hkbws.org.hk

Hungary
Hungarian Ornithological
and Nature Conservation Society
Kolto u. 21.
1121 Budapest
Tel: +36 1 275 6247
Fax: +36 1 275 6267
Email: mme@mme.hu
Web: www.mme.hu

Iceland
Fuglavernd - BirdLife Iceland
PO Box 5069
125 Reykjavik
Tel: +354 652 0477
Fax: +354 551 6413
Email: fuglavernd@fuglavernd.is
Web: www.fuglavernd.is

India
Bombay Natural History Society
Hornbill House
Shaheed Bhagat Singh Road
Mumbai 400 023
Tel: +91 22 2282 1811
Fax: +91 22 2283 7615
Email: bnhs@bom4.vsnl.net.in

Indonesia
Burung Indonesia
PO Box 310/Boo
Bogor 16003
Tel: +62 251 719 5344
Fax: +62 251 835 7961
Email: birdlife@burung.org
Web: www.burung.org

Iraq
Nature Iraq
PO Box 144652
Amman 11814
Jordan
Tel: +964 53 329 2007
Fax: +964 53 329 2007
Email: info@natureiraq.org
Web: www.natureiraq.org

Ireland
BirdWatch Ireland
Rockingham House
Newcastle, Co. Wicklow
Tel: +353 1 281 9878
Fax: +353 1 281 9763
Email: info@birdwatchireland.org
Web: www.birdwatchireland.ie

Israel
Society for the Protection
of Nature in Israel
Hanegev 2 St.
Tel-Aviv 66186
Tel: +972 3 638 8666
Fax: +972 3 687 7695
Email: ioc@netvision.net.il
Web: www.birds.org.il
& www.spni.org.il

Italy
Lega Italiana Protezione Uccelli
via Trento n. 49
43100 Parma
Tel: +39 0521 273043
Fax: +39 0521 273419
Email: lipusede@box1.tin.it
Web: www.lipu.it

Ivory Coast
SOS-FORETS
22 BP 918
Abidjan 22
Tel: +225 20 37 1835
Email: sosforets@hotmail.com

Japan
Wild Bird Society of Japan
Maruwa Building
3-9-23 Nishi-Gotanda
Shinagawa-ku
Tokyo 141-0031
Tel: +81 0 3 5436 2620
Fax: +81 0 3 5436 2635
Email: hogo@w-bsj.org
Web: www.wbsj.org

Jordan
Royal Society
for the Conservation of Nature
PO Box 6354
Jubeiha-Abu-Nusseir Circle
Amman 11183
Tel: +962 6 533 7931
Fax: +962 6 534 7411
Email: adminrscn@rscn.org.jo
Web: www.rscn.org.jo

Kenya
NatureKenya
PO Box 44486
00100 GPO Nairobi
Tel: +254 2 374 9957
Fax: +254 2 374 1049
Email: office@naturekenya.org
Web: www.naturekenya.org

Kuwait
Kuwait Environment Protection Society
PO Box 1896 Safat
Code No 13019
Tel: 00 965 484 8256
Fax: 00 965 483 7856
Email: info@keps74.com
Web: www.keps74.com

Latvia
Latvijas Ornitologijas Biedriba
PO Box 1010
Riga 1046
Tel: +371 72 21 580
Fax: +371 76 03 100
Email: putni@lob.lv
Web: www.lob.lv

Lebanon
Society for the Protection of Nature
and Natural Resources in Lebanon
Awad Bldg, 6th Floor
Abdel Aziz Street
PO Box 11-5665
Beirut
Tel: +961 1 748 308 or 309
Fax: +961 1 344 814
Email: spnlorg@cyberia.net.lb

Liberia
Society for the Conservation
of Nature of Liberia
Monrovia Zoo Lakpazee
PO Box 2628
Monrovia
Email: scnlib2001@yahoo.com

Liechtenstein
Botanish-Zoologische Gesellschaft
Im Bretscha 22
9494 Schaan
Tel: +41 75 232 4819
Fax: +41 75 233 2819
Email: bzg@adon.li

Lithuania
Lietuvos Ornitologu Draugija
Naugarduko St. 47-3
03208 Vilnius
Tel: +370 5 213 0498
Fax: +370 5 213 0498
Email: lod@birdlife.lt
Web: www.birdlife.lt

Luxembourg
Letzebuerger natur-A Vulleschutz-Liga
Kraizhaff,
rue de Luxembourg
1899 Kockelscheuer
Tel: +352 29 04 04
Fax: +352 29 05 04
Email: birgit.jacoby@luxnatur.lu
Web: www.luxnatur.lu

Madagascar
ASITY: Ligue Malagache
pour la Protection des Oiseaux
Lot IIN 184 PH Ter Analamahitsy
101 Antananarivo
BP 1074
Tel: +261 20 22 536 07
Email: zicoma@birdlife-mada.org
Web: www.asity.org

Malawi
Wildlife and Environmental Society
of Malawi (WESM)
Heritage Centre Building
CNR-Churchill Road/Partridge Avenue
Opposite Shire Highlands Hotel
Private Bag 578 LIMBE
Tel: +265 0 1843 428
Fax: +265 0 1843 765
Email: wesm-hq@africa-online.net
Web: www.wildlifemalawi.org

Malaysia
Malaysian Nature Society
PO Box 10750
Kuala Lumpur 50724
Tel: +60 3 2287 9422
Fax: +60 3 2287 8773
Email: mns@mns.org.my
Web: www.mns.org.my

Malta
BirdLife Malta
57 Marina Court
Flat 28
Abate Triq Rigord
MT-Ta' Xbiex
MSD 12
Tel: +356 21 34 76 46
Fax: +356 21 34 32 39
Email: office@birdlifemalta.org
Web: www.birdlifemalta.org

Mexico
Pronatura
Aspergulas 22 (antes Pino)
Colonia San Clemente
CP 01740
Tel: +52 55 563 55 054
Fax: +52 55 563 55 054
Email: pronatura@pronatura.org.mx
Web: www.pronatura.org.mx

Myanmar
Biodiversity and Nature
Conservation Association
A/6-2 Anawrahtar Housing
Pyay Road
Ward No 2
Kamayut Township
Yangon
Tel: +951 527 175
Email: banca@yangon.net.mm

Nepal
Bird Conservation Nepal
House Number 388 KHA
Uttardhoka Marg
Lazimpat
Kathmandu
Tel: +977 1 441 7805
Fax: +977 1 441 3884
Email: bcn@mail.com.np
Web: www.birdlifenepal.org

Netherlands
Vogelbescherming Nederland
PO Box 925
3700 AX Zeist
Tel: +31 30 693 7799
Fax: +31 30 691 8844
Email:
fred.wouters@vogelbescherming.nl
Web: www.vogelbescherming.nl

New Caledonia
Société Calédonienne d'Ornithologie
69 av. Koenig - Rivière Salée
BP3135
98846 Nouméa Cedex
Tel: +687 35 48 33
Fax: +687 35 48 33
Email: sco@sco.asso.nc
Web: www.sco.asso.nc

New Zealand
The Royal Forest
& Bird Protection Society
90 Ghuznee Street
PO Box 631
Wellington
Tel: +64 4 385 7374
Fax: +64 4 385 7373
Email: office@forestandbird.org.nz
Web: www.forestandbird.org.nz

Nigeria
Nigerian Conservation Foundation
PO Box 74638
Victoria Island
Lagos
Tel: +234 1 2642498 ext 7903
Fax: +234 1 264 2497
Email: ncf@hyperia.com

Norway
Norsk Ornitologisk Forening
Sandgata 30 B
7012 Trondheim
Tel: +47 73 52 60 40
Fax: +47 73 52 40 90
Email: nof@birdlife.no
Web: www.birdlife.no

Palau
Palau Conservation Society
PO Box 1811
Koror
Palau 96940
Tel: +680 488 3993
Fax: +680 488 3990
Email: pcs@palaunet.com

Palestine
Palestine Wildlife Society
Beit Sahour
PO Box 89
Bethlehem
Tel: +972 2 2277 4373
Fax: +972 2 2277 4373
Email: pwls@wildlife-pal.org
Web: www.wildlife-pal.org

Panama
Sociedad Audubon de Panamá
Apartado 2026
Balboa, Ancón
Tel: +507 224 9371
Fax: +507 224 4740
Email: info@panamaaudubon.org
Web: www.panamaaudubon.org

Paraguay
Guyra Paraguay
Gaetano Martino 215 esq. Tte. Ross
Asunción
Tel: +595 21 223 567
Fax: +595 21 223 567
Email: guyra@guyra.org.py
Web: www.guyra.org.py

Philippines
Haribon Foundation
2/F Santos and Sons Building
973 Aurora Blvd, Cubao
Quezon City 1109
Tel: +632 434 4642
Fax: +632 434 4696
Email: birdlife@haribon.org.ph
Web: www.haribon.org.ph

Poland
Ogólnopolskie Towarzystwo
Ochrony Ptaków
ul. Odrowaza 24
PL 05-270 Marki Warszawy
Tel: +48 22 761 8205
Fax: +48 22 845 1412
Email: office@otop.org.pl

Portugal
Sociedade Portuguesa
para o Estudo das Aves
Avenida da Liberdade 105-2ºEsq
1250-140 Lisboa
Tel: +351 213 220 430
Fax: +351 213 220 439
Email: Spea@spea.pt
Web: www.spea.pt

Puerto Rico
Sociedad Ornitológica
Puertorriqueña, Inc
PO Box 195166
San Juan
00919-5166
Tel: +1 787 254 2354
Fax: +1 787 254 2354
Email: directivasopi@yahoo.com
Web: www.avesdepuertorico.org

Qatar
Friends of the Environment Centre
PO Box 1822
Doha
Tel: +974 48 74725
Fax: +974 48 77301
Email: citysilk@hotmail.com
Web: www.myqatar.org

Romania
Romanian Ornithological Society
Str. Gheorghe Dima 49/2
400336 Cluj Napoca
Tel: +40 264 438 086
Fax: +40 264 438 086
Email: office@sor.ro
Web: www.sor.ro

Russia
Russian Bird Conservation Union
Shosse Entuziastov 60, Building 1
Moscow
111123
Tel: +7 495 672 2263
Fax: +7 495 672 2263
Email: mail@rbcu.ru

Rwanda
Association pour la Conservation
de la Nature au Rwanda
PO Box 4290
Kigali
Fax: +250 778 45 c/o M Muramira
Email: acnrwanda@yahoo.fr

Samoa
O le Si'osi'omaga Society Incorporated
PO Box 2282
Apia
Western Samoa
Tel: +685 25 897
Fax: +685 21 993
Email: ngo_siosiomaga@samoa.ws

Saudi Arabia
National Commission for Wildlife
Conservation and Development
PO Box 61681
Riyadh 11575
Tel: +966 1 441 0369
Fax: +966 1 441 0797
Email: ncwcd@zajil.net
Web: www.ncwcd.gov.sa

Seychelles
Nature Seychelles
Roche Caiman
Box 1310
Victoria
Mahe
Tel: +248 60 11 00
Fax: +248 78 01 42
Email: nature@seychelles.net
Web: www.nature.org.sc

Sierra Leone
Conservation Society of Sierra Leone
PO Box 1292
Freetown
Tel: +232 22 229 716
Fax: +232 22 224 439 fax bureau
Email: cssl_03@yahoo.com

Singapore
Nature Society (Singapore)
510 Geylang Road #02-05
The Sunflower
Singapore 389466
Tel: +65 6741 2036
Fax: +65 6741 0871
Email: contact@nss.org.sg
Web: www.nss.org.sg

Slovakia
Slovak Ornithological Society
/ BirdLife Slovakia
Mlynske Nivy 41
821 09 Bratislava
Tel: +421 2 55 422 185
Fax: +421 2 55 422 186
Email: vtaky@vtaky.sk
Web: www.birdlife.sk
and www.vtaky.sk

Slovenia
Drustvo Za Opazovanje in Proucevanje
Ptic Slovenije
DOPPS - BirdLife Slovenia
p.p. 2990
TRŽAŠKA 2
1001 Ljubljana
Tel: +386 1 426 5875
Fax: +386 1 425 1181
Email: dopps@dopps.si

South Africa
BirdLife South Africa
PO Box 515
Randburg
Johannesburg 2125
Tel: +27 11 789 1122
Fax: +27 11 789 5188
Email: secretary@birdlife.org.za
Web: www.birdlife.org.za

Spain
Sociedad Española de Ornitología
Melquiades Biencinto 34
28053 Madrid
Tel: +34 91 434 0910
Fax: +34 91 434 0911
Email: mjarmesto@seo.org
Web: www.seo.org

Sri Lanka
Field Ornithology Group of Sri Lanka
Department of Zoology
University of Colombo
Colombo 03
Tel: +94 75 342 609
Fax: +94 75 337 644
Email: fogsl@slt.lk

Suriname
Foundation for Nature Conservation
in Suriname
Cornelis Jongbawstraat 14
PO Box 12252
Paramaribo
Tel: +597 271 856
Fax: +597 422 555
Email: research@stinasu.sr
Web: www.stinasu.sr

Sweden
Sveriges Ornitologiska Förening
Stenhusa Gård
380 62 Mörbylånga
Tel: +46 8 612 2530
Fax: +46 8 612 2536
Email: info@sofnet.org
Web: www.sofnet.org

Switzerland
Schweizer Vogelschutz SVS-BirdLife
Schweiz/ASPO BirdLife Suisse
Wiedingstr, 78
8036 Zürich
Tel: +41 0 44 457 70 20
Fax: +41 0 44 457 70 30
Email: svs@birdlife.ch
Web: www.birdlife.ch

Taiwan
Chinese Wild Bird Federation
1F, No. 3, Lane 36 Chinglung St.
116 Taipei
Tel: +886 2 2930 3649
Fax: +886 2 2930 3595
Email: mail@bird.org.tw
Web: www.bird.org.tw

Tanzania
Wildlife Conservation Society
of Tanzania
PO Box 70919, Dar es Salaam
Tel: +255 22 211 2518
Fax: +255 22 212 4572
Email: wcst@africaonline.co.tz

Thailand
Bird Conservation Society of Thailand
43 Soi Chokchairuammit
Viprawadee-Rangsit Rd
Samsaen-nok, Dindaeng
Bangkok 10320
Tel: +66 2 691 4816
Fax: +66 2 691 4493
Email: bcst@bcst.or.th
Web: www.bcst.or.th

Tunisia
Association "Les Amis des Oiseaux"
Bureau des Projets
Avenue 18 janvier 1952
Center – Bureau C 208/209
2080 Ariana
Tel: +216 71 717 860
Fax: +216 71 717 860
Email: aao@topnet.tn

Turkey
Doga Dernegi
PK 640 06445 Yenisehir
Ankara
Tel: +90 312 448 05 37
Fax: + 90 312 448 02 58
Email: doga@dogadernegi.org
Web: www.dogadernegi.org

Uganda
NatureUganda
PO Box 27034
Kampala
Tel: +256 41 540 719
Fax: +256 41 530 134
Email: nature@natureuganda.org
Web: www.natureuganda.org

Ukraine
Ukranian Society
for the Protection of Birds
PO Box 33
Kiev-01103
Tel: +380 44 284 7131
Fax: +380 44 284 7131
Email: uspb@birdlife.org.ua
Web: www.birdlife.org.ua

United Kingdom
Royal Society
for the Protection of Birds
The Lodge
Sandy
Bedfordshire SG19 2DL
Tel: +44 0 1767 680551
Fax: +44 0 1767 693265
Email: (first name.name)@RSPB.org.UK
Web: www.rspb.org.uk

Uruguay
Aves Uruguay
Casilla de Correo 6955
Correo Central
Montevideo
Tel: +598 2 902 2362
Fax: +598 2 908 5959
Email: gupeca@adinet.com.uy
Web: www.galeon.com/avesurug

USA
Audubon
700 Broadway
New York
NY 10003-9562
Tel: +1 212 979 3000
Fax: +1 212 979 3188
Email: bperciasepe@audubon.org
Web: www.audubon.org

Yemen
Yemen Society
for the Protection of Wildlife
29 Alger Street
PO Box 19759
Sana'a
Tel: +967 1 44 74 23
Fax: +967 1 44 74 24
Email: wildlife.yemen@y.net.ye

Zambia
Zambian Ornithological Society
PO Box 33944
Lusaka 10101
Tel: +260 125 5981
Email: zos@zamnet.zm
Web: www.wattledcrane.com

Zimbabwe
BirdLife Zimbabwe
PO Box RVL 100
Runiville
Harare
Tel: +263 4 490 208
Fax: +263 4 490 208
Email: birds@zol.co.zw

California Condor
Ice Age Icon
Adapts to Modern World

IN 1983 I HELD IN MY HANDS AN OLD EGG. It reminded me of the eggs of Common Murre *Uria aalge* but was 20% larger. About the size and shape of an avocado, it was laid by a bird nesting in a rock-bottomed cave. It was the egg of a California Condor *Gymnogyps californianus*. The egg was from a 1905 nest in Monterey County, a large county in central California. I was researching a book on Monterey birds, and visiting the Western Foundation of Vertebrate Zoology for that project. Monterey County was where the first California Condor known to science was described in 1792, and had been a stronghold for the species. But 1905 was the last year that condors are known to have laid eggs there. Enterprising entrepreneurs had been taking some of them to sell to oologists. They described dramatic entries into nest caves, using ropes and descending 100 feet or more down vertical cliffs. The collectors felt it was worth the risk, as an intact condor egg garnered a high price.

A handwritten account accompanied the egg I was holding. Rough-hewn snippets described the events of March 25, 1905: "Nest was on face of a rugged mountain of rock about 800 feet from the creek channel, was between two large boulders which was roofed over by another boulder which rested on top of them. The crevice was about 2 ft. wide and about 7 feet long. I located the nest on the 24th from the top of another hill. I sat down on the hill opposite the nest for about 3/4 of an hour [but] could not see a bird anywhere so I gave a yell and she at once popped out on the rock where I could see her. As soon as I moved she came straight for me and soared over me until I reached the nest. After making the climb I sat down before the nest and enjoyed a good smoke while the sweat flowed freely down my face. All this while the old Vulture was flying to and fro within 30 to 40 ft. of me with feathers set forward and her legs hanging at full length. Egg was laying on some small trash of wood carried in there by rats. Only seen the one bird about the place."

By the time the book I wrote was published in

1985, only nine condors remained in the wild. Two years later the last of them were caught for captive breeding. Although that breeding program brought hopes for recovery, in the 1993 Atlas of Breeding Birds of Monterey County I wrote that it "seems unlikely that condors will nest in Monterey County again."

A new chick changes everything

I was wrong. In August 2007, I hiked to a remote hill in the Ventana Wilderness of Monterey County with an intern of Ventana Wildlife Society (VWS). We used spotting scopes to view across a landscape of deep-shaded rushing creeks and sunlit chaparral slopes to a cliff-face on the far side. High up the cliff there was a jumble of boulders at the entrance to a deep defile. The cleft itself was in the shade but every once in a while a huge wing would stretch out across the opening. It was the wing of a California Condor chick in the first wild nest known from Monterey County in 102 years.

Portrait of an adult California Condor on the Big Sur coast

How this remarkable turn-around occurred is attributable to the Ventana Wildlife Society and how just a few determined individuals brought a nearly extinct species back to the local breeding avifauna of central California.

From Ice Age to Doom

The story of the California Condor goes back to the Pleistocene. There is fossil evidence of condors as far east as Florida and New York. They reached their peak following the great herds of prehistoric grazers in what is now the western United States at a time when woolly mammoths and saber-toothed tigers roamed those plains. In this the condor was similar to the largest vultures on the African veldt. Its niche perhaps most closely matched that of today's Lappet-faced Vulture *Torgos tracheliotus*. Both this vulture and the California Condor are huge birds that dominate at carcasses; both are well equipped to devour bones left by smaller scavengers; and both breed as solitary pairs.

With the close of the Ice Age and the decline of Pleistocene herds, the California Condor's range became restricted to the wilds of the west coast of North America. Here they foraged on a new source of large carrion: beached whales, dead elephant seals, and the offal of sea lion colonies. This niche resembles that of its South American relative, the Andean Condor *Vultur gryphus*.

It was on the shores of Monterey Bay in December 1602 that a Spanish priest and geographer, Antonio de la Ascencion, writing in his journal during the exploratory voyage of Sebastian Vizcaino, first mentioned seeing a condor. Scottish naturalist Archibald Menzies collected the first specimen in 1792, from which the species was formally described by George Shaw in 1797. That bird was feeding on a beached whale along Monterey Bay. As late as 1871, early ornithologist James G. Cooper described what was then called the California (or Royal) Vulture as among "the most characteristic land birds" of the Monterey area.

Within twenty years, Cooper lamented that the condor had "rapidly grown scarce" throughout California in a paper he entitled "A doomed bird." By the end of the 19th century this decline was widely known and disturbing. The fledgling Cooper Ornithological Society, named after Dr. Cooper in his declining years, featured a condor on the cover of its first Bulletin in 1899. The Society renamed their journal "The Condor" by its next volume.

What led to this precipitous decline? A small part of the problem may have been egg collecting. At least 17 eggs were collected within Monterey County alone between 1859 and 1905. Condors can be quite wary at feeding locales, but they are not particularly shy around nest sites, which were being located more frequently. Ranchers or hunters shot other condors. Some now think that the most serious problem was a steady loss of condors from ingestion

of poison in carcasses; it may have been the ingestion of toxic lead from bullets lodged in shot deer, pigs, or waterfowl that caused the greatest long-term damage. The danger attributable to lead bullets would not be recognized for almost a century.

The turn of the 20th century saw the last of Monterey's condors. A local rancher saw ten around a dead cow near the Big Sur coast in 1910, the last time an aggregation of condors was reported on the central California coast. Breeding condors were unreported in Monterey County after 1905, and from the Pinnacles, in adjacent San Benito County in what is today's Pinnacles National Monument, after 1907. By the mid 20th century the only condors remaining were well south of Monterey, in remote mountains of southern California. By the 1970s only about 40 were thought to remain alive there. In the 1980s a large-scale effort by governmental and private agencies sought to capture condors for captive breeding. The last wild condor was captured in April 1987, bringing the zoo-held breeding population to 27 birds. This intensive effort did result in captive breeding by 1988, and by 1990 there were 26 young condors in zoos, many hatched from eggs laid in captivity, which almost doubled the world's population.

Ventana Wildlife Society responds: Peregrines, then Eagles, then Condors

Meanwhile, back in Monterey County, a small group of local wildlife enthusiasts had the unique opportunity to acquire a 240 acre in-holding within the Ventana Wilderness of Los Padres National Forest. Sal Lucido and the Petkus brothers, who met while rehabilitating injured wildlife, purchased the property with the intent of using it for preservation of local wildlife. They formed a non-profit group, called the Ventana Wilderness Society, in hopes of restoring endangered species. They identified restoration of Peregrine Falcon *Falco peregrinus*, Bald Eagle *Haliaeetus leucocephalus*, and California Condor – all listed on the Federal endangered species list – as long term goals for the central California coast. They built a hack site for releases of raptors, testing first with Prairie Falcons *Falco mexicanus*, and then in 1986 they released three Peregrines. Within two years a mated pair was nesting at a nearby eyrie.

From 1986-2000, Ventana Wilderness Society, since renamed Ventana Wildlife Society, worked to re-establish Bald Eagle as a nesting bird in central California. The last breeding Bald Eagle in Monterey County had been on the Big Sur coast in 1934. By releasing 66 eaglets taken from nests where healthy populations existed (Alaska, British Columbia), they succeeded in their goal. Bald Eagles began nesting in the local area by 1993; by 2007 there were a dozen active nests on the central coast producing young annually.

The lessons and success of the Bald Eagle project caught the attention of federal biologists. In 1994

Female condor #208, who laid the first wild egg in Monterey County in a century, perches on the lip of the cave. This dramatic shot was captured by a VWS biologist during a nest entry in spring 2007.

hey invited VWS to be part of the working group n California Condor. VWS staff biologists converted he seasonal hack site in the Ventana Wilderness n-holding to a year-round facility for the release of ondors. The first four condors arrived in September 996, and were released in January 1997.

Hurdles to restoring the condor

alifornia Condors are long-lived birds. Captives ave lived to 50 years, and they may be capable of ven greater longevity. The female lays only a single gg each breeding season, unless the egg is lost and ust be replaced. Eggs are laid on the bare floor of a cave' of some sort. Typically this is a cleft on a rocky liff, but historically condors also nested in huge equoia trees in the southern Sierra Nevada range. ecently a pair bred in a huge Coast Redwood stump ear the Big Sur coast. If an egg hatches and the oungster is fledged, the adults will spend both that ear and the next watching over it, thus missing the ext breeding season.

Condors are so large that they are at the upper mit at which flapping flight is possible. Flapping akes much energy, so most of their time in the air is pent soaring on their nine-foot wingspan. Condors orage best in areas with updrafts, such as along

foothills, and they avoid the flat (and now almost entirely agricultural) valleys that separate California's mountain ranges. Condors have keen eyesight but do not find carrion by smell, as do the smaller Turkey Vultures *Cathartes aura*. Rather, they key into the activities of Turkey Vultures, Common Ravens *Corvus corax*, or Golden Eagles *Aquila chrysaetos* to locate carcasses. It is a long learning curve to find enough food to survive in the wild. Young condors need adult mentors to learn how to find enough food, to avoid dangers, and to become integrated into the social hierarchy necessary for population survival.

Ventana Wildlife Society had to account for all aspects of a condor's natural history. Their history with Bald Eagle releases was good training. Experience had taught that carting a big bird to a release site in a crate, and just opening the lid, did not lead to much success. Rather, the VWS crew built an aerial hack site on stilts in which potential releasees were kept and fed for months, allowing them to acclimatize to their setting, and permitting previously released birds to visit and interact through a double-door entry.

The young condors brought to Monterey were hatched from captive laid eggs at the Los Angeles Zoo or the San Diego Wild Animal Park. It is another remarkable story of public-private cooperation to

San Diego Wild Animal Park, 2006

describe how those facilities managed to raise fledglings that were fit to be released into the wild, but we don't have space here. The first four released by VWS in January 1997 did not do well. They were too curious of people, encountered dangers much too easily, and had to be recaptured that June. The next five, released in December 1997, were better adapted. These had been raised by adult condors in captivity and were not imprinted on people. By 2008, over 70 condors had been released by VWS at the Ventana Wilderness release site and, since 2003, at Pinnacles National Monument. As of this writing, 44 condors were flying in Monterey and San Benito counties.

Finding wild food & avoiding mortality

As VWS was releasing birds born in captivity, food was an immediate concern. Local dairies began providing stillborn calves, and more recently non-native deer culled from federal lands have been available, but transporting these carcasses to remote feeding sites was (and remains) a major effort. It was hoped that condors would learn to exploit their original source of primary food on the central coast: dead whales and pinnipeds. In June 2000, a released condor followed vultures

Big Sur, California, 2006

Photo: © Dave Monley / Ventana Wildlife Society

Condor biologist Joe Burnett tracks local condors through radio telemetry (this shot) but most current information on condor movements relies on cutting-edge GPS telemetry.

to a dead sea-lion, and fed on it for a month. Instances of this adaptive behavior are increasing. By 2005, condors were regularly roosting on the coast at a site overlooking an active sea-lion colony. A washed-up Gray Whale in 2006 fed most of the central coast condors for nearly half a year. This year a dead Humpback Whale is attracting all the local central coast condors as I write.

Any source of mortality is of concern for a Critically Endangered species. Determining the causes of death requires finding the dead birds. Condors range widely over miles of wilderness daily. They can be monitored only by telemetry, a technique developed by National Audubon and others for monitoring the southern California population. All VWS released condors bear small radios and visible wing tags. Staff and interns follow day-to-day movements via radio telemetry, using hand-held antennas. In 2003, VWS incorporated cutting-edge global positioning system (GPS) telemetry. The GPS tags transmit data to the biologist's computers 12 times a day. These data include location (accurate to 10m), speed, heading, and altitude, and have revolutionized the way condors are tracked. The telemetry has led to carcasses of dead condors, which were recovered for necropsy, or to sick condors that can be recaptured and treated.

Many new insights on condor movements are attributable to radio and GPS telemetry. We now know that birds released on the central coast have ventured south and interacted with the populations

in southern California. Conversely, in June 2000, a mentor adult and 8 youngsters from southern California flew north and landed atop an observatory on one of the highest ridges in Monterey County. They flew south again a few hours later, and never encountered the 14 VWS-released condors that were then flying free nearby. Evidence of condor dispersal derived from tracking was a major reason the government purchased specific ranches adjacent to Pinnacles National Monument. GPS telemetry was the major factor in the discovery of recent nests. Of course, maintaining staff and interns for daily telemetry monitoring, not to mention the cost of equipment, is an expensive proposition.

The risks faced by condors have changed over time. A few condors were shot in the early release years, but publicity surrounded the prosecution and a conviction of one hunter broadened public awareness. Shooting is no longer a major concern. Collisions with power lines proved to be another problem. Aversion training at zoos and at the hack sites, where young condors receive a mild shock when perching on a fake power pole, has helped, as has the installation of protective devices on power lines.

Getting the lead out

Necropsies of dead condors proved that the greatest threat remained lead poisoning. A number of emergency chelations were required for acutely

33

poisoned birds. Chemical "fingerprinting" found that the lead came from lead bullets. Lead bullets are widely used by hunters on public and private lands. Condors do not stay within the Ventana Wilderness; they venture over montane and foothill habitats wherever food can be found. The entrails of a shot deer make an excellent meal.

In 2007, VWS joined the National Audubon Society and others pushing for laws or agency regulations that prohibited the use of lead bullets within the historic range of condors in California. In fall 2007, over the opposition of gun lobbyists, the State legislature passed a law giving the greatest possible protection to the condor from lead bullets.

It then became a question of whether governor Arnold Schwarzenegger, whose party generally opposed this legislation, would sign the bill. The United States is currently in the midst of printing quarter-dollar coins commemorating each of the 50 states. The recently minted California quarter features a design showing preservationist John Muir, Yosemite Valley, and a California Condor in flight. Proponents noted that Governor Schwarzenegger had chosen that design, and editorials urged that he sign the bill. The State chapter of the Audubon Society, honoring the Governor for his efforts on global warming shortly after the lead bill passed, presented him with a framed portrait of a condor.
    Whether these symbolic tokens mattered is unknown, but in October 2007 Governor Schwarzenegger signed the no-lead bill. It took

effect in July 2008, and although there is currently no monies for enforcement, it is hoped that the law will contribute to the effort to re-establish condors as a part of the breeding avifauna of central California.

A new world for young condors

The total world population of California Condors has now passed the 300 mark; about half in captivity and half in the wild. Beyond the releases at Big Sur and the Pinnacles, there are on-going efforts to establish populations in the coastal mountains of southern California, at the Grand Canyon in Arizona, and in northern Baja California, Mexico. These efforts are achieving success, with breeding already achieved in Arizona (2004) and southern California (2005). In 2007, a wild chick was born in Mexico.

Young condors do not attain full adult plumage for a half-dozen years, and typically don't attempt to breed until 6-8 years of age. It was once thought that condors were very sensitive around their nest sites, but the evidence does not support this. Rather, condors are amazingly tolerant of humans in the vicinity of their breeding haunts. Instead, nest locales are usually overlooked, inconspicuous and inaccessible to ordinary approach. Turkey Vulture, a smaller cathartid common locally, is similar in this aspect. Despite its abundance, very few Turkey Vulture nests are ever found.

By 2007 it had been ten years since the first releases

Three condors (plus two Turkey Vultures and a Western Gull Larus occidentalis) feed on a beached Gray Whale on the Big Sur coast in May 2006. All California Condors bear wing tags and each individual can be identified at a distance.

of condor on the Big Sur coast. Radio telemetry had led to a pair engaged in breeding behavior in spring 2006, using a huge old Redwood stump as a potential nest site, but no egg was laid. In spring 2007, telemetry evidence suggested that another pair might be nesting well inside the Ventana Wilderness. After prolonged searches a potential nest cave was located, but the situation did not permit better views. Only by entering the cave could the presence of an egg be confirmed. If there was an egg, there was also concern for eggshell thinness; studies of wild-hatched eggs in the 1960s and 1970s showed considerable contamination by the now-banned pesticide DDT and its residue. If there was an egg in the cave nest, the plans were to remove it, swap it for a dummy wooden egg, and take the egg to the Los Angeles Zoo for incubation. A ready-to-hatch captive egg would replace the dummy egg in the wild nest at the proper time, and the fledgling would be reared by the wild parents. Chicks also needed to be vaccinated against West Nile virus at the age of one month, and radio-tagged at the age of four months.

VWS biologist rappelled into the cave nest three times in 2007 - daring entries that used helicopters, safety ropes, and much skill. Dramatically, the mother condor flew to the lip of the cave while the biologist was present inside, resulting in a first-of-its-kind photograph.

More good news that spring was that the pair at the Redwood stump also laid a wild egg. Both Ventana eggs hatched in 2007, bringing much acclaim and publicity. The public voted on names in a fund-raising effort: the chick in the cave nest became "Centennia" - the first-born wild chick in 100 years in central California - and the female chick in the redwood nest became "Ventana." It was "Centennia" that I observed in August with a VWS intern who later observed that fledgling's first flight on 26 September. "Ventana" fledged on 22 October. These fledging dates are consistent with the five-and-a-half month nestling period known for California Condors.

Unfortunately, "Centennia" was attacked and apparently killed by a Golden Eagle in December 2007. Eagle attacks on youngsters, apparently to establish dominance, are a known survival threat. There is also concern that the continuing spread of Common Raven along the Big Sur coast could lead to an increased threat of egg predation. Condors also pick up small pebbles for their gizzard, and mistake trash for pebbles. When such trash is taken to the nest, it represents a threat to the chick. Raising condors in the wild remains a hazardous undertaking.

The successes of 2007 are promising for the future. In spring 2008, three new nests were discovered near the Big Sur coast, some in surprising proximity to heavily used and beautifully scenic State Highway 1. The parents of "Centennia" remain paired and have been observed in pre-breeding behavior. "Ventana" remains free-flying along the Big Sur coast, accompanied by her parents, and bearing wing

tag #1. She has already taught local biologists new information. VWS's condor biologist Joe Burnett reports that she is more wary than any other of the young condors, suggesting that youngster from wild nests might be better adapted to avoid people and man-made dangers.

VWS founder Sal Lucido has said that "with passion and tenacity, you can accomplish anything." It was that attitude that overcame the many obstacles to the return of the Condor to the central California coast. With the help of a few highly motivated individuals, the future looks brighter than it ever has for this magnificent bird. You can follow the program's progress on the VWS web site: www.ventanaws.org. Membership information and monthly updates are available there.

Acknowledgments

Lloyd Kiff graciously arranged access to the condor egg collection back in 1983. Joe Burnett, VWS's senior wildlife biologist for the condor project, and Sal Lucido graciously agreed to interviews for this article, and Burnett provided many of the photographs. The executive director of VWS, Kelly Sorenson, and staff were very helpful in locating photographs and arranging permission for use. Lucido, Burnett, Kiff, and Rita Carratello provided helpful comments on an earlier draft.

Further reading

Cooper, J. G. 1871. Monterey in the dry season. Amer. Naturalist 4: 756-758.

Cooper, J. G. 1890. A doomed bird. Zoe 1: 248-249.

Kiff, L., D. B. Peahull, and S. R. Wilbur. 1979. Recent changes in California Condor eggshells. Condor 81: 166-172.

Koford, C. B. 1953. The California Condor. National Audubon Soc. Res. Rep. No. 4: 1-154.

Pemberton, J. R., and H. W. Carriger. 1915. A partial list of the summer resident land birds of Monterey County. Condor 17: 189-201.

Roberson, D. 1985. Monterey Birds. Monterey Pen. Audubon Soc., Carmel, CA.

Roberson, D. 2002. Monterey Birds, 2d ed. Monterey Pen. Audubon Soc., Carmel, CA.

Roberson, D., and C. Tenney. 2003. Atlas of the Breeding Birds of Monterey County, California. Monterey Pen. Audubon Soc., Carmel, CA.

Snyder, N. F. R., and N. J. Schmitt. 2002. California Condor (*Gymnogyps californianus*) in The Birds of North America, No. 610 (A. Poole & F. Gill, eds.). The Birds of North America, Inc., Philadelphia, PA.

Snyder, N. F. R., and H. Snyder. 2000. The California Condor, a Saga of Natural History and Conservation. Academic Press, London.

Wilbur, S. R. 1978. The California Condor, 1966-76: a look at its past and future. U. S. Dept. of Interior, Fish & Wildlife Service, North American Avifauna 72.

Don Roberson splits his interest between his local patch, Monterey County in California, and photographing birds worldwide.
He has authored four books on Monterey or California. His web site www.montereybay.com/ creagrus features pages on world bird families.

Are All Birds Equal?

The Role of Biodiversity

WHY IS BIODIVERSITY SO IMPORTANT and what is the point of engaging in local conservation of globally common birds when there are so many rarer birds that no one cares about? Erik Hirschfeld has met with world-famous conservationist Dr. Nigel Collar who guides us through some ethical stumbling-blocks in conservation.

B iodiversity is defined as the totality of genes, species and ecosystems of a region. Why is biodiversity so important and what exactly is biodiversity when it comes to birds? How does avian biodiversity relate to 'total' biodiversity?

The term 'biodiversity', compressing the original usage 'biological diversity', is simply designed to encapsulate something rather more objective and specific than the words 'nature' and 'wildlife', both of which carry slightly different connotations ('nature' includes the inorganic environment, while 'wildlife' tends to omit plants and the smaller, less spectacular invertebrates). The concept came into being in the late 1970s and early 1980s, and it flourishes because it has proved so useful as a descriptor for all organismic matter. Its key quality has been its flexibility in relation to the notion of 'area': although originally coined to cover really huge, indeed unquantifiable, numbers of species and individuals, such as are found in great tracts of rainforest, it can also be applied to things as small as backgarden ponds or samples of mud from a riverbank.

There was (and is) also an important political dimension to the usage of the word. It emerged at a time when several major international conservation bodies were seriously concerned by the evidence that (1) increasing numbers of species were slipping towards extinction, and (2) the donor community was experiencing fatigue at this mounting list of cases to address. People began to talk about triage, letting species die out if their conservation was going to be too expensive or difficult. So 'biodiversity' was a very useful way of rescuing them under another name, with areas rather than individual species within them being put forward as the priceless things to be targeted for conservation.

Of course you can subdivide biodiversity for analytical or presentational purposes: it is legitimate to assess avian diversity, which is what many research studies on protected areas do, as a means of estimating the general level of biodiversity to be found in them. The expertise to assess other life-forms in these and other places often simply does not exist. The birds can thus be very helpful surrogates and indicators of where 'patches' of high organismic diversity might be. BirdLife pioneered this approach with its Endemic Bird Areas project, the results of which were published 10 years ago, and which have been crucial to many developments in biodiversity conservation, not least BirdLife's own Important Bird Areas programme.

There are 190 Critically Threatened birds spread over the globe. Do we have to save each one of them? Take Raso Lark (see p. 188) for example, with its small population, and less colourful plumage. What will happen if it disappears?

While we may not be able to secure every last species, or every last subspecies, or indeed every population, we should at least strive on their behalf, do our very best for them—under a kind of conservationist's Hippocratic oath. BirdLife International itself would die out if we ever took a policy decision to turn away from cases too problematic or expensive to address. The public would turn away from us in like measure, and in justified disgust. In any case, who really wants to start playing God in such a manner, inventing criteria for the sparing or spurning of taxa on the grounds of their distinctiveness, expensiveness, hopelessness and so on? No, we must fight for everything we can, to the best of our ability.

Arguments for conserving species sometimes hinge around human health (plant X may hold the cure for cancer), economics (hunt Y sustainably and the whole park comes for free) or ecological function (remove Z from the system and everything falls apart), and such things may sometimes be demonstrable. But we know there are cases where animals and plants block rather than bring economic development, we know that we can lose species from the system and nothing much happens (Raso surely would not miss its lark in any obvious ecological way), and what use is plant X to us once we finally do find the cure for cancer?

So we have to accept that there is another value that we attach to species, an unfocused and poorly articulated sense of the importance of diversity in human life whose strongest expression comes as the fear of losing it. We recoil at the Taliban shelling of the great stone buddhas; we are shocked when the owner of a van Gogh announces that it will be cremated with him. We might never see these works of art for ourselves, but their existence is somehow crucial to us, to our imaginations, to our sense of the sheer interest the world offers. The actual or potential disappearance of anything literally irreplaceable – for bird lovers right now, the Spoon-billed Sandpiper perhaps most immediately comes to mind – causes great angst in the hearts of many and probably most people. This is John Donne (Jacobean poet and preacher, 1572–1631) territory: it is we ourselves who are diminished by species loss, and it is this diminishment of ourselves which we try to prevent and, if unsuccessful, mourn. In my view it is,

*Goldfinch Carduelis carduelis
is introduced by man to New Zealand*

ultimately, a loss of our imaginative freedom, and I think of imaginative freedom as essential to our political and individual well-being—the oxygen to our capacity for happiness.

When we talk about ecosystems on earth, we tend to remove ourselves from them. But are we not inevitably part of the ecosystems ourselves, even if we destroy them by regulating rivers for safeguarding our water supplies, growing crops for our food or energy requirements, and introducing Goldfinches to New Zealand to be reminded of home? Some of our waste gets recycled and feeds back into the ecosystem. Large meteorites possibly erased dinosaurs from earth, was that part of a natural evolution or something that should have been stopped? We talk today about stopping a meteorite from hitting us, but what is the reasoning behind that from a conservation point of view? Isn't a meteorite an act of nature? If it is stopped, the reasons must surely be more selfish, i e to preserve mankind.

Of course we are a part of the planet's ecosystems and our destructive influence on them has never been greater. Our waste is not just nourishing plants right now, of course—it's also nourishing the greenhouse effect. In fact, global warming is so much more imminent a threat than a large meteorite that we may as well take that as our subject here. It is certainly 'an act of nature'. Whether it's our fault or not, it's happening, and the consequences are very likely to be utterly horrific, with mass human migration, hardship and starvation, involving serious and possibly complete economic and social collapse. This kind of scenario, where the survival of society and civilisation itself is at stake, reshapes our priorities, as when on a plane they tell you to fit your own oxygen mask before you help someone else. If we think for a moment about what rising sea-levels will do to our cities and infrastructures, and what redistributed rainfall patterns and ocean currents will do to our food security, we realise that we have to act now simply in order to save ourselves. But in the very act of doing so we give ourselves the best chance of saving the planet's biodiversity. If we fail, nobody is going to be out there guarding the world's nature reserves, and biodiversity is going to be left entirely to its fate. A huge extinction spasm will occur, and the human population that survives to the other side of it will have an unimaginably duller, poorer global environment from which to eke out its new living.

If we don't want any of this to happen, we have to make some big decisions and sacrifices now, but the collective political will is probably too weak to accept these things until the first major planetary shock, by which time it may be too late. This weakness of collective political will is of course a direct result of the selfishness to which the questions refer. Individual institutions, nations, economies, persons: all are inherently selfish, and seek to look after their best interests, which usually means those which are most immediately obvious and pressing. Meanwhile, however, individuals can make their own decisions and sacrifices, and the more we band together in support of sensible self-restraint, resulting in sustainability in the way we consume global resources, the more we have a chance of getting our views and behaviour accepted into mainstream political behaviour.

Photo: © Peter Hodum

Juan Fernandez Firecrown Sephanoides fernandensis (above) is competing with self-introduced Green-backed Firecrown S. sephanoides

Enjoying biodiversity.

How should we act, from a conservation point of view, when a self-introduced species is outcompeting an indigenous species? The example of the Least Concern Green-backed Firecrown versus the Critically Endangered Juan Fernandez Firecrown (see p. 164) springs to my mind. And if the Juan Fernandez Firecrown is helped by introduced plants which flower at times when it normally would have difficulties finding food, should we avoid eradicating these introduced plants which could have a detrimental effect on natural vegetation?

Self-introductions are probably always the result of anthropogenic changes to landscapes and habitats. We have the same thing happening on continents where clearance of forest allows two closely related non-forest species to come into contact with each other and begin hybridising, sometimes with worrying consequences for one of them. Would the alien firecrown have been able to get a lasting foothold on the Juan Fernandez islands without the habitat change that men have wrought over centuries? I doubt it—and we have to remember that, if background (i.e. natural) extinction rates are to be believed, we should only be witnessing truly man-independent extinctions every few thousand years. So, of course, if we caused it we should fix it. And in fact I think we should fix it anyway, even with species, if there are any and if we could ever be

sure, that are dying out for entirely natural reasons. Nothing is going to last forever; but the longer the diversity of the planet is with us our lives are the richer, and it seems inconceivable to me that we would wash our hands—indicating our lack of guilt or complicity—of species that are slipping into oblivion.

There are quite a few cases where indigenous birds have come to depend on non-indigenous plants. A good case is the Mauritius Fody: pretty much the only trees in which it can now nest are introduced Cryptomeria, because only these trees have properties (sticky sap on the bark, spiky needles) that prevent easy access by introduced rats. When you think about it for a minute, adaptations of this type are happening all the time, with various degrees of success. What would Barn Swallows do these days without barns, House Martins without houses? Birds and human beings are heavily interlinked that it would be impossible, really, to turn away from trying to save a species on the grounds that nature is simply taking its course.

You consider species diversity as a right of freedom. We have the freedom to enjoy biodiversity, a bit selfish perhaps, but a nice thought. But isn't this putting a western perspective on things, isn't it a luxury that we, with our basic needs fulfilled, feel? Many of the world's people see nature as something

else, as a resource. And when it comes to birds there are different ways of enjoying them; twitching is one, ringing another, egg-collection (which is hopefully not so common now) a third and hunting a fourth, all being pursued with a sense of freedom for the pursuer. Biodiversity is important for all of them. For which one of these interests should we save biodiversity?

I have already acknowledged that (1) sometimes arguments and scenarios exist by which biodiversity can be defended for the material values that it offers, in terms of health, ecological security and economic wellbeing, and that (2) these values do not, and cannot, always apply. Ultimately we have to be as honest as possible about our wish to preserve things. We do it because we love or take pleasure in the things in question, we estimate them for merely being, they bring us inspiration and comfort—and, in my final formulation, the freedom of the mind. If we are honest on these matters, we stand a chance that people who do not perhaps immediately share our values will nonetheless respect them and be willing to accommodate them. Moreover, I think it is merely an assumption that people less materially secure than westerners will automatically feel indifference to or contempt for our values. Many indigenous people deeply respect and revere nature, even while they exploit it as of course they must.

I think there is also a duty of care that we should not be shy of shouldering, without fear of being labelled western ecological imperialists. Where nature continues to be treated as a commons, accessible to all, there is scope for major conflicts of interest in which nature itself is customarily the biggest loser. But it follows that, if natural resources are depleted beyond sustainability, the users soon become big losers too. The tragedy of the commons is something we can overcome only through the medium of education and negotiation. Although conservationists may often be portrayed as standing in the way of development, it is actually they who offer human societies the best ways of maintaining the ecological equilibrium on which all our livelihoods depend. We are back to the sensible self-restraint I mentioned in a previous answer.

I do not think it is possible to say that animals or species have rights. At any rate, I prefer to argue that only people have rights. These rights include (1) the right to be assured that animals

Breeding Least Concern White-backed Woodpeckers in captivity leads to global conservation.

Photo: © Tom Svensson/Nordens Ark

Photo: © Tom Svensson/Nordens Ark

do not suffer when, in whatever way, they are coerced into contributing to human wellbeing, and (2) the right to live in a world as diverse and rich as human conservation endeavour (and self-restraint) will allow. The bearer of these rights ought ideally to be able, under law, to require governments to preserve species in viable numbers in areas under their control, and to find ways of ameliorating any actual or perceived adverse social impact of such conservation interventions. Mentioning here the rights of people to expect minimal suffering in animals helps frame my answer to the question of hunting, which is obviously not a clear-cut or easy issue. People do of course have rights, and where they do not impinge on others there is little to be said: twitching (if one discounts the carbon footprint) and ringing are both harmless pursuits that bring people satisfaction. Egg-collecting and hunting can have serious impacts on species, so the right of people to do these things has to be set against other people's rights to expect protection of the birds in question and the minimisation of their suffering.

In your writings you have touched on the subject of conserving a species locally versus biodiversity on a global scale. In many countries, local and national enthusiasts spend much effort and money on preserving globally widespread species, such as Barn Owl, Osprey and White-backed Woodpecker. Is this how we should work saving biodiversity? While other species in places where there are no enthusiasts remain neglected? What is our responsibility here?

This is an intriguing and important issue. The answer is surely that there has to be a balance. The RSPB would not be the powerhouse of conservation that it is today—in Britain, Europe and world—were it not for its dedicated campaigns to protect the Osprey and the Avocet in Britain as they made their first tentative efforts to recolonise Britain after decades of absence. The fact that these two species were never globally at risk is irrelevant: among the British public local and national pride in their return helped transform the RSPB into a major conservation body. This emotional response to a situation you can influence, if only by joining forces in a society, can produce a momentum of its own, and in due course result in exposure to all the obscurer issues and problems beyond the immediate loyalties of place and nation (i.e. you start by supporting Avocets and end by supporting Jerdon's Courser). Moreover, scientific work on these national rarities can engender great expertise that then becomes available for application in other contexts.

But this is not to minimise the need for interventions now in many parts of the world where, indeed, only one or two dedicated heroes, and sometimes no-one at all, may stand between certain Critically Endangered species and oblivion. BirdLife International has always sought to ensure that globally threatened species are the focus for major attention, and our new initiative to promote the conservation of the most highly threatened birds – the Preventing Extinctions Programme – has sprung

into life precisely in order to spread the conservation response and responsibility among a wider audience of sympathisers and well-wishers.

I am also keen to see academics doing more to set their students on highly threatened species, using money from standard educational (non-conservation) sources, since scientific research projects can be a good way of generating valuable data and even more valuable awareness and commitment. The BirdLife position – its bottom line – is that nothing shall become extinct by the consequences of human actions if it is humanly possible to prevent it. We champion the right and need to act locally and conserve local biodiversity. In many ways this really is an imperative, but we are constantly seeking to remind the richer nations, institutions and partners that the world beyond their present purview has some desperately urgent cases that we should do all we can to address.

Photo: © Karen Hsu

Nigel J. Collar is Leventis Fellow in Conservation Biology with BirdLife International, for which he has worked for 27 years. He is the senior author/editor of Threatened Birds of Africa and Related Islands *(1985),* Threatened Birds of the Americas *(1992) and* Threatened Birds of Asia *(2001), as well as* Key Forests for Threatened Birds in Africa *(1988),* Birds to Watch *(1988) and* Birds to Watch 2 *(1994), plus a string of contributions to the* Handbook of the Birds of the World, *for which he is conservation consultant. He works closely with the University of Cambridge and the University of East Anglia, and currently has PhD students working on bird conservation issues in Cambodia (3), the Philippines (2), Cyprus, Botswana and Amazonian Peru.*

Avocet (*Recurvirostra avosetta*)

Bamboo Specialists
Birds of the Atlantic Forest

THIS YEAR IN ARGENTINA, a rare event – flowering of the Takuarusu (*Guadua chacoensis*) – is giving us a unique opportunity to search for one of the world's most endangered birds, the Purple-winged Ground-Dove (*Claravis godefrida*). Like many other birds of the Atlantic forest biodiversity hotspot, the Purple-winged Ground-Dove is threatened by severe habitat destruction. Unlike most other species, however, it depends not only on the Atlantic forest, but on a key resource that fluctuates enormously over space and time: bamboo seeds.

Seeds of the Takuarembo (Chusquea ramosissima) seem to be preferred by Uniform Finches.

The Purple-winged Ground-Dove is critically endangered, with only a few undocumented records in recent years. In reviewing the published records of this dove in Argentina, we noticed that it is only recorded in Argentina every 15-18 years, coinciding perfectly with the flowering events of our two common Guadua bamboos: Takuarusu and Yatevo (*Guadua trinii*). In 2007 we set out to look for the mysterious Purple-winged Ground Dove in the first stands of flowering Takuarusu around Puerto Iguazú, in the province of Misiones. Since there seem to be no recordings of its voice, we could not use playback. Never the less, our recent sight record at Iguazú National Park encouraged further expeditions to other sites with Guadua bamboo, where we hope to tape-record this elusive bird.

Bamboo: a resource for birds

The Purple-winged Ground-Dove belongs to an interesting but poorly studied group of birds: the bamboo specialists. Bamboos are a diverse tribe of grasses, with more than 1,500 described species worldwide. They form a key component of forest ecosystems in Asia, Africa, Oceania, and South America, but reach their peak diversity in parts of Asia and South America. The Atlantic forest of Brazil, Paraguay and Argentina is one of the most important centres of bamboo diversity, and supports an unusually rich community of bamboo specialist birds.

A key feature of bamboo biology is especially critical for the conservation of specialist birds. Fast-growing and often invasive, most bamboos are semelparous. Each plant flowers only once, then dies. Additionally, many bamboos are masting plants. Over large areas, they reproduce vegetatively without flowering for many years, providing a stable and apparently productive habitat for a number of specialist insectivores. After many years of vegetative growth, plants of a given species will flower in synchrony, producing an incredible abundance of seeds and attracting many species of granivorous birds. These

Through a puppet show, members of the Proyecto Selva de Pino Paraná introduce rural school children to the White-bearded Antshrike, a little-known, globally vulnerable species that lives in Yatevo bamboo on their farms. In Argentina, environmental education is key for conserving this Yatevo bamboo specialist.

Photo: © K. Cockle

include generalist granivores like parrots, but they also include nomadic bamboo seed specialists like the Purple-winged Ground-Dove, which travel long distances between patches of masting bamboos, to take advantage of this locally abundant food resource. The period between flowering events can be up to 150 years, depending on the species of bamboo. The Takuarusu, for example, flowers synchronously over a large area every 30 years, then dies.

Bamboo-specialist insectivores

Bamboo-specialist insectivores feed on insects in, on, and around living bamboo. In Southeast Asia, the Bamboo Woodpecker (*Gecinulus viridis*) is found only in stands of bamboo. In 1973, L. Short described the close relationship between this inconspicuous bird and its bamboo habitat. The woodpecker climbs the slippery bamboo with its legs clasped around the stalk, methodically gleaning and sometimes drilling for ants. It drums on bamboo to signal, and apparently nests in cavities in bamboo. Similarly, in south-western Amazonia, the Rufous-headed Woodpecker (*Celeus spectabilis*) feeds on insects in stands of large spiny Guadua bamboos.

A diverse suite of bamboo specialist insectivores inhabit the Atlantic forest. The Yellow Tyrannulet (*Capsiempis flaveola*) hunts for insects among the leaves and stems of various species of bamboo, sometimes using bamboo fibres to build its cup-like nest on the node of the bamboo, where the leaves meet the culm. When a favoured species of bamboo dies, Yellow Tyrannulets become uncommon and move to other species of bamboo. The Large-headed Flatbill (*Ramphotrigon megacephalum*) also hunts for insects, but, at least in Argentina and Paraguay, it

Adult male Temminck's Seedeater in the understory of flowering Takuarusu at Iguazú National Park

Photo: © K. Cockle

is a specialist on Guadua bamboo and is not found in other bamboo genera. Bertoni's Antbird (*Drymophila rubricollis*) and the Dusky-tailed Antbird (*Drymophila malura*) are common understory insectivores that specialize on dense thickets of Merostachys or Chusquea bamboo, becoming rare when these bamboos die.

One of the most fascinating bamboo-specialist insectivores of the Atlantic forest is the White-bearded Antshrike (*Biatas nigropectus*). Globally, it is considered vulnerable. In Argentina, at least, it has only been found in spiny Guadua bamboo, especially Yatevo. A secretive bird, it seldom sings and is easily overlooked. What does it eat and why does it only inhabit Guadua bamboo? With so little habitat remaining, will it be able to survive through the next massive die-off of Yatevo, expected for 2018?

Bamboo seed specialists

In 1972, H. D. Jackson was one of the first to point out the specialist relationship between a seed-eating bird and the masting events of bamboo. He noticed that records of the Pied Mannikin (*Lonchura fringilloides*) in Rhodesia were closely tied to masting events of the Bindura Bamboo (*Oxytenanthera abyssinica*), which produces seeds about every 30 years.

An unusual diversity of bamboo seed specialists is found in the Atlantic forest. In 1996, F. Olmos reported large numbers of Uniform Finches (*Haplospiza unicolor*) breeding during a masting event of Chusquea bamboo in the Atlantic forest of Brazil. In Argentina, there always seem to be some patches of Chusquea ramosissima bamboo with seeds, providing a constant source of food for the Uniform Finch. The globally vulnerable Temminck's Seedeater (*Sporophila falcirostris*) and Buff-fronted Seedeater (*Sporophila frontalis*), on the other hand, like the Purple-winged Ground-Dove, appear only when Guadua bamboos are flowering. However, both species have been observed feeding on other bamboo seeds, and the Buff-fronted Seedeater has been suggested to feed on rice crops in Brazil.

Dr. Walter Braun, a retired agricultural scientist from Petropolis, has a unique perspective on bamboo seed specialists of the Atlantic forest, having watched these birds arrive during three masting events of several bamboo species in the state of Rio de Janeiro, Brazil. Dr. Braun tells of thousands of Buff-fronted Seedeaters (locally "Chanchão") arriving in 1944, 1974, and 2007, to feed on the bamboo mast, then disappearing when the seeds are gone. At these times, comments Dr Braun "the three species of flowering bamboos are like blankets covering the forest over our mountains. Flocks of hundreds of Chanchão come from several hundred meters above, descending rapidly in a spiral toward the forest, where something attracts them: either the seeds themselves, or the loud, shrill songs of the other

Alejandro Bodrati examines
a new Takuarusu culm

Takuarusu flowers (top) and seeds

Two Takuarusu plants on a small island in the Río Iguazú. The plant on the left flowered a few months later. By that time, the other plant was dead.

Photo: © J. I. Areta

In Brazil and Paraguay, nearly all of the Interior Atlantic forest has been replaced by large-scale agriculture and pastures.

Photo: © M. Debarba

Chanchãos, already inside the forest, calling for the new flock to join them."

The sound of these thousands of male Buff-fronted Seedeaters has been described by Brazilian naturalist Helmut Sick as "a unique roar that echoes strangely in the mountain forests."

Why specialise on bamboo seeds? Bamboo masting events provide an enormous abundance of large, apparently nutritious seeds. They seem to provide an excellent opportunity for nesting. Where bamboos are diverse and abundant, bamboo seed specialisation must be a good strategy, even if it requires travelling from place to place.

There is a great deal still to be learned about bamboo seed specialists. How are they different from other granivores? How do they find stands of masting bamboos? How much do they specialize on just one genus or species of bamboo? How long do they live and how far do they go in search of bamboo seeds? We know so little about the bamboo seed specialists that in many cases we do not even know which bird species belong in this group. The recent description of the Carrizal Seedeater (*Amaurospiza carrizalensis*) in Venezuela suggests that there may be several, as yet undiscovered, bamboo specialist birds.

What happens when the bamboo dies?

When the bamboo stops producing seeds in a given area, the nomadic bamboo seed specialists move elsewhere. The bamboo specialist insectivores seem to be much less mobile. How do they respond to massive bamboo death? These species have a relatively stable habitat over several generations. When their preferred species of bamboo dies, they must either move long distances or rely on less-suitable habitat, and they probably experience population declines.

We have been studying the birds of Cruce Caballero Provincial Park, in Argentina, since 2003. From 2003 to 2005, much of the understory was dominated by dense Takuapi bamboo (*Merostachys claussenii*). Bertoni's and Dusky-tailed Antbirds were abundant, and Yellow Tyrannulets were common. In 2006, the Takuapi flowered and died. By 2007, the understory was completely changed. Bertoni's Antbird, Dusky-tailed Antbird, and Yellow Tyrannulet are now uncommon, remaining only in the small patches of Guadua and Chusquea bamboo.

Threats to bamboo specialists in the Atlantic forest

Bamboo specialist insectivores are threatened by destruction of their specific bamboo habitat. While some bamboos are favoured by selective logging, the loss of more than 90% of the Atlantic forest to pasture and agriculture must have had severe impacts on many bamboo specialist insectivores, much less mobile than the nomadic birds that specialize on bamboo seeds. Clearing of Atlantic forest, and specifically bamboo stands, continues to threaten specialist insectivores like the White-bearded Antshrike.

Bamboo seed specialists like the Purple-winged Ground-Dove can move long distances, but can only

Takuarusu harvested for building materials

use each stand of bamboo for a short period of time. They need many different patches of their preferred bamboos. With the clearing of the Atlantic forest, bamboo seed specialists must travel many times farther in search of food, or make do with other food sources. The enormous loss of Atlantic forest, particularly in Brazil and Paraguay, has already disrupted the natural cycle of nomadic movements made by flocks of Purple-winged Ground-Doves, and this species may already be doomed to extinction.

Both types of bamboo specialists – insectivores and granivores – probably experience population cycles. Presumably, granivores are most abundant during masting periods of their favoured bamboos, and their populations shrink outside of those periods. Likewise, populations of insectivores like the White-bearded Antshrike presumably grow during periods between bamboo masting, and crash when their preferred bamboo dies off. Thus, to conserve bamboo specialist birds, we must work to ensure sufficient habitat so that populations do not crash to zero during periods of food shortage.

Conserving bamboo specialist birds in the Atlantic forest

Conserving bamboo specialist birds is difficult anywhere. In the Atlantic forest, the task is made even more difficult because bamboo specialist birds compete for space with the major population centres of Brazil, the most important agricultural lands in Paraguay, and some of the poorest farmers in Argentina. Conserving bamboo habitat will require efforts on several fronts. International strategies for conserving the Atlantic forest should specifically take into account bamboo habitat. Bamboo stands should be considered in the design and zoning of protected areas. Exploitation of Guadua bamboos for crafts and construction should be monitored to ensure long-term sustainability and seed supply for specialist birds. In Argentina, at least, environmental education is essential to encourage small-holder farmers to maintain, on their land, stands of bamboo for the White-bearded Antshrike, the threatened Sporophila seedeaters, and the mysterious Purple-winged Ground-Dove. Bird-watchers and scientists can help generate information to conserve these species, by taking photos of these specialist birds and photos or samples of the bamboos where they are found.

Kristina Cockle, Alejandro Bodrati and Juan Ignacio (Nacho) Areta are members of the Proyecto Selva de Pino Paraná. Based in San Pedro (Misiones, Argentina) since 2003, they work to conserve Atlantic forest birds through research on natural history and ecology, and through outreach in the local community. Kristina and Nacho are PhD candidates, Kristina at the Centre for Applied Conservation Research, University of British Columbia, and Nacho at the Universidad Nacional de la Plata. Alejandro is a naturalist with ten years experience searching for rare and threatened birds in the Atlantic forest

of Argentina and Paraguay. Kristina and Alejandro are adjunct researchers at the Fundación de Historia Natural Félix de Azara. Alejandro and Nacho belong to the Grupo FALCO, a group that aims to disseminate ornithological knowledge.

Acknowledgements
The authors are grateful to the Association of Field Ornithologists for a Pamela and Alexander Skutch Research Award that supports our study of bamboo specialist birds, to the Rufford Foundation for supporting our environmental education program in schools, and to the Administration of Parques Nacionales and the Ministerio de Ecología, RNR y Turismo, for permission to study these birds in Argentina.

Further reading
Areta, J.I. Finding a secretive bamboo specialist in the Atlantic Forest of Argentina: the White-bearded Antshrike *Biatas nigropectus*. Neotropical Birding 2: 76-79.

Areta, J. I., A. Bodrati and K. Cockle. 2009. Specialization on Guadua bamboo seeds by three bird species in the Atlantic Forest of Argentina. Biotropica, in press.

Bertoni, A. de W. 1917. El Tambú y la muerte de las tacuaras en Sud-América. Proceedings of the Second Pan American Scientific Congress 4: 812-814.

Bodrati, A., and J. I. Areta. 2006. La Mosqueta Pecho Pardo (*Hemitriccus obsoletus*) en la Argentina y comentarios sobre su hábitat y distribución. Ornitologia Neotropical 17: 597-600.

Bodrati, A., and K. Cockle. 2006. Habitat, distribution, and conservation of Atlantic Forest birds in Argentina: notes on nine rare or threatened species. Ornitologia Neotropical 17: 243-258.

Bodrati, A., and K. Cockle. 2006. New records of rare and threatened birds from the Atlantic forest of Misiones, Argentina. Cotinga 26: 20-24.

Collar, N. J., L. P. Gonzaga, N. Krabbe, A. Madroño Nieto, L. G. Naranjo, T. A. Parker, III, and D.C. Wege. 1992. Threatened Birds Of The Americas, The ICBP/IUCN Red data Book 2, 3rd Ed. International Council for Bird Preservation, Cambridge, UK.

Franklin, D. C. 2004. Synchrony and asynchrony: observations and hypotheses for the flowering wave in a long-lived semelparous bamboo. Journal of Biogeography 31: 773-786.

Jackson, H. D. 1972. The status of the Pied Mannikin, *Lonchura fringilloides* (Lafresnaye) in Rhodesia and its association with the bamboo *Oxytenanthera abyssinica*. Rhodesia Science News 6: 342-348.

Janzen, D. H. 1976. Why bamboos wait so long to flower. Annual Review of Ecology and Systematics 7: 347-391.

Judziewicz, E. J., L. G. Clark, X. Londoño, and M. J. Stern. 1999. American Bamboos. Smithsonian Institution Press, Washington, DC.

Kratter, A.W. 1997. Bamboo specialization by Amazonian birds. Biotropica 29: 100-110.

Lentino, M., and R. Restall. 2003. A new species of *Amaurospiza* Blue Seedeater from Venezuela. The Auk 120: 600-606.

Olmos, F. 1996. Satiation or deception?: Mast-seeding Chusquea bamboos, birds and rats in the Atlantic Forest. Revista Brasileira de Biologia 56: 391-401.

Parodi, L. R. 1936. Las bambúseas indígenas en la Mesopotamia argentina. Revista Argentina de Agronomía 3: 229-244.

Parodi, L. R. 1955. La floración de la tacuara brava ("Guadua trinii"). Revista Argentina de Agronomía 22: 134-136.

Vasconcelos, M.F. 2002. O pixoxó (*Sporophila frontalis*) nos municípios do Serro e Santa Bárbara, Minas Gerais: possíveis casos de extinçoes locais. Atualidades Ornitologicas 103: 2.

Vasconcelos, M. F., A. P. Vasconcelos, P. L. Viana, L. Palú, and J. F. Silva. 2005. Observações sobre aves granívoras (*Columbidae* e *Emberizidae*) associadas à frutificação de taquaras (*Poaceae, Bambusoideae*) na porção meridional da Cadeia do Espinhaço, Minas Gerais, Brasil. Lundiana 6: 75-77.

Religion, Tradition and Bird Conservation

IN 1995, THE FIRST OF A SERIES of symposia took place under the patronage of Ecumenical Patriarch Bartholomew of the Greek Orthodox Church. The Aegean Symposium, held on the ferry boat Preveli as it travelled from the Greek port of Piraeus via Istanbul to the island of Patmos, brought together representatives of the Christian, Muslim, Jewish, Hindu, Buddhist, Jainist, Sikh, Zoroastrian and Baha'i religions, with scientists, economists and policy-makers. The voyage was "an important step in the long-running effort to find common ground among religious and scientific leaders who share similar concerns about the environment, but whose historical antagonism has often blocked collaboration".

Metropolitan John of Pergamon gave the opening address. "We are used to regarding sin mainly in anthropological or social terms, but there is also sin against nature, since evil upsets the created order as a whole. The solution of the ecological problem is not simply a matter of management and technicalities, important as these may be. It is a matter of changing our very world view. For it is a certain world view that has created and continues to sustain the ecological crisis."

Six more symposia followed, in the Black Sea, Danube, Adriatic, Baltic, Amazon, and most recently (2007) the Arctic, which was chosen to highlight the rapid shrinking of polar ice under the influence of global warming and the way that pollution, no respecter of borders, can impact distant human and ecological communities. The Arctic symposium called for a commitment to "the principles of interdependence which are common to both religion and science".

It may be news to some of us in the conservation community that there is any common ground between science and religion. For many secular environmental thinkers, the publication in 1967 of the essay *The Historical Roots of Our Ecologic Crisis* had a profound and lasting effect. Lynn White, a professor of medieval history at the University of California, asserted that "we shall continue to have a worsening ecological crisis until we reject the Christian axiom that nature has no reason for existence save to serve man". Christianity, "in absolute contrast to ancient paganism and Asia's religions, not only established a dualism of man and nature, but also insisted that it is God's will that man exploit nature for his proper ends".

White could draw on plenty of examples from his homeland. But his thesis was far from true of all Christians then, and is even less true now, when the organisation A Rocha is only one of a number of Christian movements working for biodiversity with communities and with other faith groups. In recent years, even the right wing evangelical Christians of the USA, among the most implacable foes of environmentalism, have begun to be won over, thanks to the influence of some religious leaders, and of Christians among the scientific community like Edward O Wilson (author of *The Creation: An Appeal to Save Life on Earth* (2006), which takes the form of a letter to a Southern Baptist pastor).

But at the same time, the environmental protections bound into the practices of Hinduism, Buddhism, Islam and other religions have begun to break down under the pressure of globalisation. In response, Patriarch Bartholomew's Religion, Science and the Environment Movement, a multi-faith approach to changing our world view, has been joined by others like the Alliance of Religions and Conservation (ARC), which works through many faith groups to increase conservation awareness among the communities of places which are important for biodiversity, and to strengthen the traditional practices which have helped to conserve them.

Sacred groves

For some decades past, scholars in India, Ghana, Ethiopia and elsewhere have been looking into the role that sacred groves and mountains, and other sites protected from exploitation, have had in the preservation of areas of forest. These are not confined to the developing world: monasteries in Greece, Bulgaria and Romania have also protected their lands. What is striking is how many of these sacred sites form part of Important Bird Areas identified by BirdLife International.

"There are obviously profound links between people's faith, and the way they treat the environment," said David Thomas, Head of BirdLife's Environment and Sustainable Development Division. "BirdLife has barely begun to explore the link between IBAs and sacred sites, but it's clearly an extremely important one".

New areas are also being brought under the control of conservation-minded, faith-influenced management. The Society for the Protection of Nature in Lebanon (SPNL, BirdLife in Lebanon) is pioneering the revival of a traditional Islamic approach to land management, the *hima*. Once governed by tribal chiefs and religious leaders, *hima* were intended to ensure the sustainable and fair use of the land. The modern form of *hima* will be governed by municipalities and other democratically elected bodies.

SPNL's first two *hima* were the Ebel es-Saqi IBA, centred on a remote, ancient village in a migration bottleneck, where a forested hill-top provides a perfect watch-point for soaring birds such as raptors and pelicans; and the Kfar Zabad wetland IBA, a small marshland in the Bekaa Valley, part of the Syrian-African Great Rift Valley, on the main migration route for African-Eurasian water birds. SPNL has recorded the Vulnerable Syrian Serin *Serinus syriacus* and a number of regionally threatened bird species at Kfar Zabad.

BirdLife International is working with its Middle Eastern Partners to revive the *hima* across the region and elsewhere. One of the newest members of the BirdLife Partnership, Qatar's Friends of the Environment Centre, brought with it a $1 million

donation to establish *hima* in the Arab world.

Maronite Christians, major landowners in Lebanon, have also been active, establishing some the country's most important cedar forests as reserves. A Rocha has worked with SPNL to identify Lebanon's IBAs.

The Ethiopian Highlands have been largely deforested; only small islands of woodland remain. All traditional Ethiopian religions have worked to conserve patches of relict natural vegetation, but most are the responsibility of the Orthodox Church, the dominant religion of the Highlands.

In 2001 a Darwin Initiative (UK) funded project was initiated between the University of Wales and the Ethiopian Wildlife and Natural History Society (BirdLife in Ethiopia), in conjunction with the Ethiopian Orthodox Church and the Alliance of Religions and Conservation, to promote sustainable development through participatory conservation of the biodiversity of the forests preserved on sacred lands, and their establishment as a resource of value to alleviate local poverty.

Cultural diversity and biodiversity

The World Commission on Protected Areas is one of several large conservation NGOs which is analysing the relationship between sacred sites and areas that have remained worth protecting. In 2006, a number of organisations including the United Nations Environment Programme (UNEP) and IUCN-the World Conservation Union came together in an initiative to conserve ancient sacred sites, in the belief that these culturally important locations may be a key to saving the world's declining biodiversity.

Among supporters of the project, "Conservation of Biodiversity Rich Sacred Natural Sites", was the Guatemalan Nobel Peace Prize laureate Rigoberta Menchu, who pointed out that "it is not accidental that where indigenous peoples live is where the greatest biological diversity exists too. The values on which indigenous peoples have built our complex systems are founded in the ethical, spiritual and sacred nature that links our peoples with the whole work of creation."

At the launch of the initiative, Klaus Toepfer, UNEP's Executive Director, asserted that "there is clear and growing evidence of a link between cultural diversity and biodiversity, between reverence for the land and a location and a breadth of often unique and special plants and animals. Conserving sacred sites and their biological richness can play a major role in achieving the 2010 biodiversity target, and perhaps act as beacons from where good and sustainable management practices can be exported to nearby areas and beyond."

Gonzalo Oviedo of IUCN explained: "Communities managing such sites have made many efforts locally to try and boost their prospects, but to date global action has been far from the level needed to ensure a global shift in their fortunes. This project

Storks are seen as under God´s special protection, because they often choose the high roofs of churches and mosques for their nests.

aims to cement a wide alliance and mobilise the international attention so urgently needed in this neglected field."

Rules, taboos and spirit guardians

With funding from the Global Environment Facility, the analysis of sacred sites now extends to all continents except Antarctica, sometimes in partnership with organisations like ARC and the Athens-based Mediterranean Initiative for Nature and Anthropos (Med-INA), which hosts the workshops of the Delos Initiative, part of the IUCN/WCPA Task Force on Cultural and Spiritual Values of Protected Areas.

The pilot network of sacred sites included the Arquipélago dos Bijagós in Guinea-Bissau. Composed of 88 islands and a large intertidal area of mudflat and mangrove, this site has been identified by BirdLife as an IBA (GW007). BirdLife's site description says "this area is second only in importance in West Africa to the Banc d'Arguin in Mauritania (IBA MR007) for the numbers of Palearctic waders present during the northern winter. It has been estimated that up to 700,000 birds occur in the archipelago at this time. The area also includes a number of heronries as well as breeding colonies of ibises, gulls and terns."

The Bijagos community observes a range of rules.

Certain areas are off-limits or confined to those who have completed their ceremonial duties. In many of the sites certain activities are banned, including sexual relations, burials, the shedding of blood, and construction of permanent settlements.

"These traditional practices of the Bijagos effectively assist in the preservation of the sites for flora and fauna," said UNEP's Oviedo. "The most valued sites for biodiversity also happen to be the most sacred ones."

There are many other African IBAs which include sacred forests, such as Bakossi mountains (CM022), which BirdLife describes as "one of the three most important sites for the conservation of local endemics along the Cameroon chain", with species including the Endangered Mount Kupe Bush-shrike *Malaconotus kupeensis*, and Vulnerable Green-breasted Bush-shrike *Malaconotus gladiator* and Grey-necked Picathartes *Picathartes oreas*. Mount Kenya (KE005), which has enormous traditional religious significance for the Kikuyu people who live around it, has a rich montane bird fauna including the Endangered Sharpe's Longclaw *Macronyx sharpei* (see p. 230) and Vulnerable Abbott's Starling *Cinnyricinclus femoralis*.

Also identified as IBAs are some of Kenya's Kayas (Kaya Gandini KE012 and Kaya Waa KE013), patches of forest of ceremonial significance, varying in size from 10 ha to over 150 ha, and protected by tribal elders. They are of importance for Endangered

Animistic temple of the Bijagos-people on the island of Organo, which is also a national park.

The Great Hornbill occurs in Cambodia's Central Cardamoms, where Buddhist monks are teaching the importance of conservation.

Spotted Ground-thrush *Zoothera guttata* and Sokoke Pipit *Anthus sokokensis*.

Parts of Tsimanampetsotse Strict Nature Reserve in Madagascar (IBA MG069) are protected by a local fady or taboo. Eighty-eight species are known from this site, of which 35 are endemic to Madagascar, including the Vulnerable Madagascar Plover *Charadrius thoracicus*. The Endangered Madagascar Teal *Anas bernieri* has been recorded on the lake.

China's Xishuangbanna National Park includes many sacred groves protected by Buddhist villagers, where hunting, wood-cutting and cultivation are forbidden. It has been estimated that these groves amount to 100,000 hectares –or five per cent of the total area. Xishuangbanna is also an IBA (CN233), where the Critically Endangered White-rumped Vulture *Gyps bengalensis*, the Vulnerable Green Peafowl *Pavo muticus*, Rufous-necked Hornbill *Aceros nipalensis* and Giant Nuthatch *Sitta magna*, and the near-threatened Hume's Pheasant *Syrmaticus humiae* can all be found.

The Central Cardamoms IBA in Cambodia (KH013) comprises all the areas of evergreen and semi-evergreen forest in the central Cardamom Mountains above 400 metres, which is thought to be the lower altitudinal limit of Vulnerable Chestnut-headed Partridge *Arborophila cambodiana*, one of the two restricted-range species found in the Cambodia-Thailand Mountains Endemic Bird Area.

Large expanses of relatively intact lowland evergreen forest within the IBA make it a potentially important site for the conservation of Near-Threatened Great Hornbill *Buceros bicornis*. Historically both Endangered White-winged Duck *Cairina scutulata* and Critically Endangered White-shouldered Ibis *Pseudibis davisoni* were recorded within the IBA, but their current status is unknown. Monks from the Association of Buddhists for the Environment, supported by ARC, are spreading the importance of conservation among local villagers.

The Cayapas Mataje reserve in Ecuador is protected by a belief in spirit guardians which has survived the conversion of local communities to the Catholic faith. The site is a complex of estuaries and mangrove forests within the Choco-Darien-Western Ecuador hotspot. It is an IBA, with species including the Endangered Baudo Guan *Penelope ortoni*.

Kuna Park, Panama, in the Darién lowlands EBA, is managed by the Kuna people, for whom "forests are sanctuaries where the spirits hang their clothes from the tops of the tallest trees. If they cut down the trees, the spirits will punish them". Species include the Vulnerable Choco Tinamou *Crypturellus kerriae* and Spiny-faced Antshrike *Xenornis setifrons*. Both are threatened by habitat loss elsewhere in their ranges.

Europe's sacred sites include Mount Athos and the

*Some Purple Martin populations
are totally dependent on humans for nest sites.*

Meteora region of Greece. Both are IBAs (GR037 and GR053), and both important sites for breeding threatened raptors. The Meteora is also important for forest species and those associated with open montane habitats.

Rain-bringers and joy-bringers

Traditions and religious practices have played a part in establishing harmonious relations between people and a number of bird species which have adapted themselves to human-modified environments, including towns and cities. Not all of them are threatened, but as environmental conditions deteriorate and many common species have begun the slide towards conservation concern, these practices need to be strengthened and encouraged. Here we look at some examples involving common species, and a number of Critically Endangered species too.

Among the mascots Beijing chose to welcome visitors to the 2008 Olympic Games was Nini, the swallow. According to Beijing's Games organisers, Nini "reflects the popularity of the swallow shape among Beijing's traditional kite-flyers. Because of the swallow's graceful aerobatic flight, Nini has also been chosen to represent gymnastics among the Olympic events."

The Beijing Bird Watching Society used Nini to promote its contribution to the 2006 World Bird Festival. "Visitors could not only watch the Barn Swallow, the character of the festival, and see the end of their southern migration, but also enjoy a variety of activities including a display of artificial nests, and kite-making," explained Fion Cheung, BirdLife's China Programme Officer. "The idea was partly to show Beijing citizens how they can take part in conservation activity."

In fact, the swallow has a long history as a symbol of luck and happiness in China. Doors and windows were often left open in order to give them access; and people even put up ledges inside their houses to encourage the birds to nest. Barn Swallows *Hirundo rustica* are not among the world's threatened species, although BirdLife's 2004 assessment of birds in Europe gives them an unfavourable conservation status and speaks of "moderate continuing decline". But in China's cities, where traditional houses with eaves and ledges that provide nest sites are being pulled down and replaced by sheer-sided high-rise, the Beijing Bird Watching Society's promotion of artificial nests may contribute to the survival of Barn Swallow in urban environments.

East of the Rocky Mountains in North America, the Purple Martin *Progne subis* is believed to nest exclusively in artificial nest boxes; the subspecies *P.s.subis* is thought to be the only bird completely dependent on man in this respect. Fortunately there is a tremendous enthusiasm for this, with many local and national Purple Martin associations running bird-box workshops every year. According to the

Photo: © Jens and Hanne Eriksen

Northern Bald Ibis

"In Birecik in southern Turkey, Northern Bald Ibises *Geronticus eremita* lived wild on cliff ledges just above roof level, and were for centuries treated with reverence. One story to explain this tolerance is that the local people believed that the 'raven' Noah had released from the Ark was in fact this bird, Abu Mengel, and that it had guided Noah and his children there from Mount Ararat. However, birds from Birecik wintered along the Red Sea coast, and it seems likely that Turkish Moslems making the Haj noticed the birds in the lands around Mecca and bore back the news that either the ibises, too, had made the great pilgrim-

age or that they would make excellent guides for the human pilgrim." Nigel Collar, *Birds and People: Bonds in a Timeless Journey* (CEMEX-Agrupación Sierra Madre-BirdLife International, 2007).

But during the second half of the 20th Century people lost their reverence for the birds, whose nest-ledges were close to their rooftops, within reach of stone-throwing children. With the intensification of agriculture, numbers plummeted. A captive breeding programme began in the 1970s, but birds were failing to return from migration, and by 1992 the bird was extinct in the wild in Turkey. In 1994 the species was declared Critically Endangered.

In 1998, with the support of the Turkish government, RSPB (BirdLife in the UK), Doga Dernegi (BirdLife in Turkey) and others, a semi-wild population was established. The birds are free-flying for five months, breeding on natural nest sites and nest-boxes on cliffs, but are taken into captivity after the breeding season, to prevent them from migrating. Ultimately, when numbers have stabilised and the factors preventing young Northern Bald Ibises returning to their breeding sites have been addressed, the population will be allowed to migrate once again.

Bali Starling

In Bali, in the Hindu part of Indonesia, the critically endangered Bali Starling *Leucopsar rothschildi* has found a safe haven in a reinvented habitat. On the tiny and arid island of Nusa Penida, an agreement was reached in 2005 between 35 villages, two nature conservation foundations and the Balinese state authorities involved in nature conservation.

Bayu Wirayuddha, director of the Friends of the National Parks Foundation under whose auspices the Bali Starling project has been running, thinks that close co-operation with the local population, who adhere to a rather strict set of religious rules, is the only way to guarantee the bird's survival.

After a release in December 2007, there are around 50 birds flying freely in the wild, and some 90 in captivity within the park's boundaries. Prior to the release date, the birds were 'offered' to the gods and commended to their protection by means of a series of religious ceremonies performed by Hindu priests.

Traditional Balinese law (Awig-awig) provides a good basis for their protection as well. This law has a strong foothold within rural Balinese society and sanctions deter potential illegal bird catchers. The port authorities have agreed to keep a close watch on illegal trafficking and bird trade.

The Bali Starling appears to be altering its breeding behaviour to adapt to the very different conditions on Nusa Penida, and the islanders were delighted to find one pair investigating the niches of a Hindu temple in the village of Saren, in search of a suitable nesting place. They consider it a sign of good luck and a blessing from above that this bird should choose a temple location for its offspring.

Yellow-crested Cockatoo *Cacatua sulphurea parvula* and Java Sparrow *Padda oryzivora* on Nusa Penida are also said to be benefiting from the protection of the Hindu religion. However, as far as is known, Bali Starling has never been native to Nusa Penida, and the project is controversial.

Photo: © Gregory Guida / www.gguida.com

Handbook of Birds of the World, early settlers took over the practice from Native Americas, who put up hollow gourds to attract the martins. Their motives –if they had any beyond enjoying the bird's company –may have been to get warning of the approach of predators, or because the birds kept down the numbers of flying insects, although some tribes apparently ground the birds into powder which they sprinkled over animal pelts, perhaps as an insecticide.

Around the world, rooftop-nesting storks are welcomed and encouraged as a sign of favour and harmony with nature. They are regarded as under God's special protection because they often choose the roofs of churches and mosques, the highest buildings in towns and villages. In mainland Europe, people build platfoms to support the often-huge bulk of their nests. In Turkey, BirdLife Partner Doga Dernegi reports that villagers have worked with power companies to make electricity pylons safe for nesting storks.

Abdim's Stork *Ciconia abdimii* arrives on its breeding grounds in Africa with the advent of the rains, so is popularly deemed a rain-bringer and protected from persecution, and like the European White Stork *Ciconia ciconia* is encouraged to nest on rooftops. In the 1950s, monks at the Buddhist Monastery of Wat Phai Lom, Thailand, are reported to have protected the country's last colony of Asian Openbill storks *Anastomus oscitans*, saving the species from local extinction. Wat Phai Lom was established as Thailand's first protected area with the help of Dr Boonsong Lekagul, founder of Thailand's Association for the Conservation of Wildlife, forerunner of the Bird Conservation Society of Thailand (BirdLife in Thailand).

But some religious traditions can unwittingly work to the detriment of threatened species. In Ecuador, the practice of cutting the central leaves of Wax Palms for the Palm Sunday procession became so widespread that it endangered the survival both of the trees, and of the Critically Endangered Yellow-eared Parrot *Ognorhynchus icterotis* and the Vulnerable Golden-plumed Parakeet *Leptosittaca branickii*, which depend on old and dead Wax Palms for nest sites

In 2001, with the slogan ¡Si vuelan las Palmas, palman los loros! ("If the palms fly away, the parrots will too!"), Aves&Conservación (BirdLife in cuador) and the Jocotoco Foundation organised national campaign for the conservation of the Wax Palm, supported by Ecuador's Ministry of Environment. Aves&Conservación established links with the Catholic Church in Ecuador, and lobbied to receive its official endorsement to promote the use of alternatives, such as corn leaves and eucalyptus. The Botanical Garden of Quito helped supply these alternatives, which were handed out at churches.

By 2008, with the support of the Catholic Church, Wax Palm fronds were no longer used in Holy Week festivals. To reinforce the message, Aves & Conservación mounts numerous activities during Palm Sunday week, including field trips, nature walks, theatre events with an environmental theme, and wall painting competitions. However, it may be too late for the Yellow-eared Parrot, which hasn't been seen in Ecuador for more than eight years

protection provided by a taboo imposed by a former Queen of Rimatara, French Polynesia saved the endangered Rimatara Lorikeet *Vini kuhlii* - formerly known as Kuhl's Lorikeet and renamed in honour of the Queen - from extinction within its natural range. There are introduced populations on two of the Northern Line Islands, Kiribati).

The lorikeet had been extirpated from Atiu and the other Cook Islands by the 1820s, hunted for its red feathers, which were used in ceremonial robes. Since then, the tree-climbing, egg-eating Black or Ship's Rat has become widely established in French Polynesia and the Cook Islands, devastating other Pacific parrot species, and dooming most hopes of reintroduction.

Storks also nest in minarets.

In 2007, 27 Rimatara Lorikeets were released on Atiu after an absence of almost two centuries. The reintroduction proposal emerged from research by Gerald McCormack and Judith Kunzlé of the Cook Islands Natural Heritage Trust.

McCormack established that Atiu, like Rimatara, had somehow remained free of Black Rats. The vegetation on Atiu was the same as on Rimatara, ensuring that the birds would find the nectar and fruit they needed.

But the reintroduction would not have been possible without the permission of the people of Rimatara, for whom the lorikeet is a symbol of joy and wellbeing.

In 2005, Cook Islands Prime Minister Jim Marurai delivered a letter from McCormack to the French Polynesian President Oscar Temaru. He in turn passed it to MANU (BirdLife in French Polynesia), who approved the programme and joined the reintroduction project. Other key partners included TIS (BirdLife in the Cook Islands), and the Zoological Society of San Diego. BirdLife International added the reintroduction to their regional programme 'Saving the Pacific's Parrots', the beneficiary of the 2006 British Birdfair.

The lorikeets were caught in mist nets in April 2007. Air Rarotonga donated two flights to transport the birds, the project team, and island representatives. "Cook Islands protocol has elaborate welcoming ceremonies, but in this case the Atiu community agreed to postpone the welcome until after the release of the birds," says Gerald McCormack. "All 27 birds flew strongly to the nearest tree, where they spent several minutes preening, orienting and exploring the immediate surroundings, before they flew out of the area."

There have been regular sightings since, with flocks of up to 13 being reported on sunny days. Gerald McCormack says the birds have spread over the whole 30 km² of the island –and four birds flew 50km to the neighbouring island of Miti'aro, where there are currently unconfirmed reports of breeding.

We have only begun to appreciate what conservationists owe to religious communities and their practices. Whether they are practical codes intended to ensure fair distribution and avoid excessive exploitation of natural resources, or involve animistic reverence for entire landscapes, they have helped preserve viable habitats and biodiversity in a rapidly degrading global environment. We must build better bridges with faith groups, and give them our support.

Nick Langley is a journalist and editorial consultant for BirdLife International.

Birdfair
and Conserving Rare Birds

WHAT DO DJIBOUTI FRANCOLIN, Restinga Antwren, Belding's
Yellowthroat, Bengal Florican, Dwarf Olive Ibis, Araripe Manakin,
Sociable Lapwing, Spoon-billed Sandpiper, Tuamotu Kingfisher and
Azores Bullfinch all have in common? Certainly, they are all rare
birds! Indeed, they are all Critically Endangered species (and are thus
included in this book) but all of them have also appeared on the posters
advertising the British Birdwatching Fair during the last two years.
Martin Davies tells the story.

The reason for this is that "The Birdfair" (as it is
now more commonly known) has taken on the
role of becoming the main global programme
sponsor of the new BirdLife International Preventing
Extinctions Programme, which was launched at
the BirdLife World Conference in Buenos Aires in
September 2008. The species on the Birdfair posters
are amongst those that will either benefit directly
from funding raised by the Birdfair or through
sponsorship deals with commercial companies that
the Fair has helped to secure.

Birdfair 2007 raised an amazing total of £226,000 for
the Preventing Extinctions Programme and the Fairs
in 2008 and 2009 will continue to raise funds to help
meet this global challenge. The 2008 Fair again had
a record attendance, so the organisers are hopeful
of another good outcome once all the accounts are
finalised.

2008 also saw the celebration of the 20th Birdfair, the
latest in the series of these annual three-day events
that take place in August every year at Rutland
Water, UK. For all this time, the Fair has been jointly
organised by The Leicestershire and Rutland Wildlife
Trust and The Royal Society for the Protection of
Birds and every year since its inception, the Fair has
raised funds for international conservation projects,
with the overall total now topping £2 million. The
2008 Fair was attended by some 320 companies and

organisations as exhibitors and around 20,000 overall
visitors, making it the biggest event of its kind in the
world focussed on birdwatching and conservation.

This all seems a far cry from the rather more modest
beginnings at Rutland in 1989 that marked the
first ever Birdfair (anywhere!). Like a lot of good
ideas, the original notion to launch an event called
a Birdfair was hatched up by a couple of friends
over a pint of beer in a pub – in this case, the rather
appropriately named "Finches Arms" in the village
of Hambleton on the shores of Rutland Water. When
Tim Appleton (Reserve Manager of the Leicestershire
and Rutland Wildlife Trust Reserve on Rutland Water)
and myself (of the Royal Society for the Protection
of Birds) decided to join forces to co-organise the
event, we had a number of ambitions we hoped to
realise. First and foremost, we wanted to support
a celebration of birds and birdwatching, to help
encourage more and more people to take an interest
in the natural world.

In the earlier years of the mid-1980s, our initial
efforts had taken the form of a few activities centred
on the Wildlife Trust reserve at Rutland Water but by
1989 it was becoming clear that that there was a gap
in the market for an actual fair focussed on birds and
wildlife. We began to realise the enormous potential
of staging such an event and set about making plans.
We wanted to provide a shop window for the rapidly

OFFICIAL PROGRAMME 2008

Sponsored by **Birdwatch** Magazine

20th ANNIVERSARY

Your guide to the **BIGGEST** birdwatching event in the world

RSPB

Birdfair

THE wildlife TRUSTS
LEICESTERSHIRE AND RUTLAND

THE BRITISH BIRDWATCHING FAIR

BIRDFAIR 2007–2009 SUPPORTING BIRDLIFE INTERNATIONAL

Preventing Extinctions: Saving the world's most threatened birds

Anglian Water Birdwatching Centre, Egleton Nature Reserve, Rutland Water
Friday 15 to Sunday 17 August 2008 9 am–5.30 pm daily

www.birdfair.org.uk

Artwork of Critically Endagered birds by Robert Gillmor; Birdfair Official Programme cover design by Maythyme Creative.

increasing range of commercial companies involved in birds and birdwatching and also the growing number of conservation groups, but we also decided to see if we could use the event to fundraise to help conserve birds and we focussed right from the start on the needs of international conservation.

RSPB membership was growing rapidly and popular birdwatching magazines were reaching Britain's news-stands, funded by a boom in advertising for binoculars and birdwatching holidays. *Swarovski Optik* offered us some sponsorship to help get the idea off the ground in that first year. Bruce Hanson of binocular retailers *in focus* joined the team bringing both additional sponsorship but also a sound commercial perspective and contacts throughout the industry, which helped us get the whole thing properly organised and establish its credibility. It is hard to remind ourselves of the efforts we had to go to in that first year to explain what we thought a Birdfair would be like and to encourage all kinds of people to join us in taking a risk by backing the idea. Thank goodness they did! To our astonishment, some 3,000 people attended the first Birdfair in 1989 and we were delighted to raise £3,000 to support the Maltese Ornithological Society in their efforts to counter bird-killing in the Mediterranean.

Securing the initial support from many of the other big brand names in binoculars and telescopes and in the emerging bird tourism market was crucial in creating that critical mass of important exhibitors that the visiting public would want to come and see.

We also got support even in those early years from a range of TV wildlife personalities and other well-known names in the birding scene. However, the 2008 Fair must certainly go down as one of the best yet, not least in the fantastic support from wildlife celebrities at the Fair. Not only were we delighted and proud to have Sir David Attenborough as our Guest Celebrity Lecturer on the Saturday night, the Fair itself saw guest appearances from Bill Oddie, Simon King, Chris Packham, Nick Baker, Mike Dilger, Janet Sumner, Jonathan Scott, and Rory McGrath.

All the fun of the Fair

Exhibitors now flock to Rutland from all over the world – more than 40 different countries were represented in 2008! Alongside the numerous trade stands (50 when we started out but now over 320!) we also put together extensive programmes of lectures, workshops and numerous other entertainments events which helped make a visit to the Fair a really great day out for anyone with an interest in birds and the countryside. And so it has remained ever since (except now you need to come for several days to have any chance of sampling it all!). For the last 7 years, all the artists at each Fair combined forces during the three days to paint a beautiful mural (16 feet x 4 feet) each year portraying the species and habitats of the project in question. Over the last two years, the two murals have now been completed showing all the 190 Critically Endangered Birds in effectively one painting (32 feet x 4 feet) - it is an impressive image, but it also brings home the scale of the challenge we are taking on!

Visitors enjoying the Trade Stands in Marquee 3, Birdfair 2008

Simon King signs his autograph for a young admirer on his stand at Birdfair 2008.

Photo: © Newton Maxwell-Harris

Despite the early successes of the Fair, in our wildest dreams we could never have imagined how over the years the Birdfair at Rutland would grow and grow … and grow. Thankfully, the growth has mostly happened gradually and incrementally, making it more manageable and easier to adjust our planning and the detailed on-site facilities. If you visit the showground at any other time of year, you will see some beautiful hay-meadows and could be forgiven for wondering where the Fair is held! But for a few weeks in August these fields are transformed into a temporary village of 20,000 people under huge marquees.

Local marquee contractors *Kingsmead Marquees* supply all the tentage, ably supported by numerous other professional local companies who provide electrical systems, PA systems, radio communications, temporary phone lines, AV facilities, catering, toilets, security, fencing and other safety systems, temporary offices, transport buggies, flooring, carpets, tables, chairs, display panels, waste disposal, etc., etc. – altogether, an amazing array of gear! Although the professional reserve team at Rutland coordinate the detailed arrangements on the ground to set up the showground (and restore it back to being a reserve afterwards!), the whole event also depends hugely on the efforts of tremendous teams of volunteers. Two staff are now employed by the Fair to run all the administrative aspects throughout the year. Various other staff from LRWT and RSPB also support particular elements, such as finance and publicity.

How does the Birdfair raise funds for conservation?

More than half the money the Fair produces for the chosen conservation project each year comes from the entrance fees paid by visitors who come into the Fair each day. 100% of these tickets fees go to the project, so it really is true that everyone attending the Fair is helping conservation. The rest of the funds comes from profits on the exhibitors stand fees, merchandising (Birdfair mugs and t-shirts, etc), the Birdfair auction, and celebrity lecture tickets. The tremendous support in kind from volunteers giving their time to help also helps a lot, saving thousands of pounds that would otherwise have to be paid in salaries to get all the various organisational tasks done.

Other than visitor ticket money, the other major source of funding is the fantastic support the Fair receives from its sponsors. These have grown steadily over the years, from just a few companies at the outset to more than 14 different enterprises in 2008, including many of the biggest brand names in the industry. *in focus* have been main sponsors from virtually the beginning but in more recent years have been joined in this role by *Viking Optical*. Associate sponsors include now *Swarovski Optik*, *Zeiss*, *Leica*, *Pentax*, *Nikon*, *Minox*, *Kowa*, *Bushnell* and *Olympus*, alongside *BBC Wildlife Magazine*, *Wildsounds* and *Naturetrek*. *Birdwatch magazine* are sponsors of the

Official Programme. Many other bird and wildlife magazines, such as, *Birds Illustrated*, *Bird Watching*, *British Birds*, *Dutch Birding*, *World Birdwatch* and *Birds* help with advertising support in their publications. Many of these sponsors have supported the event for many years, others have joined in more recently but we are enormously grateful to them all. Together their support gives us great confidence as organisers to take on the challenge of staging the event and makes a major contribution to the conservation fundraising successes.

Threatened species help Birdfair

Since almost the very beginning, the distinctive posters for the Fair have featured the wonderful artwork of Robert Gillmor, and especially the watercolours and striking linocut prints for which he is rightly famous. Over the years these have included some memorable and eye-catching images of rare birds, such as Wallace's Standardwing, Rimatara Lorikeet, Gurney's Pitta, Ivory-billed Woodpecker and Wandering Albatross. These same graphics have adorned the highly collectable Birdfair merchandise such as mugs, T-shirts and car stickers.

Until recently, each year we have selected a new international conservation project to be the focus of our fundraising efforts and of course this needed new images to help promote the cause. But the new project every year also helped the Fair because it meant we had a new story to tell and this resulted in lots of additional coverage in the birdwatching

press and even national daily newspapers. The Fair helps promote the project, but the project also helps promote the Fair!

Everyone working together for a common cause

LRWT and RSPB jointly co-organise the Fair, but do not directly fund it, nor do either organisation benefit financially from it. So, a local conservation group and a national one are working together to stage the Fair but all the funds raised go to support an international conservation project through the BirdLife International Partnership. We established this formula right from the start and it may be one of the secrets of the Fair's durability and success. The project helps give a tremendous focus to everyone's efforts and generates a fantastic feeling of engagement in something really worthwhile amongst everyone involved – organisers, exhibitors, celebrities and visitors alike and the tremendous team of volunteers are all united in a common goal – to help the birds we all care about. And it is amazing to reflect on just what has been achieved as a result of quite a lot of people for a few days each year standing around in some fields in Rutland, Britain's smallest county! As a direct result of the funds and publicity raised by the Birdfair over the years, new National Parks and other protected areas have been established in places as diverse as Spain, Poland, Vietnam, Madagascar, Halmahera and Sumatra (Indonesia) and Brazil.

Robert Gillmor producing a linocut print of the Critically Endangered Rimatara lorikeet for the 2006 Birdfair poster.

1993 Corncrake, Poland

1994 Wallace´s Standardwing, Halmahera

1996 Vietnamese Pheasant

1997 Andean Cock-of-the Rock, Ecuador

1999 Seven-coloured Tanager, Brazil

2000 Wandering Albatross

2001 Ivory-billed Woodpecker, Cuba

2002 Red-naped Trogon, Sumatra

2003 Madagascar Plover & Madagascar Heron

Paintings and linocut prints by Robert Gillmor

69

Critically Endangered Chatham Albatross and (insert) Graham Wynne (RSPB Chief Executive), Eliot Morley MP (then UK Fisheries Minister) and HE Cheryl Carolus, High Commissioner, Republic of South Africa at the opening of Birdfair 2000. Their discussions led to a conference and eventually a new international treaty, the Agreement on the Conservation of Albatrosses and Petrels.

Many of these projects have focussed on conservation of threatened bird species and habitats. Indeed, the majority of the species used in the publicity designs as flagship birds for the various projects are on the list of Globally Threatened Birds. From Red-breasted Geese and Great Bustards in Europe to Red-naped Trogons and Vietnamese Pheasants in the forests of South-east Asia, the most important actions that we can support to help these birds is to protect the sites and habitats where they are found in the wild.

Making a Difference

Sometimes the actions needed are to focus publicity and attention to counter direct threats to the individual birds. Such was the case in the year 2000, when Birdfair raised £122,000 to support the launch of the BirdLife International Save the Albatross Campaign. Some 300,000 seabirds are killed annually by being caught in long-line fisheries and as a result 19 of the 22 albatross species are now globally threatened, with four of them Critically Endangered. In 2001 a new international treaty under the legally-binding Bonn Convention was adopted – the Agreement on the Conservation of Albatrosses and Petrels (ACAP) was signed in South Africa, where BirdLife South Africa had been the main beneficiary of the funds raised by Birdfair. This was no coincidence! The agreement to hold the first conference that led to the ACAP treaty was made at Birdfair 2000, by the UK Fisheries Minister and

the South African Ambassador, who opened the Fair that year! BirdLife International and the RSPB this year doubled the number of countries in which the Albatross Task force will work and autumn 2008 saw a crucial step in the ratification of ACAP by Brazil, a country whose neighbouring seas are hugely important for many seabird species. All this started a long way from the sea in those fields in Rutland!

In 1998, the Birdfair project was to give overall support to BirdLife International's work on Globally threatened birds. BirdLife's reputation as the compilers of the hugely authoritative Red Data Books for birds was already well established. Birdfair funding went particularly to support the research and publication costs of the first ever book to illustrate all the globally threatened birds in colour and document their status in one volume - "Threatened Birds of the World". The BirdLife's CD and web-based versions that have followed are now the baseline references used by key decision makers worldwide to help focus conservation priorities for threatened birds.

From 2006 onwards, Birdfair joined forces with RSPB to establish an annual grant programme which provides small grants to ornithologists overseas for research on Critically Endangered birds. This has resulted in some exciting finds such as the rediscovery of the Chinese Crested Tern in Fujian, China, the discovery of important staging posts of Sociable Lapwings in Syria, new sites for the Fringe-

backed Fire-eye in Brazil and identification of key wintering sites for the Scaly-sided Merganser in China.
(for further details see http://tinyurl.com/6j3oru)

Why a Preventing Extinctions Programme?

So why one might ask, 10 years later, do globally threatened birds now need a Preventing Extinctions Programme and what part will Birdfair funding play in this? The short answer is that, although a great deal of good work has been and is being done to save threatened bird species, it is clearly not enough. More birds are edging towards extinction and still more species are being added to the threatened categories as each year goes by. Even more worrying is that the number of species in the most threatened category of all (Critically Endangered) is also increasing. Even where some action is taking place this most often involves research and surveys, essential preparation for other interventions, but not directly improving the species status. Conservation actions do work however and elsewhere in this book, there are some heartening stories of how the trends of decline can be reversed with well focussed projects. What is needed is greater concentration

of conservation effort on these species on the edge and increased resources to make all this happen. The Species Guardians will take responsibility on the ground to implement the necessary conservation action and the Species Champions will take on the challenge of providing or securing the financial resources to make this work possible. That is where we come in!

Birdfair 2007, 2008 and 2009 will be devoting all of the funds raised from the three Fairs to supporting the BirdLife Preventing Extinctions Programme. Two-thirds of the funds raised will go to support direct actions on the ground for species (and this work has already started); the remaining third will go to finance the Programme overall and efforts to secure Species Guardians and Species Champions for all the remaining species for which such an approach is appropriate (and that's most of them!).

So, Birdfair funds have already gone towards conservation actions for 12 Critically Endangered species, including Bengal Florican, Belding's Yellowthroat, Restinga Antwren, and Djibouti Francolin (all on the 2007 poster!), but also to Mindoro Bleeding-heart, Royal Cinclodes, Dwarf Olive Ibis, Puerto Rican Nightjar, White-shouldered Ibis, Long-billed Tailorbird, Balearic Shearwater, and Fiji Petrel.

Photo: © Newton Maxwell-Hassis

Johannes Davoras of Swarovski Optik and Norbert Schaffer of RSPB are presented pictures of Sociable Lapwing to acknowledge them becoming Species Champions for this bird. Graeme Gibson and Margaret Atwood, joint Hon Presidents of BirdLife's Rare Bird Club, make the presentations.

Sir David Attenborough talking with Robert Gillmor at Birdfair 2008

Now, Sir David Attenborough, the face and voice of the BBC Natural History Unit for more than half a century and surely one of the most influential, admired and best-liked people on British Television, is among the individuals, companies and organisations who have become Species Champions. He announced at this year's Birdfair Celebrity lecture that he would be backing efforts to conserve the Araripe Manakin in Brazil.

in focus have stepped forward to become a Species Champion for White-shouldered Ibis, *Birdwatch magazine* for Azores Bullfinch, *Swarovski Optik* and *RSPB* for Sociable Lapwing, *Wildsounds* for Spoon-billed Sandpiper, *The Peter Smith Charitable Trust* for Dwarf Olive Ibis, *Leeds Castle* for Blue-crowned Laughing Thrush, *The Reissing Family* for Blue-billed Curassow, *Dr Urs-Peter Stäubler* for Restinga Antwren, and *The James Gibson Charitable Trust* for Yellow-crested Cockatoo,

NHBS, Rare Bird Alert, Permian, Porzana Ltd, Rockjumper Birding Tours, Peter Oakley, Rare Birds Yearbook (i.e. this publication!), *Edward Keeble, Colin Shields, Arbutus Images, S G Shields (Benfleet) Ltd, Disney Worldwide Conservation Fund, The David and Lucile Packard Foundation* and the *Olewine Family* are helping as Species Champions to sponsor the overall programme. So, considerable progress had been made in the first year, but there are still many Critically Endangered species without a Species Champion and much more help is needed. But, what

we are starting to prove is that it can be done!

It is tempting sometimes, when listening to tales of gloom and doom about the impact that man's actions are having on the natural world, that it seems almost impossible to stem the tide of habitat destruction and species loss. But the record of what has been achieved by dedicated conservation action suggests otherwise. Birdfair funding over 20 years for BirdLife International's conservation projects has demonstrated that well researched, targeted actions can make a real difference. The next 20 years will be a crucial time for many species – let's all do our best to help! We can all play our part in helping to maintain the extraordinary diversity of wildlife with which we share this planet.

Photo: © Newton Maxwell-Harris

Martin Davies, a zoologist by training, has worked for more than 30 years for RSPB and is now Head of International Programme Development. Together with Tim Appleton (of LRWT), he started the Birdfair 20 years ago and the two of them have overseen the event ever since. Martin is a keen traveller and photographer, lecturer and tour leader and is a devoted butterfly-watcher as well as birder. He lives near Cambridge (UK) with his wife and two children.

THREATENED BIRDS
OF THE WORLD

Painting by Robert Gillmor.

RSPB Birdfair

The wildlife TRUSTS

THE BRITISH BIRDWATCHING FAIR

*The 1998 Birdfair gave overall support to BirdLife's work on Globally threatened birds including helping
to fund the research and publication costs of the book "Threatened Birds of the World."*

Haribon

My Encounter With a
Critically Endangered Species

AT THE FIRST VANTAGE WE SEARCH patiently without success. The threat of more rain looms behind heavy cloud. Far down the Valley the rasping clank of the Mindanao Tarictic Hornbill echoes against riverrock. The sound is guttural and harsh; raw and prehistoric. It mingles with the lush sound of fast white water, invoking the feeling of an alien and pristine wilderness. But it belies the deforestation around us.

We press up the hill. Giant flocks of Eyebrowed Thrush work cleared fields, while here and there Mountain White-eye fill the empty spaces of tropical shrub. We near the trail's upper watch and the bright chatter of Colasisis fill the canopy of a lonely old tree in a clearing. We wait. Carlito disappears in a high thicket of Lemongrass while the rest of us gaze into the valley. Fisher stands just upslope leaning on a rough hewn staff of tropical hardwood. There is a look of careful resignation on his face. Coupled with his modest paunch and silver hair it lends him a comforting air of durable authority. Again and again Carlito screams out the call of Haribon over the forest. It is an inhuman sound that must have required years of careful listening and cultivation. But still there is no Eagle. Eventually Fisher and three of our party resume the march toward the walls of Kitanglad. Carlito remains invisible. Two of us lag, desperately scanning the treetops before reluctantly resuming our assent.

There are moments in life for which even the most opulent superlatives are empty shadows. There are no words to capture the delicate and fragile brilliance of a Coquette bathing in a mountain stream or the resplendent wildness of the dawn chorus in virgin woodland. What words can truly describe the crane's silhouette against the carmine of a full setting sun, or convey what we glimpse in the eye of an Eagle? There are none. Yet ill-suited though they may be, words are often all we have. And there are certain creatures whose grace and importance demand attention.

The Great Philippine Eagle has compelled the fascination and plaudits of men from the very beginning. When Whitehead dispatched science's first on Samar, at the close of the 19th century, he prompted one of the greatest sensations in London's ornithological circles, at a time when ornithology was still near its zenith as a gentile avocation. That a flying giant of such fantastic proportions could have escaped centuries of notice confirmed for many wide-eyed explorers that the wilderness still hid great secrets awaiting their discovery. As Whitehead's specimen was unpacked a half-world away from its jungle home there seemed no end to its novelty or limits to its grandeur. The creature possessed the most fiercely enormous bill of any forest raptor thence – or since-known. Tremendously deep and broad wings defied all known dimensions and wrought in the beast a maneuverable poise that

Near Mount Kitanglad, 2007

seemed impossible for its size. The resolute eyes, set against a sinister black mask, cast an unfamiliar and decidedly un-avian air of menace. Perhaps most fantastic of all was its immaculate feathered crown- a sublime cocoa and cream mane raised by the Eagle rarely but triumphantly when provoked.

And *Pithecophaga jeffreyi* would prove far more than the sum of its remarkable parts. Rumor of its strange behavior fueled the scientific commotion. From the Native People of Samar, Whitehead was told of the bird's chilling taste for the flesh of primates. Thus it was, and is, in some circles still known evocatively as the "Monkey-Eating Eagle". It soon became clear the Eagle was a classic apex predator that suffered no natural rivals to its seat atop the ecological food chain. It ruled the Filipino skies supreme and unchallenged. Years later, when one animal perished after decades in captivity, it was posited that individual birds may live as long as a half century.

By the 1960's its accelerating rarity only fueled global interest in its fate. Jungles on the Philippine islands were falling to the hunger and greed of humanity at a catastrophic rate. Great champions of the creature's survival emerged. Charles Lindbergh famously called it, "Earth's noblest flier" and did all he could to draw global attention to both its magnificence and its plight. Lindbergh's words were

apt, for noble indeed the bird was. But there were some who spoke the essence of the creature even better. To the Filipinos whose ancestors had known it for time immemorial, it was simply "Haribon", the King of all Birds.

Lindbergh was the Eagle's first and most famous benefactor. Today, whether intended or not Haribon finds one of its best advocates in a decidedly unassuming man named Tim Fisher. His notorious charm and quiet attention to the birds of the Philippines has brought travelers from across the globe to Haribon's imperiled dominion. Despondently confronted with yet another 4:00 AM departure into the jungle, one of his former clients told me, "all it takes is a smile from Tim for you to remember why you're there, and know everything will be alright." After having spent a month with Fisher on 7 islands staggering through innumerable buffalo wallows and up leach-laden trails in the equatorial heat, I knew what she meant. The jovial look of his face aglow in the light of a campfire buttressed by the therapeutic verve of his unending Tanduay Rhum supply is enough to quiet even the most petulant traveler.

Tim has helped make a place called Kitanglad the Wilderness Mecca for Haribon. The name belongs to a giant Volcano and also the web of mountains that spread out from it like tendrils in the heart of Mindanao. The nominate peak soars

Hunting grounds of Philippine Eagle

Jon King, Volker Schmidt and Tim Fisher searching for Haribon at Mt. Kitanglad

nearly 9,000 feet in the vast Budkidnon highlands. There is something defiant in its posture not unlike the great Bird to which it belongs. Rising over a sea of deforestation and an ever-growing human mass both Kitanglad and the Philippine Eagle itself remain besieged but living, breathing monuments to a tropical island wilderness that not long ago would have rivaled the most fanciful musings of Conan Doyle, made all the more marvelous for their reality. One need only gaze at the Mountain, or into the eyes of the Eagle, to know they are filled with a force and living cadence that will not be lightly relinquished.

Fisher's camp is situated near the lowermost limit of the Kitanglad Eagles' territory. To reach it requires a day's hike with sturdy Filipino ponies and a group of even hardier porters from the surrounding villages. Above the campground, a well-worn trail traces the rim of a plateau, towering high above a great river chasm and rising gradually before it eventually yields to the still wild places high on the mountainside. Much of the land en route has been slashed bare in recent decades and now a mosaic of crops and huts dot a treeless expanse that once supported thriving forest. Lately as these scars on the land have grown and festered, the resident pair of Philippine Eagles has moved ever higher up the chasm. It often now requires several hours of hiking upslope from camp to even chance a glimpse.

Both on and off the trail, the inestimable value of Fisher and his contacts impresses itself forcefully, time and time again. Tim's partner at Kitanglad goes by Carlito. He is a tall and thin older man, with an elegant face set below jet black and silver hair. Tim has relied on Carlito as his "man on the ground", here for a very long time. Now joined by his nephew Danny, Carlito leads Fisher's troops into Kitanglad's remnant forest enclaves in search of famously endangered endemics. On frayed flip-flops and with chipped, ancient binoculars they discern Blue-capped Wood-Kingfishers and White-cheeked Bullfinches where a more careless eye would find only backlit leaves and twisted vines. Perhaps the most unexpected of Carlito's skills is a miraculous gift for mimicking the call of Haribon. It is a raucous and high, enormous clarion. Martial and resonant but melodious, it dwarfs the familiar chanting cries of lesser eagles. It was a sound that filled the morning of December 23.

The Philippine Eagles here may be the most seen

of their kind in the wild, though even they are infamously elusive. As with their kin, the pair raises and nurtures an heir semi-annually. The solitary fledge will spend several years before maturing into a full grown "King". The year before our arrival there had been no nest and it was hoped this season the pair would once again conceive and rear a vigorous successor. Our early winter expedition coincided perfectly with the height of breeding season. I even nurtured the hope of finding a nest. But as mid-day drew closer, doubt and fear whispered in my ear. I was beset with the worry that after having come so far we could miss Haribon all together. We were the first this season to search for it. No one had ventured up Kitanglad since before the long, violent Typhoon season that can stretch from June through November and I knew all too well the risk of missing such a rare animal in the vastness of the Budkidnon country.

The trail up the canyon widens twice into small overlooks, some distance apart, known as the "eagle watch points". After some time at the first we had moved up the hill to the second, smaller viewing area. Carlito, utterly invisible in a thicket began to call but with no apparent effect. The sky over the chasm remained painfully empty and still. We all strained behind binoculars and scopes as our minds' eyes rendered spikes of dead wood jutting above the forest panorama into resplendent Eagles. Eventually Tim pressed up the hill. I was the last to follow. Seconds later it is not the mimicking cry of the Eagle, but rather the word… "Eagle", we hear from Carlito behind us. The jubilance in his voice is unmistakable. I rush back down the trail. My heart pumps like the deafening rumble of a timpani crescendo. My breath is uneven and weak under the knowledge that a definitive moment in life has arrived. Now I would either miss or catch a moment tossed by destiny.

I would witness one of creation's most glorious jewels or leave the Philippines having missed it by seconds. Dust from our heavy, frantic steps rose from the trail like a cloud and we reached the viewpoint. And there is Haribon. Sailing slowly but with direction very close, just above the cliff's edge. I see the rich mane in repose. I see the blue and black mask that reaches up from the great bill that had so impressed Whitehead more than a century ago. I see the broad wings, deeper than perhaps any raptor on Earth. I have heaved a massive camera and lens up the hill. It hangs at my side, forgotten and obsolete. This is one of life's rare eternal moments not to be complicated by the ponderous worries of composition and aperture. Seconds pass and Haribon has drawn even closer. The air is motionless and the Hornbills are silent. There is only the quiet sound of water moving over stone.

In the shadow of Kitanglad, Haribon tilts his head and looks at me. I could have kept examining the seemingly countless beautiful predatory aspects that have borne it through the millennia and brought it the admiration of men the world over. But now it is only the white eyes that I see. They glow like the fire from another world.

I can only smile. Then and now there are no words for the light I see in Haribon's eyes.

Photo: © Don Roberson

Blake Matheson is an American presently pursuing his degree in Environmental Law. He previously studied ethics and philosophy at Santa Clara University in California and Oxford in England. As life allows, he travels the world in search of Earth's most magnificent and endangered animals.

Near Mount Kitanglad, 2007

Rare Birds Yearbook
Photo Competitions

Most of the pictures and artwork you
see in this book have been received through
the competition at www.rarebirdsyearbook.com.
This competition has over the two years seen over 2,000 images
submitted from more than 500 photographers/artists from all
over the world. The winners of the 2009 competition
are announced on the web site.

The competition prizes have kindly been sponsored by

MINOX
www.minox.com

BirdLife
INTERNATIONAL
www.birdlife.org

Lynx
www.hbw.com

The Fifty Rarest Birds of the World

www.inventas.co.nz/50rarestbirds/index.htm

The 2010 edition of Rare Birds Yearbook
will be published in May 2010. Please check
www.rarebirdsyearbook.com from June 2009 onwards
for news about new competitions
with new, exciting prizes.

Categorisation of the species

THIS BOOK TREATS THE CRITICALLY ENDANGERED birds of the world. They are thus the rarest living birds, many on the border of the next level above, which is *Extinct/Extinct in the wild*. The category *Critically Endangered* belongs to a classification system of species by the IUCN (The International Union for the Conservation of Nature and Natural Resources) also known as the World Conservation Union.

The IUCN Red List of Threatened Species provides taxonomic, conservation status and distribution information on species that have been globally evaluated using the IUCN Red List Categories and Criteria (see below). This system is designed to determine the relative risk of extinction, and the main purpose of the IUCN Red List is to catalogue and highlight those species that are facing a higher risk of global extinction. The IUCN Red List also includes information on species that are categorized as Extinct or Extinct in the Wild, Data Deficient and Near Threatened.

IUCN Classification System

EXTINCT (EX)
A taxon is Extinct when there is no reasonable doubt that the last individual has died.

EXTINCT IN THE WILD (EW)
A taxon is Extinct in the Wild when it is known only to survive in cultivation, in captivity or as a naturalized population (or populations) well outside the past range.

CRITICALLY ENDANGERED (CR)
A taxon is Critically Endangered when the best available evidence indicates that it meets any of the criteria for Critically Endangered, and it is therefore considered to be facing an extremely high risk of extinction in the wild. Possibly Extinct (PE)

ENDANGERED (EN)
A taxon is Endangered when the best available evidence indicates that it meets any of the criteria for Endangered, and it is therefore considered to be facing a very high risk of extinction in the wild.

VULNERABLE (VU)
A taxon is Vulnerable when the best available evidence indicates that it meets any of the criteria for Vulnerable, and it is therefore considered to be facing a high risk of extinction in the wild.

NEAR THREATENED (NT)
A taxon is Near Threatened when it has been evaluated against the criteria but does not qualify for Critically Endangered, Endangered or Vulnerable now, but is close to qualifying for or is likely to qualify for a threatened category in the near future.

LEAST CONCERN (LC)
A taxon is Least Concern when it has been evaluated against the criteria and does not qualify for Critically Endangered, Endangered, Vulnerable or Near Threatened.

DATA DEFICIENT (DD)
A taxon is Data Deficient when there is inadequate information to make a direct, or indirect, assessment of its risk of extinction based on its distribution and/or population status.

NOT EVALUATED (NE)
A taxon is Not Evaluated when it is has not yet been evaluated against the criteria.

The species in this book are considered Critically Endangered and that means that they meet any of the following criteria:

A. <u>Reduction in population size based on any of the following</u>:

1. An observed, estimated, inferred or suspected population size reduction of > 90% over the last 10 years or three generations, whichever is the longer, where the causes of the reduction are clearly reversible AND understood AND ceased, based on (and specifying) any of the following:
   (a) direct observation
   (b) an index of abundance appropriate to the taxon
   (c) a decline in area of occupancy, extent of occurrence and/or quality of habitat
   (d) actual or potential levels of exploitation
   (e) the effects of introduced taxa, hybridization, pathogens, pollutants, competitors or parasites.

2. An observed, estimated, inferred or suspected population size reduction of > 80% over the last 10 years or three generations, whichever is the longer, where the reduction or its causes may not have ceased OR may not be understood OR may not be reversible, based on (and specifying) any of (a) to (e) under A1.

3. A population size reduction of > 80%, projected or suspected to be met within the next 10 years or three generations, whichever is the longer (up to a maximum of 100 years), based on (and specifying) any of (b) to (e) under A1.

4. An observed, estimated, inferred, projected or suspected population size reduction of > 80% over any 10 year or three generation period, whichever is longer (up to a maximum of 100 years in the future), where the time period must include both the past and the future, and where the reduction or its causes may not have ceased OR may not be understood OR may not be reversible, based on (and specifying) any of (a) to (e) under A1.

B. <u>Geographic range in the form of either B1 (extent of occurrence) OR B2 (area of occupancy) OR both</u>:

1. Extent of occurrence estimated to be less than 100 km², and estimates indicating at least two of a-c:
   (a) Severely fragmented or known to exist at only a single location.
   (b) Continuing decline, observed, inferred or projected, in any of the following:
      (i) extent of occurrence
      (ii) area of occupancy
      (iii) area, extent and/or quality of habitat
      (iv) number of locations or subpopulations
      (v) number of mature individuals.
   c. Extreme fluctuations in any of the following:
      (i) extent of occurrence
      (ii) area of occupancy
      (iii) number of locations or subpopulations
      (iv) number of mature individuals.

2. Area of occupancy estimated to be less than 10 km², and estimates indicating at least two of a-c:
   a. Severely fragmented or known to exist at only a single location.
   b. Continuing decline, observed, inferred or projected, in any of the following:
      (i) extent of occurrence
      (ii) area of occupancy
      (iii) area, extent and/or quality of habitat
      (iv) number of locations or subpopulations
      (v) number of mature individuals.
   c. Extreme fluctuations in any of the following:
      (i) extent of occurrence
      (ii) area of occupancy
      (iii) number of locations or subpopulations
      (iv) number of mature individuals.

C. <u>Population size estimated to number fewer than 250 mature individuals and either</u>:

1. An estimated continuing decline of at least 25% within three years or one generation, whichever is longer, (up to a maximum of 100 years in the future) OR

2. A continuing decline, observed, projected, or inferred, in numbers of mature individuals AND at least one of the following (a-b):
   (a) Population structure in the form of one of the following:
      (i) no subpopulation estimated to contain more than 50 mature individuals, OR
      (ii) at least 90% of mature individuals in one subpopulation.
   (b) Extreme fluctuations in number of mature individuals.

D. <u>Population size estimated to number fewer than 50 mature individuals</u>.

E. <u>Quantitative analysis showing the probability of extinction in the wild is at least 50% within 10 years or three generations, whichever is the longer (up to a maximum of 100 years)</u>.

Source: www.iucnredlist.org

Critically Endangered
- the 190 rarest birds in the world

Using the directory

Sources

The facts for compiling this section of the book have been taken from the fact sheets published by BirdLife International at **www.birdlife.org** and published volumes of *Handbook of the Birds of the World* published by Lynx Edicions. The editor has also corresponded with scientists, amateurs and NGOs worldwide. These persons are acknowledged on pp. 10-11 and are or will be acknowledged in current or future versions of the BirdLife fact sheets where the references used in compiling the fact sheets and *Threatened Birds of the World* by BirdLife International and Lynx Edicions are found. These references are excluded from this book in order to provide space for information concerning the species themselves and readers are strongly urged to check out these sources when in need of references.

Amount of space allocated each species

The 190 Critically Endangered species are presented on either two, one or half pages. The number of pages devoted to a species depends on the availability of photos, new information since 2008 and whether the species is new to the Critically Endangered list or not. They follow an approximate taxonomic order, with some consideration given to technical aspects such as available photos and layouts. This may mean that some species do not appear within the established taxonomic order. Furthermore, 60 species are listed on pages 222-223. These species were covered in greater detail in *Rare Birds Yearbook 2008* and as, at the moment, there is no new information to add to that already provided in the 2008 edition these birds are merely listed in this edition to provide more space for new photographs and facts for those species where there are more developments to report. Those readers seeking more information about them should consult either of the *Rare Birds Yearbook 2008*, *Handbook of the Birds of the World* or the BirdLife fact sheets at **www.birdlife.org**.

Reasons for listing as Critically Endangered

Population: ⬇ 200	REASON FOR CR-LISTING		
	DECLINE	POPULATION	RANGE
THREATS Infrastructure development, agriculture, persecution, plant-gathering, disturbance, dams & water management			

See pp. 80-81 for an explanation of the IUCN categories and criteria. For each species the IUCN criteria are summarised so they can be understood at a glance. The population number refers to the number of mature individuals. The arrow refers to the current direction of the population trend. The box "Reason for CR-listing" interprets the criteria used by BirdLife International to list this species as Critically Endangered. For example, for a species with a declining population it may not be the decline which is the strongest reason for its being listed as Critically Endangered; it may rather be because of its small range or population. The criteria are subdivided further than the fields presented in the box in Rare Birds Yearbook, and those readers wishing to study this in more detail are strongly advised to visit **www.iucnredlist.org** which provides more detailed information. Finally, a box shows the threats most important to the species (those threats coded by BirdLife International as 'medium to high' and 'current'). In many cases there are numerous threats of lower importance (or that took place in the past) though these have been omitted here for reasons of clarity and replaced by "No high/medium-impact threats". Again, all threats can be found in full at **www.iucnredlist.org** and **www.birdlife.org**. The threats are, in some cases, expanded on in the text even if they are of lower concern than the ones listed in the box.

Illustrations

Most of the pictures in this book have been provided by professional and amateur photographers from all over the world. I have strived to find new images for all the species covered since last year. In some cases, paintings have had to be used.
The material has chiefly been obtained by a photo competition, sponsored by Minox, Lynx Edicions, Inventas Media and BirdLife International at **www.rarebirdsyearbook.com**. Being a book of rare birds, the photos will of course vary in quality. Photos of birds at nests have generally been avoided, but when they occur the Editor remains assured they have been taken responsibly.

Maps

Satellite images taken from Google Earth Pro have been used. Distribution polygons have kindly been provided by BirdLife International and any corrections or updates should be sent to **science@birdlife.org**. In general, only breeding range has been depicted as the majority of species are non-migratory. Distribution outside of the breeding range is usually mentioned in the text.

Trinidad Piping-guan
Pipile pipile

Grande Riviere, Trinidad, 2007

Population: ↓ 70-200	REASON FOR CR-LISTING		
	DECLINE	POPULATION	RANGE

THREATS
Agriculture, hunting or persecution, logging

History

1784 – Dutch scientist Nikolaus Joseph von Jacquin desribes the species.

1963 – legal protection of the species is awarded.

1989 – a stamp featuring the Trinidad Piping-guan is released.

2004 – the Matura National Park is declared an Environmentally Sensitive Area.

2007 – the Pawi Study Group web site (www.geocities.com/pawisgtt/) is launched.

2007-8 – two-year study of the Pawi funded by Environmental management Authority of Trinidad and Tobago takes place.

The Trinidad Piping-guan, also known as the Pawi, is the only species endemic to the island of Trinidad. Historically it was distributed over most of the island except for possibly the western parts. It now occurs in the north-eastern part and is confined to an area which only holds c.150m² of suitable habitat at elevations ranging from 10-900m. It was last recorded in southern Trinidad in 2000 and in central Trinidad in 1983. Its´ preferred habitat consists of steep, hilly areas with streams, closed canopy and lianas and epiphytes. It has also been recorded in semi-cultivated lands near primary forest and seems to tolerate humans as long as canopy trees are available and it is not hunted. Very little is known about its breeding which seems to take place in most months and incorporates laying two eggs. Most of the time is spent in forest canopy and it can be actively feeding after dusk. Food consists mainly of fruits, though flowers and leaves are also consumed.

The main causes of the species's decline is hunting and, to some extent, habitat destruction.

Most of the current population lives in forest reserves or state forests, although the laws for protecting these areas are not always enforced. One such area is the Matura National Park, which comprises 9,000 ha and contains the largest intact Mora forest in Trinidad and Tobago. Public awareness campaigns and ecotourism (especially in the Grande Riviere region) are proving to be beneficial for the conservation. Trinidad Piping-guans can be individually identified, based on the white on the wing-coverts, and this will be used in combination with telemetry to find out more about its requirements and biology. Because virus, bacteria and parasites can have devastating effects on small populations, more research is being conducted into the health of the current population by zoologists and veterinaries and will no doubt facilitate the captive-breeding programme when it eventually gets underway. A captive breeding programme, telemetry monitoring and more public awareness campaigns are actions that need to be undertaken to save this species.

Blue-billed Currasow
Crax alberti

RNA El Paujíl, 2004

Photo: © Fundación ProAves www.proaves.org

Population: ↓ 1,000-2,499	REASON FOR CR–LISTING		
	DECLINE	POPULATION	RANGE

THREATS
Infrastructure development, agriculture, energy, hunting or persecution

History
1852 – British Zoologist Louis Fraser (1810 -1866) describes the species.

2004 – Fundacion ProAves purchases 1,201 ha and establishes the El Paujíl Nature Reserve to protect the species.

2008 – A campaign to expand the Paujil Reserve is launched and so far four properties have been acquired to expand the reserve a further 1,215 ha with another 3,000 ha awaiting acquisition.

This species, in which the sexes have different plumages, formerly bred in northern Colombia, but is today restricted to two main areas. One is El Paujíl Bird Reserve, named after the local name for Blue-billed Currasow. It lives in humid forest up to 1,200 metres. Breeding takes place during the dry season in December – March with family parties being observed until August. Two or three eggs are laid which the female incubates for a month and there is only one brood per season. It feeds on the ground on fruit, shoots, invertebrates and perhaps carrion. Roost sites, situated in foliage in trees, are near feeding areas and are used for several days.

The main threat to this species has been the clearing of forest for agricultural, both legal and illegal activities. Hunting has also played a part. Few males have been located in the field since 1998 which suggests that hunting is still a problem. Gold mining has also affected the habitat at the Serranía de San Lucas which has become settled and altered.

The species occurs or is believed to occur in several reserves, but it only gets full protection at the El Paujíl reserve. More surveys are planned to identify additional IBAs which may hold Blue-billed Currasows. Actions that need to be taken include surveying more areas for birds especially in the south-western limits of the range, protecting them and initiating public awareness campaigns to limit hunting and provide resources to replace the need for habitat conversion.

White-winged Guan
Penelope albipennis

Population: ↓ 150-249	REASON FOR CR-LISTING		
	DECLINE	POPULATION	RANGE

THREATS
Agriculture, logging, invasives

Photo: © Alejandro Tabini

Chaparrí Lambayeque, Peru, 2007

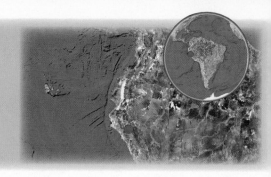

This South American species lives in dry, forested slopes near permanent water and deciduous forests in north-western Peru. It breeds from January to August and feeds on fruits, berries, flowers, buds, leaves and seeds. Movements are believed to take place but are poorly understood.

The range is now greatly fragmented and overhunting and habitat destruction are the main threats. The Peru Congress declared the conservation of White-winged Guan as of "National Interest" in 2003. Three IBAs hold the species; Laquipampa, Olmos and the Chaparri Private Conservation Area. The Laquipampa Wildlife Reserve, where a first group of eight birds were reintroduced in February 2007, houses 22 individuals and is the only site where both the bird and its habitat are legally protected. Around 70 individuals live in captivity and are used for breeding for release into the wild. An intensive awareness campaign commenced in 2008 via radio in the distribution area and is hoped to significantly contribute in halting the decline. One unprotected site, known as Limon, harbours approximately 25 guans and is protected as locals receive income from ecotourism.

Future actions include drawing up a national conservation plan and surveying possible areas where it could occur, e.g in southern Ecuador.

Djibouti Francolin
Francolinus ochropectus

Population: ↓ 250-999	REASON FOR CR-LISTING		
	DECLINE	POPULATION	RANGE

THREATS
Agriculture, logging, disturbance, pollution, climate change

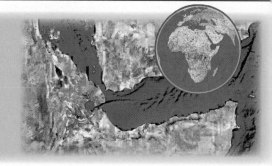

Photo: © Houssein Rayaleh

Day forest in Goda mountain, Tadjourah region, Djibouti, 2006

The Djibouti Francolin is confined to two areas of Djibouti, Forêt du Day and the Mabla Mountains with the former being the stronghold from where it was first described in 1952. It occurs in juniper woodland above 950 m, it is very shy and breeds from December to February.

The juniper woodland is under heavy pressure from grazing, collection of firewood and probably climatic changes as well. It is uncertain whether dead woodland holds the species, but there are indications that if junipers are undisturbed from grazing the woodland may recover. Hunting may also pose a threat.

Research to clarify the species' range and population numbers is ongoing. In May 2008 a 1,000km^2 area near Day village was set aside for a tree nursery. Promotion material on the francolin was produced in 2008 and has been spread and used in schools and attempts to establish a local Djibouti Francolin group took place at Djibouti University in June 2008. Future conservation actions include implementation of protected status of Forêt du Day, conduct ecological studies of the species and work with local communities to restore and protect juniper habitat and the francolin.

Laysan Duck
Anas laysensis

Population:		REASON FOR CR-LISTING		
600-700 ⬆		DECLINE	POPULATION	RANGE

THREATS
Invasives

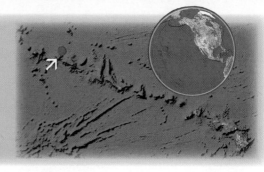

Photo: © James H Breeden Jr.

Midway Atoll NWR, 2006

The only remnant, wild population is on Laysan, Hawaii Islands but a reintroduced population is now established on Midway atoll. In the 20th century the population fluctuated between a few and 743 adult birds. Only the females tend to the young and usually lay three to four eggs. Introduced birds on Midway have been found to breed at an earlier age and lay larger clutches which is perhaps due to more easily available food and a lower population density than on Laysan.

As it occurs in only two small populations, stochastic events such as tsunamis, drought, global warming, diseases and accidental introduction of competitors or predators are risk factors. Broods are reared primarily at freshwater wetlands. Its future was extremely precarious when a Bristle-thighed Curlew *Numenius tahitiensis* trampled and destroyed the last female's eggs in 1930, but the female managed to lay another clutch. Over 160 Laysan ducks died from avian botulism on Midway in August 2008 while 28 were rehabilitated.

One species of native grass has been eliminated from Laysan, but other invasive weeds occur. The current captive population is inappropriate for reintroductions and a new captive stock derived from wild stock is needed. Other future conservation measures include population monitoring, restoring habitat and ecosystems at Laysan, Midway and other mammal-free islands to establish four additional populations as well as strict control of alien species to these sites.

Madagascar Pochard
Aythya innotata

Population:		REASON FOR CR-LISTING		
< 50 ?		DECLINE	POPULATION	RANGE

THREATS
Agriculture, hunting & persecution, fisheries bycatch, dams & water use, invasives, pollution

Photo: © Lily Arison René de Roland

Madagascar, 2008

This rather tame diving duck is endemic to Madagascar where it was found at Lake Alaotra in the northern part of the island. It became extinct from there in 1991 but was rediscovered at another site approximately 300 km away in 2006. This new site is a volcanic lake, quite different from lake Alaotra in character, and with less cultivation and disturbance around it and the birds breeding there visit other lakes as well.

It breeds in October-January in vegetation at the lake's edge and lays a clutch of 6-8 eggs with nests two to four metres apart. Males are strongly territorial, their aggression confining rivals to their nests. The food consists of invertebrates and plants/seeds which are obtained by diving, often two birds feed together. Lake Alaotra has undergone major changes which are believed to have contributed to the decline of Madagascar Pochard; rice cultivation along the shores, soil erosion from surrounding, deforested hillsides, introduced mammals, intensive fishing and introduced plants. Hunting is probably also causing pressure. There are no captive populations and genetic degradation could be a threat considering the small size of the known population. The new site is being monitored closely through the Peregrine Fund and Durrell Wildlife Conservation Trust and permanent staff is in place to prevent hunting.

Further conservation actions that need to be taken are surveys of potential new sites and restoration of those parts of lake Alaotra which are least disturbed, should the species chose to come back.

Campbell Islands Teal

Anas nesiotis

A group of Campbell Islands Teals that were released on Codfish Island in 1999 as a temporary measure while the island that has given the species its name was being cleared from rats, started breeding and thrived so much that they remain there.

Photo: © Simon Fordham

Codfish Island, 2007

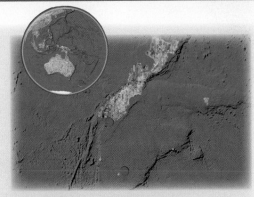

History

1810 – Campbell Island is discovered and rats are introduced shortly thereafter.

1868 – rats are well established on Campbell Island.

1886 – the first specimen is collected on the coast of Campbell Island.

1935 – Canadian ornithologist James Henry Fleming (1872-1940) describes the species.

1944 – second and last record for many years from Campbell Island.

1972 – it is rediscovered on Dent island, a few km from Campbell.

1984 – three males and one female are taken in to captivity – no breeding this year.

1990 – a survey reveals not more than 25 breeding pairs on Dent and estimates population to between 60 and 100. Four males and three females are taken into captivity.

1994 – the first captive breeding takes place.

1997 – a survey on Dent locates only three birds, which may indicate a drop in numbers.

1999 – the first 12 birds, four males and eight females are released on Codfish Island and start to breed almost immediately.

2003 – Campbell Island is declared rat-free.

2004 – 50 (22 from the wild and 28 captive bred) birds are released on Campbell Island.

2005 – another 55 (22 from the wild and 33 captive bred) birds are released on Campbell Island.

2006 – at least four cases of breeding takes place on Campbell Island, another 54 birds, all captive-bred, are released.

2007 – further breeding and dispersal recorded.

2008/09 – a survey of Campbell Island is planned.

This flightless duck, sometimes treated as a subspecies of Brown teal *Anas aucklandica*, occurs on three islands of New Zealand; Dent Island where a wild population was found in 1975 which numbers approximately 25 pairs and Codfish and Campbell islands where introduced birds breed since at least 2000 and 2006 respectively. Even if the birds are capable of swimming 3 km to other islands, the Dent population was believed to have been isolated for 150 years. Codfish Island was intended to be an intermediate site for holding teals while Campbell was being eradicated from rats, but the released population has made itself at home there and remains. It is nocturnal, feeding primarily on invertebrates and can be found feeding offshore. Captive birds lay three to four eggs in a clutch and are known to have lived for over 15 years. Threats include rats, disease and climatic events. Potential predators are Brown Skua *Catharacta lonnbergi*, Kelp Gull *Larus dominicanus*, and Northern Giant Petrel *Macronectes halli*.

Seven males and three females caught in 1984 and 1990 contributed to a captive population, but nearly all have now been released onto Codfish Island with only around 20 birds retained as backup. A survey of Campbell Island was planned for the season of 2007/08 but had to be postponed. Recent visits on Campbell Island have, however, resulted in records of both adults and ducklings at several locations around the island and it is expected that this population is doing well. All released birds have been screened for disease, but have so far not shown any negative signs. Radio transmitters have been used to follow movements, and batteries have been replaced. Birds were located by telemetry, trained dogs and people with nets.

Future conservation actions include tracking the fate of released birds and monitoring the health of birds in all sub-populations to ensure that they are not suffering from disease.

Codfish Island, 2007

Photo: © Simon Fordham

Willowbank Wildlife Reserve, Christchurch, New Zealand, 2007

Photo: © Ian R. McHenry

Brazilian Merganser

Mergus octosetaceus

This shy and secretive merganser is highly adapted to life in the fast lane. It lives in fast-flowing waters of South American rivers but lays its nest in a hollow in a tree.

Photo: © Adriano Gambarini

Parque Nacional da Serra da Canastra, Minas Gerais, Brazil, 2007

Population: ↓ 50-249	REASON FOR CR-LISTING		
	DECLINE	POPULATION	RANGE
THREATS			
Agriculture, logging, disturbance			

History

1817 – French ornithologist Louis Jean Pierre Vieillot (1748-1831) describes the species from specimens probably taken in Brazil.

1891 – the first record is made in Paraguay.

1948 – the species is rediscovered.

1984 – the second Paraguayan record is made when Nancy López sees a bird in Rio Carapá.

1993 – a survey along 376 km of river in Argentina only produces one bird.

1995 – a small population was discovered on the Rio Tibagi, Paraná, Brazil.

2001/02 – 81 individuals estimated in a survey around Parque Nacional da Serra da Canastra, Minas Gerais, Brazil.

2002 – the first record for ten years is made in Argentina in the Uruzú river. Interviews with locals in Paraguay indicate that the species may still exist there.

2007 – a new breeding site is found in Goiás state.

This river-living merganser, that likes to hide under overhanging vegetation, has a fragmented distribution in Brazil, Argentina and possibly Paraguay. Its stronghold is believed to be in the Goiás province of Brazil. In extensively surveyed Argentina, the species was rediscovered in 2002 after an absence of ten years. A pair will use 8-14 km of river and it is a non-migratory bird preferring upper tributaries of watersheds and small rivers surrounded by forest although it appears to be able live by rivers lacking forest and running through cerrado habitat. A pair that was studied in Serra da Canastra National Park, Minas Gerais, Brazil managed to fledge 70 young over five years. Young birds have been encountered between August and November and its diet consists of fish and invertebrates.

It is threatened by activities like damming, diamond-mining and tourist activities which result in perturbation and pollution.
Brazilian Merganser is protected in all three countries where it occurs, and the Brazilian population is found in five areas that receive some protection. Parts of the Arroyo Uruzú in Argentina runs through protected areas. An action plan has been developed and a Brazilian Merganser Recovery Team aiming to plan its recovery has been set up.
Future actions include survey and monitor populations, build nest boxes to assist birds outside of protected areas, restore riverine habitats and embark on awareness campaigns. In Paraguay, surveys should be performed to confirm reports of the species and captive breeding should be considered a conservation tool.

Parque Nacional da Serra da Canastra, Minas Gerais, Brazil, 2007

Photo: © Sávio Freire Bruno

Waved Albatross
Phoebastria irrorata

The chicks of this medium-sized albatross are very hardy. It has been recorded that they can survive up to 14 days in unincubated eggs and their parents´ behaviour of rolling around the eggs during incubation subjects them to risks.

Galapagos, 2005

Population: 34,700 ↓	REASON FOR CR-LISTING		
	DECLINE	POPULATION	RANGE

THREATS
Fisheries bycatch, climate change

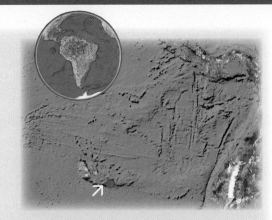

History

1883 – the species is first described by British ornithologist Osbert Salvin (1835-1898).

1924 – first record of a Waved Albatross at Isla de la Plata, 27 km off Ecuador, in November.

1970/71 – estimated 12,000 pairs.

1978 – goats are eradicated from Española.

1990 – ten breeding pairs reported from Isla de la Plata.

1994 – estimated 15,600 – 18,200 pairs. On 13th June, an individual ringed in 1961 being at least five years old was retrapped, thus establishing the longevity record of 38 years for the species.

1995 – 25,000 adults.

2001 – several non-breeding adults seen on La Plata off Ecuador and on Isla Genovesa. The population consists of 31,000 – 35,000 adults (6,857 pairs).

2007 – 6,045 pairs were estimated to breed, which is 88% of those estimated at the last census, in 2001.

2008 – a meeting of stakeholders related to the Agreement for the Conservation of Albatrosses and Petrels (ACAP) convened to finalize the ACAP Waved Albatross Plan of Action for the management and conservation of the species.

This medium-sized albatross breeds on Española Island in the Galápagos and possibly in small numbers on Isla de la Plata and off Ecuador. This is one of the most numerous species covered by this book, but decreasing trends and a very limited breeding distribution qualify this beautiful bird for inclusion on the Critically Endangered list. Adults travel to the Peruvian upwelling for feeding and non-breeding birds are found off Ecuador and Peruvian coasts. It feeds on fish, crustaceans and squid although it has recently been found that scavenging food disgorged by other species such as boobies is also an important food source. Nesting is colonially in both rocky sparsely vegetated areas and thick scrub vegetation. The hardy embryos can survive for six days in un-incubated eggs, with cases of live embryos being recorded up to a fortnight after the egg was abandoned. Birds attempt breeding for the first time at five or six years of age even if they can return to colonies, typically late in the season, already at two years of age.

Humans threaten the species through both accidental by-catch and by harvesting it for the food and feather markets. The small Isla de la Plata population is affected by illegal collection of eggs and young and predators such as rats and cats. The adults' behaviour of moving around eggs during incubation can also damage the eggs when they get lodged between rocks and for some reason males are more susceptible to incidental and intentional catching, which has a severe effect on a species where both parents tend their young.

Española Island is part of the Galápagos Marine Reserve and industrial, but not artisanal, long-lining is prohibited there. Long-lining does, however, affect dispersing albatrosses away from the Galapagos. Española is free from alien fauna and tourism is well regulated, which should mean that the species is safe from these threats, while the situation on Isla de la Plata, in this respect, needs improving.

Future conservation actions include monitoring the population with improved techniques, developing a species action plan, protecting the Isla de la Plata colony and evaluating the threat of incidental and deliberate capture in connection with fishing. It is essential that the adult mortality of such a long-lived species be reduced.

Española Island, Galápagos, 2006

Photo: © Marvin Hyett

Española Island, Galápagos, 2006

Photo: © Marvin Hyett

Tristan Albatross
Diomedea dabbenena

Hidden cameras at
nests revealed one of
the horrific reasons for
this species´s decline;
up to ten giant house
mice were filmed taking
bites from live Tristan
Albatross chicks until
the chicks succumbed.

Daniel Bengtsson

Population: ↓	REASON FOR CR-LISTING		
9,000-15,000 ▼	DECLINE	POPULATION	RANGE

THREATS
Fisheries bycatch, invasives

History

1995 – Gough is classified as a World heritage site.

1998 – the species is split from Wandering Albatross *Diomedea exulans*.

2000 – the first complete survey of breeding numbers since 1956 is performed.

2004 – the split is formally recognised.

2007 – a feasibility study on eradicating mice from Gough is under way.

his magnificent albatross, locally called Gony, was ʃlit from Wandering Albatross in 2004. It breeds on ʃough Island in Tristan da Cunha and occasionally, ʃreeding has taken place on Inaccessible Island. disperses to South American and South African ʃaters outside the breeding season and there is also a agrant record from Australia.

reeding occurs every second year in December to ʃbruary. Around 1,600-1,700 breeding instances are ʃcorded each year and around 600 of these hatch. ʃe oldest breeding bird, ringed as an adult, is close ʃ 40 years old and annual survival is expected to be ʃpproximately 91%.

ʃung birds are predated by the House Mouse *Mus ʃusculus*, which arrived with ships in the 19ᵗʰ century, ʃd fledging success average around 30%. Up to ten ʃice have been filmed attacking and eating from ʃe albatross chicks. Pigs and humans are probably ʃsponsible for the disappearance from Inaccessible, ʃthough pigs have now been eradicated. Breeding ʃeas can also be disturbed due to weather. Adults are ʃighly susceptible to long-lining as satellite data show ʃat their dispersal areas coincide with areas of long-ʃe fishing and there are several recoveries of Gough-ʃnged birds in connection with fishing off Brazil. The longevity of this species is being detected only now and there will be a time-lag before the species will show signs of recovering.

Cats have been eradicated from Tristan, Gough is a World Heritage site and Inaccessible a Nature Reserve. The RSPB, in partnership with University of Cape Town and Tristan's Agriculture and Natural Resources Department, are heavily involved in investigating the possibility of eradicating mice and rats from the islands.

More information is needed on this species's dispersal with more interaction from fisheries. Mice should be eradicated from Gough. Decoy birds could perhaps be used to lure Tristan Albatrosses back to former breeding areas.

Gough Island, 2007

Photo: © Daniel Bengtsson

Fledgling Tristan Albatross, Gough Island, 2003

Photo: © Angel/Wanless

Amsterdam Island Albatross
Diomedea amsterdamensis

Population: ⬇	REASON FOR CR-LISTING		
80	DECLINE	POPULATION	RANGE

THREATS
Fisheries bycatch, invasives

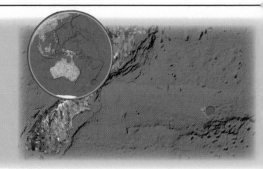

Amsterdam Island, 1982

Photo: © Eric van der Vlist

The Amsterdam Albatross breeds only on Amsterdam Island, French Southern Territories. Approximately 80 individuals are mature and only 18-25 pairs breed each year as this bird is a biannual breeder. The pair bonds are life-long and the breeding season starts in February. It forages up to 2,200 km away from Amsterdam Island. Geo-locators that have been attached to birds in recent years have shown that they range from the coasts of South Africa to south o Western Australia in non-breeding years.

The primary threat today is disease. Avian Cholera an the bacterium *Erysipelothrix rhusiopathidae* already affect a nearby Indian Yellow-nosed Albatross *Diome dea chlorohynchos* colony and signs are that increase chick mortality in recent years can be explained by this. Other threats include human disturbance, the degradation of nesting sites by cattle and especially predation by feral cats. Interaction with fisheries may be responsible for a decrease a few decades ago.

All birds are ringed and fences have been set up to prevent cattle from entering the breeding area.

A resolution from the Indian Ocean Tuna Commission requiring long-line vessels to use preventive measure to avoid by-catch of seabirds in June 2008 may be important for this species.

Future actions include continued monitoring, preventing spread of disease and cat eradication.

Chatham Albatross
Thalassarce eremita

Population: ↔	REASON FOR CR-LISTING		
11,000	DECLINE	POPULATION	RANGE

THREATS
Climate change

Off Kaikoura, New Zealand, 2003

Photo: © Brent Stephenson / www.wrybill-tours.com

The only breeding site for this species is a stack called the Pyramid, in the Chatham Islands, New Zealand. When not breeding it disperses east over the Pacific to the Humboldt Current off Chile and Peru. Satellite telemetry indicates that the journey from the non-breeding grounds takes place via a more northerly route to reach the breeding areas from July to Augus Breeding starts in September and the eggs hatch in November-December with fledging in March-April. The earliest breeding age recorded so far is seven years, but birds return to the colony at four years of age. The main foods are fish and cephalopods. Historically, the species was harvested for food. Storm and extreme weather are considered a threat and this may cause poorer quality nests that collapse in dry weather. There are no introduced mammalian predators on the island. In 2007, 12 birds were killed by longline vessel in New Zealand EEZ which is the largest single mortality since records begun.

The only nesting site is privately owned but the owners are co-operative towards studies being undertaken on the island. A program of satellite tracking and demographic analysis is ongoing.

Aerial surveys are impractical due to the terrain and difficulty in recognising these dark-headed birds from the air.

Galapagos Petrel
Pterodroma phaeopygia

Galápagos Islands, 2005

Photo: © Daniel Bengtsson

Population: 2,500-9,999 ⬇	REASON FOR CR–LISTING		
	DECLINE	POPULATION	RANGE

THREATS
Agriculture, invasives

History

1876 – British ornithologist Osbert Salvin (1835-1898) describes the species.

1978-1980 – estimated 27,000 pairs.

1979 – Galápagos Islands is declared a World Heritage Site.

1980 – the Galápagos National Park Service begin an intensive predator control programme on Floreana and Santa Cruz.

1982 – predator control is introduced in one colony at Cerro Pajas, Floreana.

1985 – 3,500 pairs estimated.

1997 – analysis of banding data since 1962 show that 3% of juveniles return to colonies on Santa Cruz and Floreana.

2005 – the population at Santa Cruz is surveyed and totals 700 pairs.

2008 – local NGOs study effects of wind power units on birds and mammals

This gadfly petrel is endemic to the Galápagos, Ecuador, where it breeds on at least five islands. It breeds between January and May in burrows, craters or ledges at altitudes of 300-900 metres and in close proximity to the plant *Miconia*. One egg is laid. It disperses to the coasts of South America and Mexico, reaching at the furthest 2,000 km south of Galápagos. The food consists mainly of fish and squid. Introduced mammals predate (rats, cats, dogs, pigs) or disturb (cattle, horses, goats, donkeys) nesting sites. Galapagos Hawk *Buteo galapagoensis* and short-eared Owl *Asio flammeus* may take adult birds. Habitat changes through clearing for agriculture or grazing reduces nesting sites and El Niño events can also have a detrimental effect on breeding. The local plant *Miconia* is being eradicated by grazing cattle.

Santa Cruz is affected by a wind-power development project which could threaten the population. Long-lining in the feeding areas is also a potential threat. Predator control has been launched at least one site and the Galápagos is a World Heritage Site which encourages protection of the species.
Future conservation activities include close monitoring of colonies and searches for new nesting grounds. The last - incomplete - censuses were in the 1980s and 1990s, which is why a new and complete survey is required. Wind-power plants should be situated so that they do not affect nesting areas or sites with *Miconia* and transmission lines from them should be buried so petrels will not risk colliding with them at night when they fly to and from their colonies.

97

Magenta Petrel
Pterodroma magentae

Despite its colourful name, this drab gadfly petrel is not a stunningly coloured bird. It got its name from the Italian warship turned research ship Magenta from which the first specimen was collected in July 1867.

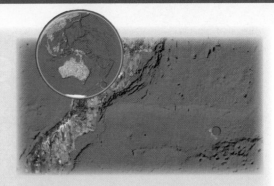

History

1867 – the first individual is collected in the Pacific on 22 July midway between New Zealand and South America. On 3 and 11 August similar-looking birds are seen south of Easter Island and north of Juan Fernandez respectively.

1869 – Italian zoologists Giglioli and Salvadori describe the species.

1903 – the last recorded mutton-birding trip result in the harvest of 300 chicks.

1969 – David Crockett and volunteers start searching for the Taiko.

1973 – the team sees four birds attracted by light, but is unable to catch them.

1978 – David Crockett rediscovers the Magenta Petrel (Chatham Island Taiko) in the south-west corner of Chatham Island on New Year's Day after nine years' and seven expeditions' efforts.

1984 – 1,238 hectares of land is donated by landowners Manuel and Evelyn Tuanui to protect breeding Taiko.

1987 – radio transmitters attached to tail feathers of birds result in the first nest being found in October.

1994 – four breeding pairs known.

1998 – The Chatham Island Taiko Trust is established to support private initiatives in Magenta Petrel conservation, and complement the work done by the Department of Conservation.

1999 – 17 new burrows discovered, mostly occupied by single males.

2004 – 12 breeding pairs known.

2007 – eight chicks successfully moved to the predator-fenced Sweetwater Conservation Covenant, from which they fledge.

2008 – 15 pairs laid, producing 13 chicks, all of which are transferred to Sweetwater Conservation Covenant and fledge successfully.

This rare gadfly petrel is also known as Taiko and is confined to one site on Chatham Island, New Zealand. First breeding attempts take place at five to ten years of age. Males visit the colony for the first time at four to five years and females at six to nine years. Males occupy burrows, up to five metres long, in dense forest four to six km from the coast for up to three years before breeding, which takes place in September to May. The pairs form a life-long bond and one egg is laid per year, incubated by both parents. The fledging chicks climb trees from which they launch themselves to fly out to sea. Post breeding dispersal may be as far as off the west cost of South America.

In the absence of management, introduced predators such as rats, weka, possums, cats, pigs and dogs would take chicks, eggs and adults, and compete for and destroy burrows. The pastoralisation of Chatham destroyed many colonies, and local Moriori and Maori people harvested thousands of chicks for food. Recent DNA analysis has shown that 95% of non-breeding adults are males.

Most breeding burrows are within the Tuku Nature Reserve, and intensive predator control is undertaken. Infrared cameras and transponder readers are used to monitor activities and identify predators. Hand-rearing of chicks of the closely related Grey-faced Petrel *P. macroptera* was undertaken to develop techniques to rescue abandoned Magenta Petrel chicks, and to safely transfer them before fledging, to establish a new breeding population. A potential breeding area at Sweetwater Conservation Covenant has been surrounded by a predator-proof fence and a playback sound system is installed.

Future conservation actions include ongoing predator control, and ground searches and telemetry to find new burrows and collect data on birds. Trained dogs are also used to find burrows. All the chicks produced in 2009 will also be translocated to Sweetwater Conservation Covenant a few weeks before fledging. The 2011 target for the Taiko is to establish a self-sustaining population of at least 250 individuals.

Chatham Islands, New Zealand, 2005

Photo: © Brent Stephenson/www.wrybill-tours.com

Chatham Islands, New Zealand, 2005

Photo: © Brent Stephenson/www.wrybill-tours.com

Chatham Petrel

Pterodroma axillaris

This nocturnal petrel faces competition from over 300,000 Broad-billed Prions that breed earlier in the season and occupy nesting sites. Fights over nesting burrows result in casualties and broken pair bonds.

Rangatira, Chatham Islands, 1984

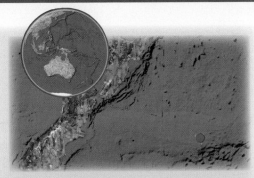

1892 – commercial collector William Hawkins collects the first specimens.

1893 – English naturalist Osbert Salvin (1835-1898) describes the species.

1999/2000 – a major search effort using radio-tracking found 120 active breeding burrows, double the number previously known.

2001 – first burrow with neoprene flaps installed.

2002-05 – 200 chicks are transferred to a predator-fenced site on Pitt Island.

2006 – the first locally reared chick fledges from Pitt Island.

2007 – four pairs nest in the predator exclosure and rear four chicks. One of the pairs is unringed and has not been raised in this safe area; the birds are presumably lured to it by the sound attraction system.

2008 – seven chicks fledge from the exclosure on Pitt Island. 47 chicks are moved from Rangatira to the predator-fenced Sweetwater Conservation Covenant on Chatham Island.

This gadfly petrel is today restricted to Rangatira (South East Island) Nature Reserve, Chatham Islands, New Zealand although it previously inhabited Chatham, Pitt and Mangere Islands according to subfossil records. Over 800 individuals have been banded since 1990 and over 100 chicks fledge each year thanks to intensive management. It nests colonially among other seabirds in December to June and lays one egg in a burrow.

The extirpation of Chatham Petrels from Chatham, Pitt and Mangere is thought to have been caused by human consumption and introduced predators. The main threat now on Rangatira is competition for nest burrows with the 330,000-strong population of Broad-billed Prions *Pachyptila vittata*, which breed earlier in the year than Chatham Petrels. These confrontations have resulted in killed birds, both chicks and young, and broken pair bonds.

Artificial burrows have been constructed around existing Chatham Petrel nest chambers, using neoprene flaps at the burrow entrances to deter Broad-billed Prions from entering, but allowing Chatham Petrels to access their nests. Broad-billed Prions found in managed burrows are culled. Breeding success has improved from 10-30% to 70-80% in the past ten years. Intensive searches have located 160 burrows of the resident population of c.250 pairs; all newly found burrows are converted into artificial burrows and guarded against prions. A second population has been created on nearby Pitt Island, and chick translocations have begun to Chatham Island.

Future actions include continued monitoring, by banding, and completing the establishment of the third colony. Further studies into the species's at-sea distribution should also be made.

Chatham Islands, 1984

Photo: © Colin Miskelly

Fiji Petrel
Pseudobulweria macgillivrayi

Population: ↓	REASON FOR CR-LISTING		
< 50	DECLINE	POPULATION	RANGE

THREATS
No high/medium-impact threats

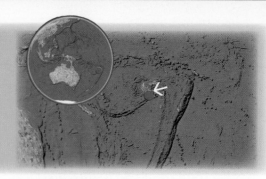

Photo: © Dick Watling

Only known from Gau island, Fiji where one was collected in 1855 and from which 12 records have been made since 1983; the most recent in 2007. Breeding is thought to take place in or around October in the forested interior of Gau and the species could occur on other islands in the region. There are ten claims of birds at sea from Bougainville, Papua New Guinea and Tonga.

Feral cats, rats and pigs probably constitute the greatest threat; cat access to nests may have been facilitated by the recent construction of a telecommunications transmitter on the summit of Gau.

Awareness of the species has been spread among locals and it is featured on a Fijian bank note. This awareness has probably helped in finding birds that have crashed in villages. A recovery plan was drawn up in 2003 and in 2004 an awareness campaign was initiated together with US-based conservation organisation RARE.

The main targets for future conservation action are identification of the breeding grounds of the species and collecting information from grounded birds that are submitted. Spotlighting, radio tracking and trained dogs could be used for looking for breeding grounds. The waters off Gau were investigated in summer 2008 using chumming to attract seabirds but the attempts had to be aborted after three days due to mechanical problems with the boat. New attempts will take place in 2009.

Beck´s Petrel
Pseudobulweria becki

Population: ↓	REASON FOR CR-LISTING		
50-249	DECLINE	POPULATION	RANGE

THREATS
No high/medium-impact threats

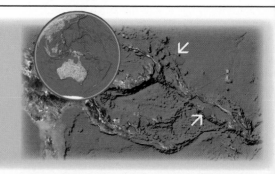

Bismarcks, 2007

Photo: © Hadoram Shirihai

Previously known only from two records in 1928 and 1929 respectively, this species was confirmed as rediscovered in August 2007 when a dead bird and several individuals were observed in the field and photographed by Hadoram Shirihai. It is suspected to breed in the montane forests of New Ireland and has been observed at sea (most recently in 2008) around the Bismarck archipelago where, judging from fledged birds, breeding should take place. Its appearance is very similar to Tahiti Petrel *P. rostrata* which may account for the long absence of records. At sea it seems to congregate in groups more than the Tahiti Petrel, which it outnumbers.

Until nesting sites are found, predation from introduced cats and rats are assumed to be threat factors.

Future actions required include surveys of at-sea occurrences, including taking photographs of encountered birds. The taxonomic validity of the taxon should also be investigated as a prioritised action and breeding grounds sought after.

Balearic Shearwater

Puffinus mauretanicus

This Mediterranean-breeding shearwater may in fact benefit from waste from human fishing activities as its natural food becomes scarce, so an uncoordinated spring fishing ban may not help it in the short term.

Isle of Wight, August 2007

Population: ↓	REASON FOR CR-LISTING		
4,000-4,800	DECLINE	POPULATION	RANGE

THREATS
Fisheries bycatch, invasives, climate change

History

1921 – Dr. Percy Roycroft Lowe (1870-1948) describes the taxon as a subspecies of Manx Shearwater *Puffinus puffinus*.

1990 – Yelkouan Shearwater *Puffinus yelkouan* is split from Manx Shearwater as a species of its own, and Balearic Shearwater is treated as a subspecies of it.

2004 – Balearic Shearwater is split from Yelkouan as a species in its own right.

2000 – the Iberian Government declares three new Special Protection Areas which include all colonies.

2007 – 12,500 birds were counted passing Gibraltar westwards from mid May to mid July.

2008 – an unprecedented influx to England and France occurs in January with over 700 birds involved. Over 16,000 birds are counted passing out into the Atlantic at Gibraltar since May 15th by Fundacion Migres.

The Balearic Shearwater breeds on islands in the Balearic Islands, Spain in the Mediterranean. Counts of migrating birds in 2007 and 2008 show that the breeding population estimate may be lower than true numbers. After breeding the majority of birds migrate past Gibraltar out into the Atlantic and the Bay of Biscay to moult from where some turn up as far north as the British Isles and southern Scandinavia. It spends the winter months (November- February) around the Balearics, and off the north-eastern coast of Spain, between Valencia and Catalonia in particular. Adult birds start breeding in their third year, and lay a single egg. It feeds on small, pelagic fish and as these are becoming scarce, the species is more and more dependant on fish waste from commercial trawlers. Adult survival is unusually low for a *Procellaridae* and this is a main concern. Modelling predicts declines of up to 80% in the coming 50 years, which corresponds to three generations of Balearic Shearwaters. The reasons for these declines are several: at breeding sites predation from genets, cats and rats occurs and rabbits can also compete for nesting sites and deteriorate nesting habitat. Some colonies also experience clepto-parasitism from Yellow-legged Gulls *Larus cachinnans*. A reduction of fish waste from trawlers, in combination with a two-month spring fishing ban, could make food resources scarce, as could a planned reduction of the number of nutrients discharged in the Ebro delta. Building on or near breeding colonies disturb the birds and brings mammalian predators closer. The northwards shift of the non-breeding areas in summer may be associated with global warming and can also result in the birds travelling further north to find ample food resources. The Iberian government has declared Special Protection Areas to protect colonies. Rat eradication has been successfully applied to several breeding islands whilst on other islands rats are under control. International and National/Local Action Plans have been developed and Spain and Portugal had a joint LIFE project aiming at identifying marine IBAs for this species (among others) in 2004-2008. Migratory routes and systematic counts of birds leaving the Mediterranean to moult have been conducted since 2007 and will hopefully contribute to understanding this species's at-sea distribution outside the breeding areas. Actions that are required include in-depth studies of the by-catch effects of long-line fishing as indications are that this kills the species and to embark on an awareness campaign among fishermen concerning this. Nesting sites must be effectively protected and monitored. Small pelagic fish populations in the western Mediterranean should be studied and the spring fishing ban should be co-ordinated to avoid a complete lack of fish waste at certain times. More investigation into pollution by heavy metals, especially off the Ebro delta, is also required.

Photo: © Kris Gillam

Isle of Wight, August 2007

Photo: © Kris Gillam

Isle of Wight, August 2007

New Zealand Storm-petrel

Oceanites maorianus

Hauraki Gulf, New Zealand, 2007

Rediscovered from a photograph and field observations in 2003, over 100 years after it was first found, this storm-petrel is fairly easy to see in the Hauraki Gulf in New Zealand but its breeding grounds and life history are still unknown.

Photo: © Stefan Oscarsson

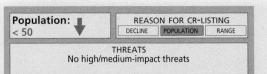

Population: ↓ < 50	REASON FOR CR-LISTING		
	DECLINE	POPULATION	RANGE
THREATS No high/medium-impact threats			

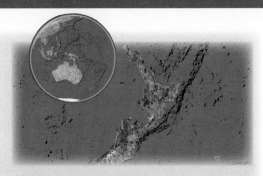

History

1827 – the first two specimens are collected by French ornithologists J. R. C. Quoy (1790-1869) and J. P. Gaimard (1796-1858) on board the ship Astrolabe in January – March, probably along the east coast of North island.

1895 – a third specimen is brought to the British Museum at Tring. This is the type specimen.

1932 – G. M. Mathews describes the species as *Paeleornis maoriana*. The following years scientists are uncertain whether it is a subspecies of Wilson's Storm-petrel *Oceanites oceanicus* (Murphy and Snyder 1952), a distinct species (Oliver 1955) or a separate genus.

2003 – a storm-petrel, thought to be Black-bellied *Fregetta tropica* is photographed by Brent Stephenson on a pelagic birding tour off Mercury Islands, North Island on January 25th. This, and more records in the Gulf later this year, leads to the conclusion that it is the lost New Zealand Storm-petrel.

2005 – first bird in the hand is obtained when fisherman

Geordie Murman captures a bird that has flown into his cabin.

2006 – three birds are captured at sea in January and are fitted with transmitters. National Geographic-funded efforts to capture birds in October-November fail, but several at-sea records are made.

2007 – a search of both published and unpublished historical records for black and white storm-petrels has revealed a number of probable earlier sightings for northern NZ waters during 1969-90. Three birds are caught but not fitted with transmitters as they do not show signs of breeding.

2008 – a group from UK travel operator Wildwings photograph what may be the first, unconfirmed New Zealand Storm-petrel away from New Zealand, south of New Caledonia on 8th April.

This species is thought to breed during the summer months between October-April in the Hauraki Gulf area, North Island, New Zealand. It was rediscovered after more than 100 years when a bird was photographed in 2003. Nothing is known about its breeding biology but it seems to occupy warmer waters which come into the Hauraki Gulf during the summer and its absence at other times indicates that it is migratory. It is thought to feed on crustaceans and plankton and is attracted to chum slicks.

No threats are known, as breeding sites have not been identified, but predators on the nesting sites could be eventual threats. Organised ecotourism trips have helped reveal much of what is known about this species.

It is possible that the species has benefited from rat eradication programmes already successful on offshore islands in the Hauraki Gulf. There are 211 islands with an area in excess of 2 hectares which have never had rats. Because of the large number of potential breeding sites, telemetry has been judged the most efficient way of finding breeding sites. Seven birds have been caught and attempts to follow them by telemetry to find their breeding grounds were made, but were unsuccessful.

Future actions include clarifying the taxonomic position and, above all, locating breeding grounds.

Hauraki Gulf, New Zealand, 2007

Photo: © Stefan Oscarsson

Hauraki Gulf, New Zealand, 2004

Photo: © Brent Stephenson / www.wrybill-tours.com

Townsend´s Shearwater
Puffinus auricularis

Population: ↓ 46,000	REASON FOR CR-LISTING		
	DECLINE	POPULATION	RANGE

THREATS
Invasives

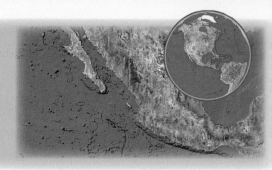

Socorro, 2007

This shearwater breeds in a small area on Socorro Island, having previously bred on the neighbouring islands of Clarión, and San Benedicto, also in the Revillagigedo islands, Mexico. It is closely related to the Hawaiian Shearwater *P. newelli* which was split from it in 2004. It breeds in burrows near forest edge and disperses over the continental shelf of Mexico when not breeding.

Introduced animals such as cats, sheep and pigs have contributed to the decline. Ninety two per cent of investigated cat scats collected between 1993 and 199? contained shearwater remains and there is an estimate of 350 female shearwaters being killed each year. Pigs contributed to the extirpation from Clarión by destroying burrows. The San Benedicto population was obliterated by a volcano eruption in 1952. Since 1994 the Revillagigedo Islands have been a biosphere reserve. Breeding surveys by Endémicos Insulares (www.endemicos.org) took place in 2008 and will form the base for an efficient recovery plan. It is considered most likely that prospectors will arrive to Clarión once burrows on the ground are safe. For San Benedicto it is believed that more time is required for vegetation to grow before the species can recolonize. Pigs and sheep are now eradicated from Clarión, but rabbits still remain. Surveys and cat-trapping are planned for both Clarión and Socorro.

Junín Grebe
Podiceps taczanowskii

Population: ↓ 100-300	REASON FOR CR-LISTING		
	DECLINE	POPULATION	RANGE

THREATS
Dams & water use, pollution, climate change

Lake Junín

This flightless grebe is confined to just one site, Lake Junín in the Junín highlands of Peru. The population fluctuates depending on climatic conditions, with lowest numbers in dry years. It breeds from November to March in flooded reed-beds and lays two eggs per clutch. Lake Junín is a shallow lake bordered by reeds and situated at an altitude of 4,080 metres. The grebes forage mostly in open water and feed on small fish and invertebrate larvae.

Lake Junín is affected by pollution from mining activities and fluctuating water levels, and climatic variations can also be detrimental. The pollution is clearly the principle threat to the species, as the densest population of grebes is found at the southern end of the lake, the furthest point from the mine. The species's inability to recover in years with high water levels is considered problematic in those cases when several poor years follow each other.
Lake Junín is a National Reserve and hunting and fishing is regulated. The Peruvian government passed an emergency law to protect the lake in 2002.
A previous attempt to translocate Junín Grebes to another lake failed as the gill-nets used there for fishing also impacted Junín Grebes.
Local fishermen indicated in spring 2008 that a new census is required and dead birds, possibly killed by pollution, have also been found recently. NGO ECOAN is working with awareness including education and a photo exhibition of Junín Grebe.

Chatham Islands Shag
Phalacrocorax onslowi

Population: ↓ 540	REASON FOR CR-LISTING		
	DECLINE	POPULATION	**RANGE**

THREATS
No high/medium-impact threats

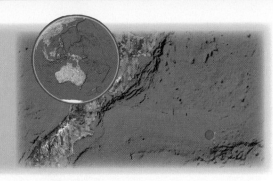

Chatham Islands, 2006

Photo: © Brent Stephenson / www.wrybill-tours.com

This black and white cormorant breeds on three islands in the Chathams but the breeding range only encompasses one ha and the feeding range is 24 km². It is a colonial nester on rocks on headlands, small islands or cliff-ledges and lays eggs between August & December. Birds feed alone but roost communally.

The largest breeding colonies are found on predator-free islands, but the Chatham population is disturbed by humans, feral cats, weka, farm animals, pigs and agriculture. When shags stampede from their nests, gulls often move in to take advantage of the broken eggs. One colony, on Stars Keys, has been disturbed by Fur Seals *Arctocephalus forsteri* who have moved in and taken over the breeding ground. Accidental by-catch in fishing occurs, and there may also be decreases in the main food source which would ensue in a decline in numbers.

A recovery plan running until 2011 was published in 2001.

Future conservation actions include performing a regularly recurring census of the population and annual monitoring of the colonies. Legal protection of all colonies and fencing, where predators are a problem, is also needed, as well as careful supervision of ecotourism.

Dwarf Olive Ibis
Bostrychia bocagei

Population: ↓ 50-249	REASON FOR CR-LISTING		
	DECLINE	**POPULATION**	RANGE

THREATS
Persecution

Ribeira Peixe, São Tomé, 2006

Photo: © Nik Borrow

This forest-living ibis has been split from Olive Ibis *B. olivacea*. It is endemic to São Tomé, São Tomé e Príncipe where it was only known anecdotally from observations made by local people until 1990 when the first confirmed sighting was made. It now occurs in the central and south-western parts. It feeds

on slugs, snails and invertebrates on forest floor, especially where wild pigs have disturbed the ground or in swampy areas. Night roosting is communal. Threats include clearing of lowland forest for cocoa plantations and land privatisation which may result in clearing of trees, although primary forest has been spared so far. Introduced mammals and hunting are also threats.

A national park and protection of primary forest as a "zona ecologica" have been proposed. A training course, sponsored by the A. P. Leventis Conservation Foundation took place in summer 2008 aiming at involving locals in carrying out their own monitoring and research projects on local, endemic birds, including this species.

Awareness of the species, study of its ecology and identification of key sites and protecting them are essential, as well as getting the species listed as a nationally protected species.

Giant Ibis
Thaumatibis gigantea

Chhep, Cambodia, 2005

Population: ↓ 200	REASON FOR CR-LISTING		
	DECLINE	POPULATION	RANGE

THREATS
Infrastructure development, agriculture, persecution, plant-gathering, disturbance, dams & water management

History

1877 – French Zoologist Jean-Frédéric Émile Oustalet (1844-1905) describes the species.

1993 – after being feared extinct for some years, it is rediscovered in Laos.

1997 – the hitherto only known breeding record is reported from Laos.

2001 – a relict population of 40-70 birds is discovered in Cambodia.

2003 – Omaliss Keo starts a PhD study of the species and contributes much knowledge on its biology.

2006 – intensive studies of feeding habits are performed with the help of camera traps during January to April.

This ibis occurs in northern Cambodia and southern Laos with a recent record from Vietnam. It wanders outside of the breeding season, but very little is known about this. It is found in wetlands and seasonal water-meadows in open, predominantly deciduous, dipterocarp lowland forest. It feeds in soft mud on, among other animals, eels, mole crickets and frogs. The nest is built in a tree and in one study area it uses five out of the 78 tree species available.

It appears to be highly sensitive to disturbance. Deforestation, drainage of wetlands and hunting has caused its decline. Plans entailing clearing dry lowland forest for teak plantations exist in the Western Siem Pang IBA where it occurs, and demand for produce such as rice, cashew, rubber and cassava may also affect its feeding and breeding habitat greatly. Its choice of large trees makes it vulnerable to logging and resin-tapping and nests that had been protected

by predator-exclusion devices seemed to fare better than those without. Drainage of pools during the dry season can also reduce the opportunities to find food. It occurs in a few protected areas and is depicted in public awareness material aiming to stop hunting of large waterbirds in Laos and Cambodia. In the Tmatboey region it, together with White-shouldered Ibis (p. 112-113), benefits from ecotourism.

Further surveys to locate and quantify remaining populations in Laos and Cambodia are required. More studies on its breeding, demography and seasonal movements are also essential and nests should be protected from predators and humans. Furthermore, efforts to keep pools, both man-made and natural, wet during the dry season should be made and the abundance of its main prey in these monitored. Awareness and education needs to be spread among the inhabitants of its range.

White-shouldered Ibis
Pseudibis davisoni

This ibis is probably the most threatened waterbird in South-East Asia and has its current stronghold in Cambodia, where ecotourist projects help to create awareness of it.

Tmatboey, Cambodia, 2005

Photo: © James Eaton / www.birdtourasia.com

Population: ↓ 50-249	REASON FOR CR-LISTING		
	DECLINE	POPULATION	RANGE
THREATS			
Agriculture, mining, logging, disturbance, pollution			

History

1836 – German taxidermist Salomon Müller (1804-1864) collects and observes the species in Borneo in December.

1875 - A. O. Hume describes the species in his journal *Stray Feathers*.

1899 - an adult male is collected in Yunnan province, China in April.

1901 – several eggs are taken by collectors in Myanmar in March.

1937 – last record from Thailand.

1946 – Malaysia's only confirmed record is a bird in Sarawak in November.

1999 – last confirmed records from Vietnam.

2006 – 108 birds are recorded at two sites in Cambodia on 1st November.

2007 – work on establishing Western Siem Pang as

a protected forest begins. The ecotourism project in Tmatboey receives the Wild Asia Responsible Tourism Award in November.

2008 – breeding is confirmed at two sites in Cambodia. Survey work in the Siem Pang district produces 86 sightings in 53 days. A PhD study commences in October to study the relationship of the ibis with human activities.

This is probably the most threatened waterbird in South-East Asia as its decline has been rapid. It formerly occurred in Thailand, Laos, Vietnam (almost certainly extinct as a breeding species), Cambodia, Myanmar, Yunnan (China), Kalimantan (Indonesia) and Sarawak (Malaysia). Today the few birds remaining are to be found in Vietnam, Cambodia, extreme south Laos and Kalimantan (Indonesia). In the Siem Pang district of Cambodia, the species has increased in recent years, from 23 in 2003 to 108 in 2006, and this unprotected area is known as the most important site in the world for this species. On the other hand, in Kalimantan it has decreased due to El Niño Southern Oscillation induced forest fires. It is currently strongly associated with dipterocarp forest while water, rivers, floodplains, rice fields and marshes have been important for it in the past (and may continue to be so). It breeds from November- April (the dry season). It has been associated with large ungulates, which keep, create and maintain short-sward grassland feeding areas that the ibises depend on. There are no indications of seasonal movements.

It is often found close to human habitation, so disturbance, logging and infrastructural projects are probably now the greatest threats. Hunting is currently less of a threat as arms have been confiscated across Cambodia and education campaigns are taking place. The lack of high density of wild ungulate populations in deciduous dipterocarp forests in Southeast Asia has also affected the species negatively.

It occurs in several protected areas and public-awareness material depicting it has been distributed in Laos and Cambodia. However, Cambodia with 25% of its land protected, is looking to develop rather than protect its land. Nest protection schemes, involving incentives for the local population, are being established and foraging ecology research

has been undertaken in Cambodia. Ecotourism has managed to bring in funds to villagers at at least one Cambodian site, Tmatboey. Each tourist pays $30 to the community.

Future actions include surveying, especially in Borneo, Cambodia and Vietnam to determine if there could be remaining populations, awareness campaigns aimed at wetlands disturbance and large waterbird exploitation in Indo-China, more studies into the species's ecology and the establishment of more protected areas, including establishing Siem Pang as a Protected Forest.

Photo: © Jonathan Eames

Northern Bald Ibis
Geronticus eremita

When first presented in a drawing in Europe half a millenium ago, the Northern Bald Ibis was believed to be a hoax. In the Middle East it was thought it had guided Noah from Ararat and that there were connections with Mekka which lies along its migration route.

Durrell, Jersey Zoo, 2007

Photo: © Gregory Guida / www.gguida.com

| Population: ↓ | REASON FOR CR-LISTING | | |
| 208 | DECLINE | **POPULATION** | RANGE |

| THREATS |
| Infrastructure development, agriculture, persecution, disturbance, dams & water use, invasives, pollution |

History

1504 – Archbishop Leonard of Salzburg publishes a decree protecting the species.

1555 – Konrad von Gesner of Switzerland publishes a drawing and description of Bald Ibis, widely believed to be a hoax.

1758 – first described by Carolus Linneaus (1707-1778).

1839 – William Francis Ainsworth mentions the Birecik colony.

1854 – a colony is discovered in Syria.

1930 – Moroccan population numbers 1000 birds.

1940 – 38 colonies known in Morocco.

1975 – 250 pairs and 100-150 non-breeding birds in 15 colonies in Morocco.

1989 – one wild bird remains in Birecik, Turkey.

2002 – although now believed to be extinct from Syria, a new colony is discovered near Palmyra and successfully protected until 2004.

2005 – a wild bird, presumed originating from the

Moroccan population is recorded in Extremadura, Spain February to May. The Syrian population's breeding fails, probably due to Raven depredation.

2006 – successful protection and tagging programme in Syria; three chicks fledged from two pairs, three breeding adults are satellite-tagged and four adult birds are tracked to wintering grounds in Ethiopia.

2007 – just two pairs with two chicks each plus three subadults are present in Syria in 2007. Four adults are found at a wintering site in Ethiopia.

2008 – Syrian breedings fail with four chicks dying, most probably due to Raven depredation. A pair in a Spanish reintroduction scheme lay two eggs near Cadiz, the first nesting in Spain since the 15th century.

oday, there are two wild populations of this species. One, the more numerous, in Morrocco which consists of four colonies and another, very small, in Syria. The Moroccan population is mainly resident, a stray record from Spain in 2005 probably relates to a wandering individual from it. Syrian birds, wintering in Ethiopia, are present from February to July and 24 offspring have been produced since 2002 with five subadults and two new recruits returning between 2004 and 2008. Records in late autumn 2007 of untagged birds in Israel and Djibouti could refer to Syrian juveniles or another, yet undiscovered, population. The Syrian population feeds on beetles, grasshoppers and toads. There is also a semi-captive population in Turkey which is confined to aviaries in winter in order to prevent it from migrating. In captivity there is a good representation of the western population, but very few of the eastern. It feeds on invertebrates in semi-arid littoral steppes or agricultural land.

In Morocco, illegal building, loss of eggs to predators, poor chick survival and human disturbance near the colonies are the main threats. Overgrazing by sheep and collection of firewood in Syria are threats to habitat and hunting is also considered a threat. Danger on the perilous migration route of the Syrian population also poses risks. The low return rate and unknown wintering areas of juvenile birds is also worrying.

The breeding project of the semi-captive population at Birecik, Turkey is planned for being used in reintroductions and captive birds are bred in Austria, Spain, Italy and Bavaria, Germany with similar intentions. The Syrian breeding area is now an officially Protected Area which also the Oued Massa National Park in Morocco is.

Main actions to be taken include increasing the Turkish colony and using it for reintroductions in historical sites or augmentation of the Syrian population, protecting the species from hunting on its migration, protect Ethiopian wintering areas and find out where young birds from the Syrian population go after fledging. There is a fairly high population density in the Ethiopian wintering site and awareness and monitoring of the future use of pesticides there will be crucial. Young, Syrian birds, should be tagged to determine their wintering quarters.

Tamri, Haha, Morocco, 2008

Photo: © Ray Tipper

White-bellied Heron
Ardea insignis

Previously treated as a subspecies of Great-billed Heron, this very large heron can be found only along undisturbed and inaccessible rivers where it gathers in flocks in winter.

Northern Kachin State, Myanmar, 2005

Population: ↓ 50-249	REASON FOR CR-LISTING		
	DECLINE	POPULATION	RANGE

THREATS
Agriculture, mining, logging, disturbance, pollution

History

1878 – British ornithologist A. O. Hume (1829-1912) describes the species.

1929 – the first nest of the species is found in Myanmar.

2006 – 16 birds were believed to constitute the total population in Bhutan in February. Three active nests in Bhutan in May held eight chicks in total.

2006 – a video about the species to be used in public awareness campaigns in Bhutan is produced.

2007 – the species is upgraded from Endangered to Critically Endangered.

breeds from February to May in India, Bhutan, angladesh and Myanmar, with historical records rom Nepal and possible occurrence in south-east ibet, China. Six active nests were recorded in Bhutan n 2007, resulting in six chicks and the population here is thought to number 30. There are six known reeding sites from two rivers in Central Bhutan. In Myanmar there has been a decline and the species s now absent from large areas of suitable habitat despite an increased number of surveys having taken lace. Local people's reports support this decline. It s found along rivers, often with sand or gravel bars, adjacent to broadleaved forest. It favours inaccessible nd undisturbed areas and flocks in winter. In Bhutan dults and juveniles were observed feeding in small orest streams while non-breeding birds visited larger ivers.

Widespread loss, degradation and disturbance of orest are thought to be the main reasons for the decline. Wetlands are also degraded due to pollution nd over-exploitation. Natural forest fires have been known to destroy nests in Bhutan, and disappearance of shallow sandbars in rivers can also have a negative effect. In some areas poaching can be a problem and the use of waterways for transport and electrical power also causes disturbance.

It probably breeds in an area already protected as a Tiger Reserve in India and Myanmar and it occurs outside of the breeding season in other protected areas. The Royal Society for the Protection of Nature, the World Wildlife Fund, the Felburn Foundation and the International Crane Foundation run a project in Bhutan to study the species and the Bhutan government has declared an important riverbed which functions as a feeding zone as protected habitat. Future conservation actions include extensive surveys in India, Tibet and Myanmar to establish distribution, ecology and populations. Satellite telemetry could be useful for establishing movements and awareness campaigns are essential as well as improving already protected areas in Myanmar by e.g. creating buffer zones.

Bhutan, 2007

Photo: © Andy Bunting

Christmas Island Frigatebird

Fregata andrewsi

Christmas Island Frigatebirds have been equipped with satellite transmitters to study their dispersal patterns and a female flew a 4,000 km non-stop route in 26 days before returning back to Christmas Island.

Christmas Island, 2007

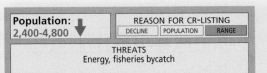

Population: ↓ 2,400-4,800	REASON FOR CR-LISTING		
	DECLINE	POPULATION	RANGE

THREATS
Energy, fisheries bycatch

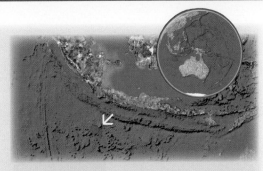

History

1910 – around 4,500 breeding pairs are estimated, down from estimated 6,300 pairs before settlement.

1914 – Australian amateur ornithologist Gregory Macalister Mathews (1876-1949) describes the species.

1978 – around 1,500 pairs are estimated.

1980 – Christmas Island National Park is established.

2003 – 1,171 breeding pairs are estimated.

2006 – the most recent, complete census is made. The first record from Vietnam is made in August.

2007 – four more birds are satellite-tagged.

2008 – one bird is satellite-tagged.

This frigatebird is endemic to Christmas Island, Australia where it breeds in three sub-colonies. Two thirds of the nests are in one colony making it particularly vulnerable. It is extremely adapted to an aerial life and cannot roost on water. It is difficult to ascertain trends, but models indicate a 66% decrease since 1945, with some fluctuations. Breeding starts in February/March and females breed bi-annually while males are suspected to breed annually. Non-breeders are widely distributed over South-East Asian seas, north to Indo-China and south to Australia. The distribution to the west in the Indian Ocean is unknown but vagrants have been recorded as far west as Kenya. It breeds in trees and raises one fledgling. Food consists of squid and fish, often chased to the surface by subsurface predators, which it snaps while on the wing and it is also a kleptoparasite. Satellite tracking has shown that Christmas Frigate birds can fly thousands of kilometres from the colony and one female with a chick even flew a 27 day, over 4,000 km long mission. The population recovers slowly after declines as the replacement rate is thought to be 15-25 years.

A quarter of the breeding area was cleared before 1946. Phosphate mining has been the main commercial activity on Christmas Island and one of the breeding colonies was deserted when subjected to fallout from mining. An application to mine 250 ha of rainforest on Christmas Island is currently under review. Poaching ceased in the 1980s and is not longer considered a threat. The Crazy Yellow Ant *Anoplolepis gracilipes* has been introduced, but has not been proven to be a threat so far. Fishing (entangling in nets), marine pollution and illegal hunting on roost islands are also potential threats.

The National Park covers two of the three colonies which correspond to 90% of the population.

A recovery plan has been completed and there is ongoing work to eliminate Yellow Crazy Ants. Future actions include continuing the ant eradication programmes and developing and implementing techniques for monitoring colonies and ecology.

Christmas Island, 2004

White-collared Kite
Leptodon forbesi

Brazil, 2008

Population: 50-249 ⬇	REASON FOR CR-LISTING		
	DECLINE	POPULATION	RANGE
THREATS Agriculture, logging			

History
1922 – Henry Kirke Swann (1871–1926) describes the species.

2007 – a three-week survey of twelve forested sites in Pernambuco and Alagoas states found kites at ten sites with 30 birds recorded.

This kite is closely related to Grey-headed Kite *Leptodon cayanensis* and some authors consider it a subspecies of the latter. It is known from seven, fragmented sites in the north-eastern Atlantic rainforest of Brazil. Very little is known about its ecology, but it occurs in humid forests up to 600 metres.

The disappearing forests are the main concern, as is fire from neighbouring sugar cane plantations which destroys what forest remains. The forest cover within its range has been reduced to 1% of its former total and the largest remaining forest fragment in Alagoas and Pernambuco are 30 and 40 km² respectively.

A large area in Murici is protected by the Brazilian government and surveys took place in 2007 and 2008 in Alagoas and Pernambuco states. A local NGO IPMA (Instituto para a Preservação da Mata Atlântica) is working to create forest reserves on privately owned land.

Further surveys are required in forest patches larger than ten hectares in Pernambuco and Alagoas, but also in neighbouring Paraiba and Sergipe to determine if birds exist in these forests and sites. Murici should be designated as a biological reserve and protection enforced.

Madagascar Fish-eagle
Haliaeetus vociferoides

Madagascar, 2005

Photo: © Pete Morris

Population:	REASON FOR CR-LISTING		
222 ↓	DECLINE	**POPULATION**	RANGE

THREATS
Agriculture, persecution, logging, fisheries bycatch

History

c.1841 – Mr. Louis Rousseau collects a specimen which is sent to the Natural History Museum in Paris.

1845 – French ornithologist Marc Athanese Parfait Oeillet des Murs (1804-1878) describes the species.

1978-1986 – a survey along the northern coast of Madagascar by Olivier Langrand locates 40 pairs and 10 singles.

1991-1995 – surveys by The Peregrine Fund find at least 222 adults in 105 sites, of which 99 pairs bred.

2006 – in the Manambolomaty Lakes Complex conservation area where The Peregrine Fund works with local communities, 8 of 11 territorial pairs managed breeding, raising five young.

2007 – 12 pairs are observed in 2007 at the Manambolomaty Lakes Complex conservation area.

2008 – 27 nests in the Antsalova district.

This eagle is restricted to the western coast of Madagascar where it occurs in low densities in three main regions. It breeds in wooded areas adjacent to lakes, rivers, and marine environments and feeds predominantly on fish, especially introduced Tilapia and ample fish resources and large trees for perching are crucial. The nest is built in a tree or large cliff and nesting takes place from May to October. The clutch is usually one to two, but a clutch of three was observed in 2005. Only one chick fledges and one third of breeding attempts result in no eggs being laid. Deforestation, soil erosion and development of water bodies into rice fields have destroyed nesting and foraging habitat. Humans compete for fish and there is also persecution of nestlings, shooting of fledged birds and accidental catches in connection with fishing which has affected the populations. Being high up in the food chain it can be affected by water pollution. Surveys are made approximately every fifth year with the most recent one in 2005. Survival to fledging has successfully been increased in two cases when young have been taken from a nest and released when on the wing, thereby preventing siblicide.

There is a target of establishing up to 28 pairs in the Antsalova region, by making use of traditional laws of local communities to protect the birds. Manambolomaty (The Three Lakes Complex) is a Ramsar site which held 12 pairs in 2007. This site and Tambohorano would make up one of two Systems of Protected Areas in Madagascar to protect 12 and six pairs respectively.

Vultures in general

The drug diclofenac, used to treat cows against disease, has been found to cause kidney failure followed by death in vultures which has contributed strongly to the rapid decline of populations in especially the Indian subcontinent. It is assumed that less than one in 100 carcasses need to be treated with diclofenac to cause serious effects.

Laws banning the manufacture of diclofenac have been passed in Nepal, India and Pakistan. However, the drug was still widely used in some places in 2007. In Nepal, a successful drug replacement programme has managed to decrease the use of diclofenac by 90% which has enabled the number of nests of White-rumped and Slender-billed Vultures to be doubled during just two years. An alternative drug, Meloxicam, which does not effect vulture populations according to trials on African White-backed Vultures *Gyps africanus*, is available. In April 2008, Indian customs started to levy an anti-dumping duty on Chinese diclofenac dumping, the result of an intensive advocacy campaign.

Vulture restaurants, where vultures are provided alternative food, have been useful to promote ecotourism and awareness as well as providing vultures with an alternative, poison-free food source but should not be isolated actions as birds will also feed in the neighbouring areas. The restaurant consists of a livestock carcass that is monitored for 4-5 days by local community rangers which record the visiting vultures. In Cambodia, there are currently seven restaurants. Three breeding centres for vultures are now established in India. The first chicks, of White-rumped Vulture, hatched in a centre in Haryana managed by the Bombay Natural History Society and the Royal Society for Protection of Birds in early 2007. This centre holds 53 White-rumped, 54 Indian and 14 Slender-billed Vultures. The second centre is in West Bengal and holds 21 White-rumped, 17 Indian and 12 Slender-billed Vultures. These birds are still too young to breed. The third centre was inaugurated in Assam and currently houses two White-rumped and two Slender-billed Vultures. In Cambodia, no captive breeding centres are established as the threats to wild vultures are considered to have stabilised and conservation actions in the wild are deemed more suitable.

Additional work with satellite-tagging to determine vultures' movements and ecology is needed as well as public awareness campaigns dedicated at vultures and their place in the ecosystem. DNA collected from feathers dropped at vulture restaurants will be analysed and will assist in determining populations and establishing how reliable traditional censuses are.

Red-headed Vulture
Sarcogyps calvus

Population: 2,500-9,999 ⬇	REASON FOR CR-LISTING		
	DECLINE	POPULATION	RANGE

THREATS
Agriculture, persecution, other ecosystems modification, pollution

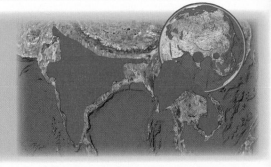

Bandhavgarh Tiger Reserve, Madhya Pradesh, India, 2007

Photo: © Santosh Saligram

This vulture is widespread over south Asia from Pakistan to the west to Vietnam in the east. The latest authenticated record since 1980 from Pakistan was, however, made in 2002 when a pair were observed in Sind province. It is very local in Cambodia, nearly extinct from Thailand and extinct from Malaysia and Singapore. It is less territorial than *Gyps* vultures and occurs at lower densities, breeding in March to April. The extent of movements is unknown.

An overall decline in the Indian subcontinent has followed with figures being recorded at 94% between 2000 and 2003. Competition with *Gyps* vultures at carcasses may explain initially slower decline rates than these. The South Asian populations have probably declined due to the decline of large ungulates while diclofenac probably plays a role in the Indian populations' decline.

The populations are monitored in protected areas and feeding of vultures is taking place in northern Cambodia and Nepal. There are no Red-headed Vultures in captivity that can be used for reintroductions but a captive-breeding programme could be useful.

White-rumped Vulture
Gyps bengalensis

India, 1996

Population: ↓ 2,500-9,999	REASON FOR CR-LISTING		
	DECLINE	POPULATION	RANGE

THREATS
Pollution

History

1788 – German physician Johann Friedrich Gmelin (1748-1804) describes the species.

1985 – White-rumped Vulture is considered to be the world's most common bird of prey numbering in the millions.

1996-97 – the colony at Keoladeo National Park has declined by 97% in ten years.

2000 – the species is listed as Critically Endangered.

2000/01 – Toawala in Pakistan houses 445 pairs.

2003 – the colony at Keoladeo, Haryana, India becomes extinct.

2004 – the largest known remaining colony is of 160 pairs at Toawala in Pakistan, 285 pairs less than four years earlier.

2007 – the year gets off to a good start when two chicks are hatched in captivity at a breeding centre in Pinjore, Haryana, India. However, a survey in northern and central India between March and June shows that numbers are down to one thousandth of the 1980 figures.

2007 – five birds have their wings amputated after having been injured by kite strings.

This vulture is widespread over south Asia from Pakistan via India, Bangladesh, Nepal, Bhutan, Myanmar, Thailand, Laos and Cambodia to Thailand. In the Indian subcontinent it has declined by 99.9% since 1992. The most viable population is today thought to be in Cambodia, where numbers in censuses increased from 90 in 2004 to 160 in 2007. It is a social species, usually found in conspecific flocks at carcasses and roosting communally. It feeds on both fresh and putrid flesh and lays one egg during breeding which takes place in October-March. Previously it was heavily relied on in the Indian subcontinent to clean both human and animal carcasses.

The declines in South-East Asia predated the current, rapid decline in other parts of Asia and it is thought that intensive agriculture and use of chemicals there has decreased the natural population of large ungulates, which in its turn and in connection with modern animal husbandry practices probably has caused a food shortage and resulted in a downturn of the vulture population.

See p. 122 for information on threats, conservation actions and proposed conservation actions.

Indian Vulture
Gyps indicus

Kanha National Park, India, 2008

Population: ↓	REASON FOR CR-LISTING		
2,500-9,999	DECLINE	POPULATION	RANGE

THREATS
Ecosystem modification, pollution

History

1995/96 – the population at Keoladeo national park is 816 birds.

1998/99 – population down to 25 birds in Keoladeo national park.

2001 – the species is split from Long-billed Vulture *Gyps tenuirostris*, which it previously has been considered a subspecies of.

2002 – the species is listed as Critically Endangered.

2003 – a colony of 200-250 pairs is discovered in Pakistan.

2008 – around six to seven Indian Vultures are spotted at Ramanagaram, near Bangalore and thought to breed.

This vulture breeds mainly in India, with a small colony in adjacent parts of southeast Pakistan. As with other South Asian vulture species it has faced serious declines in recent years. It nests in cliffs and ruins from November to March but has also been reported to nest in trees where cliffs are not available. It often associates with White-rumped vultures *Gyps bengalensis* at carcasses.

In common with White-rumped vulture (p. 123), its decline is largely attributed to the use of diclofenac and the same threats and actions to be taken are applied to the Indian Vulture.

See p. 122 for information on threats, conservation actions and proposed conservation actions.

Bandhavgarh National Park, Madhya Pradesh, India, 2007

Slender-billed Vulture
Gyps tenuirostris

Bhadoi Pach Ali, Duliajan, Assam, 2007

Photo: © Kulojyoti Lahkar

Population: ⬇ 2,500-9,999	REASON FOR CR-LISTING		
	DECLINE	POPULATION	RANGE

THREATS
Ecosystem modification, pollution

History

1844 – George Robert Gray (1808-1872) describes the species.

2001 – Long-billed Vulture *Gyps tenuirostris*, is renamed Slender-billed Vulture and Indian Vulture *Gyps indicus* receives specific status.

2002 – classified as Critically Endangered.

2006 – 18 Slender-billed Vultures are caught for captive breeding in Haryana state, India.

2007 – five nests are found in Cambodia, the first for the country. 36 individuals are counted in Cambodia December.

2008 – 51, the highest number ever, are counted at vulture restaurants in Cambodia.

his species which is closely related to and formerly onsidered conspecific with Indian Vulture, occurs in orthern India (c.1,000), Nepal, Bhutan, Bangladesh nd Myanmar to Laos and (recently) Cambodia. It reeds in November to March and places its nest in arge trees, often near villages. Movements are poorly nderstood and it is not known whether there is an xchange between the different populations. his species has probably, like White-rumped 'ulture, been affected by the disappearance of large ngulates in Cambodia although the use of diclofenac as caused the major declines the last decades. Since 992 in northern India a decrease of 97% has been bserved. Recent findings in Nepal show that the umber of nests of this species and White-rumped 'ulture (p. 123) have doubled in an area where the se of diclofenac has been reduced by 90% since 2006. ee p. 122 for information on threats, conservation ctions and proposed conservation actions.

Kaziranga, 2008

Photo: © Amano Samarpan

Philippine Eagle

Pithecophaga jefferyi

This magnificent bird, also known as Monkey-eating Eagle, is affected by hunting.
A farmer that shot and ate a released bird in 2008 risks a prison sentence of many years.

Near Mount Kitanglad, Bukidnon, Philippines, 2007

Population: ↓	REASON FOR CR-LISTING		
180-500	DECLINE	POPULATION	RANGE

THREATS
Agriculture, logging, pollution

History

1896 – British explorer and naturalist John Whitehead (1860-1899) observes the first Philippine Eagle. A few weeks later, his servant Juan obtains the first specimen.

1897 – W. R. Ogilvie-Grant shows the eagle skin in a London restaurant. It gets its latin name two weeks later, commemorating Whitehead's father, Jeffery.

1965 – famous aviator Charles Lindbergh champions the cause of the Philippine Eagle together with Philippine scientist Dr. Dioscoro Rabor.

1969 – Monkey-eating Eagle Conservation Programme is initiated.

1992 – first two captive-bred Philippine Eagles bred through artificial insemination and are raised by the Philippine Eagle Foundation.

1995 – Presidential Proclamation declares the Philippine Eagle as the country's national bird.

1999 – first successful hatching of an eaglet out of an eagle couple naturally paired in captivity.

2004 – first release of a captive-bred bird, called "Kabayan" on Earth Day April 22nd into the forest of Mount Apo, Mindanao

2005 – the released male "Kabayan" is accidentally electrocuted in early January.

2008 – rehabilitated male eagle "Kagsabua" is released in Mt Kitanglad, Mindanao on March 6, but is then lost to a farmer with an airgun who eats it. The farmer risks 6-12 years in prison. The first translocation of a rescued young eagle, called "Tinuy-an" takes place from the forests of Bislig City to Mt Kitanglad, Mindanao on June 20th.

his spectacular eagle (see also pp 74-78) is endemic to the Philippines where it is known from Luzon, Leyte, Samar and Mindanao. The main part of the population is found on Mindanao. The complete breeding cycle lasts for two years and breeding starts September to February with some differences in timing between Mindanao and Luzon birds which may depend on rainfall and prey availability. It forms monogamous bond for life with sexual maturity for females at about five years and for males about seven years. The young fledge after four to five months, but stay in the nest vicinity for almost a year and a half. It can probably be long-lived as captive birds have reached more than 40 years of age. It lives in dipterocarp and mid-montane forests, from the lowlands to steep mountains up to 1,800 metres. Disappearance of forest through agricultural expansion, logging and mining pose threats. They are also vulnerable to accidental captures in native traps intended for wild pig and deer. Accumulation of pesticides could affect breeding results and it is also hunted for food and, formerly, trade and zoos. Naïve juvenile birds and adults nesting near forest edges are very vulnerable to shooting and trapping. All these factors suggest that recruitment into the breeding population may be low.

It occurs in some protected areas, but a large proportion of the population is in habitats lacking management regimes. A Philippine Eagle Foundation performs captive-breeding, test releases, monitoring of wild populations, public education and community-based habitat conservation. There are currently 32 Philippine Eagles at the breeding centre, of which 18 are captive-bred birds.

More research into ecology, numbers and threats is required and more protected areas need to be created. Eagle-friendly practices should be integrated into forest policy and more work on awareness and advocacy would support conservation.

Philippines, 2006

Ridgway's Hawk
Buteo ridgwayi

Los Haitises, Dominican Republic, 2008

Population: ↓ 160-240	REASON FOR CR-LISTING		
	DECLINE	POPULATION	RANGE

THREATS
Agriculture, logging

History

1883 – American ornithologist Charles B. Cory (1857-1921) describes the species.

2003 – 93 individuals are recorded in Los Haitises National Park, north-east Dominican Republic, including 37 pairs, 30 of which attempted nesting with eight successful pairs fledging 10 chicks.

2005 – 83 fledglings were produced from 45 successful (out of 66) attempts in Los Haitises NP.

2006 – 114 pairs recorded, and a total of 241 birds documented.

2007 – 322 birds documented including (157 pairs and eight individuals) of which 131 attempted nesting with

87 pairs successfully fledging 122 young.

2008 – field research was carried out between January-September. Four young were released in a forested area 50 km southeast of Los Haitises National Park.

This species occurs in the Dominican Republic, but has previously been reported from Haiti, Cayman Islands and Ile-a-Vache and (a single record) from Culebra off Puerto Rico. The annual decline is rapid, with 5-10% of pairs lost in one study site in Los Haitises National Park. It occurs in humid forest, secondary habitat and agricultural habitats. Lizards, snakes, frogs, and rodents are the main prey items but centipedes and small birds are occasionally taken too. The nest is built in crowns of tall trees or on the top of Palmchat *Dolus dominicus* nests, with two to three eggs laid in February to April. Both sexes in-cubate and usually manage to raise one to three chicks.

Large-scale habitat loss through clearing for agricultural activities as well as persecution are the main

reasons for its decline. The Los Haitises National Park is the only stronghold, but protection must be enforced and proactive. A publicity campaign by Sociedad Ornotilogia de la Hispaniola, aimed at providing awareness and stopping persecution, continues. Over 30 individuals have been sampled genetically. Ongoing DNA work is comparing the extent of genetic variation remaining in the current population with the historic population to determine if poor genetic diversity should be a concern for species recovery.

The Peregrine Fund *www.peregrinefund.org* is very involved in this species's protection. Public education and awareness campaigns continue annually. Sites are being identified in order to establish populations outside of Los Haitises National Park.

Bengal Florican
Houbaropsis bengalensis

Cambodia, 2008

Population: ↓ 250-999	REASON FOR CR-LISTING		
	DECLINE	POPULATION	RANGE

THREATS
Agriculture, persecution, plant gathering

History
1789 – German naturalist J. F. Gmelin (1748-1804) describes the species.

1985 – the species is given legal protection in India.

1997 – an estimated 3,000 individuals in Cambodia.

2005/2006 – Cambodian population is down to 700 individuals.

2007 – an official patrol team is established in February, covering four IFBAs. A survey at three sites in Nepal show a 56% decline since 1982 and a 30% decline since 2001.

2008 – eleven birds are caught between February and March and are fitted with eight radio and three satellite transmitters.

here are two disjunct populations of this species; ne in India and Nepal (and, historically, Bangladesh) nd one in Cambodia (294 adult males) and possibly ietnam. The trend is stable in India whilst decreasing Nepal and Cambodia. It lives in dry or seasonally undated low-land, both natural and semi-natural rasslands. Local movements take place in the ambodian and Nepalese populations while the dian population is believed to be resident. It breeds March to June laying one-two eggs.

ne main threat is loss of grasslands through onversion to agriculture, grazing, inappropriate tting and burning regimes and flooding. Research Cambodia showed that the effect of human sturbance was weak but that annual burning of rasslands was important.

veral protected areas in Nepal, India, Cambodia and (possibly) Vietnam harbour the species. A programme in the Tonle Sap floodplain of Cambodia is aiming at reducing habitat loss and hunting pressure on the species by creating Integrated Farming and Biodiversity Areas (IFBAs) which will cover currently unprotected and important wet grasslands. In 2008 there were five such IFBAs protecting a third of the males' display sites.

More research is needed into the species ecology, habitat utilisation and breeding productivity. Radio and satellite telemetry will be used in 2008 to identify movements in the non-breeding (wet) season and find out more about females' habitat selection and nest site selection, which can be incorporated into conservation management plans. Population surveys and grassland management are essential as well as keeping human disturbance to a minimum.

Siberian Crane
Grus leucogeranus

This is the most aquatic of the crane species and it is consequently severely affected by degradation and loss of wetlands. Of the two or three disjunct populations, the global majority of the population is found in the eastern one.

Japan, 2004

Population: ⬇ 3,200	REASON FOR CR-LISTING		
	DECLINE	POPULATION	RANGE

THREATS
Infrastructure development, agriculture, dams & water use

History

1773 – Russian zoologist Peter Simon Pallas (1741-1811) describes the species.

1977 and 1978 – Russian eggs are flown to the International Crane Foundation in the USA for incubation and hatching.

2002 – Angelo D'Arrigo, a hang glider pilot, makes the world's longest hang-gliding flight from Tuymen to Iran showing captive-raised juveniles the way to wintering sites. The last observation of the "central" breeding pair is made in summer.

2006 – only two Siberian Cranes (both males) return to the wintering site in northern Iran in October, one disappears later

2007 – two captive-bred Siberian Cranes are brought to

Fereydoon Kenar in Iran, where a female is released and paired with a male in February. Both leave, but only the male returns on 3rd November. A captive-bred male is released with the wild male on 14th November.

2008 – one wild and one released bird leaves the wintering site in Iran on 23rd February. A new release of one bird is planned there for the autumn. 3,119 Siberian Cranes are counted in winter in Poyang lake, China.

hree populations are known, with one of them probably extinct; a western one ranging between the uymen region of Siberia, Russia and Iran, a central ne ranging from the basin of the Kunovat river, iberia, to India (extinct) and an easternmost one etween the rivers Kolyma and Yana and China. There ave been unsubstantiated reports of Siberian Cranes rom countries along the western flyways, so there is small chance that a population may still exist there. t lays two eggs in May-June, but usually fledges only ne chick. Both sexes take part in incubation, with he male taking care of defending the nest against danger. It is very specialised, being aquatic and preferring shallow waters for feeding on vegetarian natter and insects, fish and small mammals.
he degradation and loss of wetlands, caused by e. g. he Three Gorges Dam project in China, are the main hreats for its staging areas and wintering sites. The Poyang Lake basin in China is an important site, but he birds have to move to different areas of it during heir stays to adapt to the changing hydrological onditions. Hunting on passage was a key threat

to western populations, with the use of pesticides a problem in India. Poisoning targeting other waterbirds in China is also a threat. Oil exploration on or near Siberian breeding grounds another.
A captive-breeding facility is in place in Oka Biosphere Reserve in Russia. All States within its range have legally protected Siberian Cranes and several high-level programs have been implemented to safeguard its migration by conserving 16 important flyway wetlands from Iran to China used on its migration. Water-level management is underway in Poyang Lake, China and captive-bred birds are released in Iran in order to augment the wild population.
Actions required are to identify possible west Siberian breeding sites, especially in the Anabar-Olenek basin of Yakutia, and to enforce conservation measures in connection with the Three Gorges Dam project. Awareness campaigns with the aim of reducing hunting pressure on possible remaining western populations should be initiated. It is still unknown where subadults of one to two years of age summer, and these areas should be identified for protection.

Mongolia, 2006

Black Stilt
Himantopus novaezelandiae

Central Otago, New Zealand, 2005

Population:	REASON FOR CR-LISTING		
40 ↑	DECLINE	POPULATION	RANGE
	THREATS		
	Invasives		

History

1841 – British ornithologist John Gould (1804-1881) describes the species.

1940s – the species has retracted to a remnant population in the Mackenzie Basin and may number fewer than 500-1,000 birds from this decade onwards.

1979 – 8 eggs which are taken in October are successfully reared and result in 5 males and 3 females.

1981 – just 23 birds are known and intensive management begins.

2001 – the wild breeding population consists of just seven productive pairs.

2002 – 125 birds are recorded in the wild. The captive population consists of 25 adults.

2004/5 – 11 productive pairs breed.

2005/6 – 14 productive breeding pairs in the wild and 7 breeding pairs in captivity.

2006/7 – 17 productive breeding pairs in the wild.

2007/8 – 77 subadults and 16 juveniles are released into the wild, supplementing wild populations. 20 wild pairs and six captive pairs breed.

This wader, known locally as Kaki, today only breeds on South Island, New Zealand with a few wintering on North Island. It breeds on braided riverbeds, swamps and wetlands with some birds wintering on the coast on inter-tidal mudflats. It pairs for life with breeding taking place between August and February and laying up to four eggs. The food consists of insects and fish. Introduced mammals and Australasian Harrier *Circus approximans* and Kelp Gull *Larus dominicanus* are the main threats, while the impact of habitat loss has exacerbated declines. Recreational activities in riverbeds, hydroelectric development, drainage, weed growth and flood-control programmes disturb nesting. A previous skewed sex ratio was determined to have been caused by random effects due to a small population size and the ratio came back into balance in 2008. Hybridisation with Black-necked Stilt

H. himantopus can affect the genetic purity, although cases of hybridisation have declined in recent years. Wild-laid eggs are collected and incubated and raised in captivity with releases into the wild at about nine months of age for subadults and two-three months for juveniles. This has enhanced survival rates which have currently reached 80-100%. Some are given supplementary feeding after release to increase their chances of survival. Predators are trapped around wild nests and research is ongoing to determine the nature of these threats. Hybrids, now numbering less than 20 within the Black Stilt's range, are controlled. It is crucial to continue with captive-breeding efforts, improving wild recruitment and survival and to use expert practice management to keep this species from extinction.

St. Helena Plover
Charadrius sanctahelenae

St Helena, January 2007

Population: ↓ 200-220	REASON FOR CR-LISTING		
	DECLINE	POPULATION	RANGE

THREATS
Infrastructure development, ecosystem modifications

History

1638 – first official mention of the species.

1656 – British traveller Peter Mundy visits the island in 1634, 1638 and this year. He describes a small landbird, 'somewhat like a lark in colour, shape and note that runs off like a lapwing'.

1873 – British conservationist James Edmund Harting (1841–1928) describes the species.

1988/89 – a census tallies 450 birds.

1998 – 340 individuals are counted.

2007 – the species is uplisted to Critically Endangered.

2008 – an action plan is launched in January.

This small plover is the only endemic landbird to St. Helena. The decline between 2000 and 2005 was 40%, whilst between 2007 and 2008 the population seemed to increase. It occurs in dry, short-sward pastures where it feeds on invertebrates. It can breed at any time of the year and lays two eggs. More than one clutch may be laid a year.

Livestock grazing may have deteriorated nesting and feeding habitat and promoted scrub encroachment. Infrared cameras at nests have shown that cats, sheep and Common Mynas *Acridotheres tristis* disturb or predate nests. Building of housing and recreational use of off-road vehicles are threats as well as a probably increasing feral cat population.

All birds on St. Helena are protected. In 2007 a research programme was begun as a partnership between the University of Bath, the RSPB and the St. Helena National Trust. A feral cat trapping programme has become irregular and research began in 2007 to investigate the species' ecology and demography. This has involved setting up cameras at nests and colour-ringing birds so their individual movements can be tracked. The Action Plan, launched in January 2008, aims to have the species down-listed by 2017.

Future conservation actions include regular monitoring, habitat management, trapping of feral cats and restrictions in off-road driving.

Sociable Lapwing
Vanellus gregarius

A satellite-tagged bird's signals alerted Turkish ornithologists to go out looking for it in the field, and they were astonished to find not just the bird but a flock totalling a record 3,200 Sociable Lapwings.

Gujarat, India, 2007

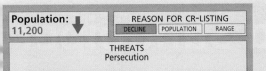

Population: 11,200 ↓	REASON FOR CR-LISTING		
	DECLINE	POPULATION	RANGE
THREATS Persecution			

History

1771 – German Zoologist Peter Simon Pallas (1741-1811) describes the species.

2004 – an intensive research project at the breeding sites in central Kazakhstan is initiated.

2005 – a survey of historical breeding sites in the South Urals is conducted.

2006 – funding for three years is awarded to the Kazakhstan research project through the Darwin Initiative programme.

2007 – surveys in northern Syria and south-eastern Turkey in March records over 1,500 and 1,000 individuals respectively, raising the possibility that these countries may form part of the regular wintering area. In October, a satellite-tagged bird led observers to discover it was with a flock of 3,200 birds in Turkey. 45 birds, the largest flock in India so far, are seen in the

Rann of Kutch on November 22.

2007/08 – new wintering grounds in Sudan are discovered when two satellite-tagged birds turn up there on November 2nd, after having been observed in a flock of 3,000 in Turkey.

2008 – one bird in the far east of Kazakhstan is tagged. It is hoped the latter belongs to the population wintering in India. One of the birds satellite-tagged in 2007 is still alive and moving around in the breeding area.

This lapwing breeds in Russia and Kazakhstan and migrates through a number of Central Asian states to winter in Israel, Eritrea, Sudan and north-west India. Single birds can be found in winter in Pakistan, United Arab Emirates and Oman. There are three flyways leading to wintering areas; a western wintering area for the majority (85%) of birds in Eritrea and Sudan, a central area in the Arabian Gulf region and an eastern area in India and Pakistan. It breeds semi-colonially in steppes where bare saline areas occur near water-bodies and it prefers to be close to livestock. It lays two to five eggs and breeds during April to August. Wintering sites consist of dry plains, sandy wastes and short-grass areas often close to water. The main food items include beetles, locusts and spiders. The key causes of the great declines, in Kazakhstan 40% between 1930 and 1960 then another 50% between 1960 and 1987, have not been fully explained. On the breeding ground the conversion of steppe to agricultural lands could have been one cause, although since the collapse of the Soviet Union

these are reverting to natural steppe habitat. This may explain increasing breeding numbers locally in Kazakhstan. On the other hand, short-sward grass for nesting is mainly found near villages now and this may lead to trampling of nests and human disturbance. Remotely photographed nests have shown that sheep are responsible for the main trampling incidents. Illegal hunting on migration and in winter may be the current primary threat. Studies in 2005 and 2006 show that one chick per female hatches successfully, which can be considered good for the species's survival. Future conservation actions include continued research of its ecology and distribution and coope-ration with local shepherds to minimize breeding disturbance. Satellite-tagging has been used to determine its migration and the areas used as staging and wintering sites and will provide more detailed knowledge on its movements. National Species Action plans should be developed in those countries where it occurs on migration and hunting controlled.

Photo: © Jens and Hanne Eriksen

Oman, 2004

Photo: © Dhritiman Mukherjee

Gujarat, India, 2007

Spoon-billed Sandpiper
Eurynorhynchus pygmeus

The situation for this charismatic species is rapidly worsening with less than ten birds seen on the regular migration sites in South Korea in spring 2008.

Photo: © Choi Soon-Kyoo

South Korea, 2003

<table>
<tr><td>Population:
50-249 ↓</td><td colspan="3">REASON FOR CR-LISTING</td></tr>
<tr><td></td><td>DECLINE</td><td>POPULATION</td><td>RANGE</td></tr>
</table>

THREATS
Infrastructure development, agriculture, dams & water use

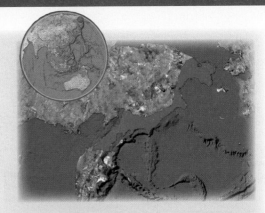

History

1758 – described by Carolus Linnaeus (1707-1778) as *Platalea pygmea*.

1821 – Swedish zoologist Sven Nilsson (1787-1883) places it in the genus *Eurynorhynchus*.

1914 – two Spoon-billed Sandpipers are collected from a flock of ten in Alaska, USA on August 15th.

1970s – the population is thought to number 2,000 – 2,800 pairs.

2000 – numbers are estimated at less than 1,000 pairs.

2003 – 402-572 pairs are estimated.

2004 – a juvenile Spoon-billed Sandpiper leg-flagged in Chukotka, Russia in July is seen on Yuboo Island, South Korea in September. Four wintering birds in southern India disappear after the tsunami.

2005 – 350-380 breeding pairs.

2007 – perhaps less than 100 pairs are estimated. A breeding male from Chukotka is shot in Russia near the Chinese border on southbound migration.

2008 – 84 Spoon-billed Sandpipers are found at Myanmar wetlands in January by the Spoon-billed Sandpiper Recovery Team. The wetlands are deemed to be in a healthy state. At least 15 birds are seen in a shorebird flock in Bangladesh in April. Surveys in South Korea fail to find the usual spring influx, only three and four birds are found at Saemageum and Geum respectively.

This peculiar sandpiper breeds in north-eastern Russia and migrates along the Pacific to winter in South-East Asia where the most important known occurrences are in Myanmar. It has probably always been scarce due to its specialised ecology, but the decrease has been marked over the last 40 years in all colonies. Breeding success is low, with 0.66 fledged young recorded per nest in 2005 and it seems that the return rate of juveniles is low, meaning that the population is ageing and rapidly declining. It breeds in June-July and lays four eggs in a nest. It has never been recorded more than seven km from the coast and favours lagoon spits with crowberry-lichen vegetation or dwarf birch and willow sedges, together with adjacent estuary or mudflat habitats that are used as feeding sites by adults during nesting.

The main concern is the disappearance of important staging sites, mudflats and lagoons that are reclaimed for industry, infrastructure and aquaculture purposes and which have become polluted. The Saemangeum and Geum estuary of South Korea is one such important staging site that has been destroyed recently. It is not directly targeted for hunting, but in Myanmar it may be caught among other waders trapped for consumption. On the breeding grounds nests can sometimes be destroyed by reindeer or herder's dogs. Human disturbance of breeding grounds has also occurred, including collection of eggs of one colony for "scientific purposes" which wiped it out completely. Climate change and associated habitat shifts are expected to impact negatively on this species which depends on tundra habitat for breeding. There are several protected areas in its breeding grounds and along the migration routes.

Actions required are close monitoring of the breeding grounds and stopping the collection of birds and eggs for scientific purposes and asserting that field researchers do not disturb the birds. Legal protection must be awarded for all known sites and surveys of wintering areas in India, Myanmar and Bangladesh should be performed. Legal protection should be established in all range states and new sites, especially in South Korea, should be protected as well as old ones restored. Awareness campaigns to stop shorebird hunting would surely benefit this species.

Photo: © Chaiwat Chinuparawat

Baan Pak Taley, Phetburi Province, Thailand, 2006

Photo: © David Bakewell

Kapar Power Station, Selangor, Malaysia, 2008

Kittlitz´s Murrelet
Brachyramphus brevirostris

Population: 13,000-35,000 ▼	REASON FOR CR-LISTING		
	DECLINE	POPULATION	RANGE

THREATS
Fisheries bycatch, pollution, climate change

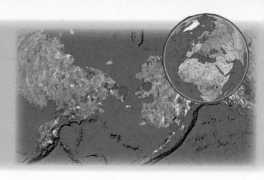

Photo: © Robert Tizard

Alaska, 2007

This alcid is restricted to the Bering Sea where it occurs in both Russia and the USA. Seventy per cent of the population occurs in Alaska, but it has declined by 80-90% in the past 15 years. The wintering distribution is unknown, but there are winter records from Kamchatka, the Kuril islands, Hokkaido (Japan) and the continental shelf of northern Alaska. Only 25 nests have ever been found, probably because it nests in unvegetated screes near or on mountain tops in glacial

regions. It lays one egg and feeds on fish and macro-zooplankton and it often feeds by diving in groups. Strong links have been made between glacial recessions, possibly as a result from global warming, and this species's decline. Other threats are habitat degradation and repeated disturbance due to recreational and commercial tour boat traffic, accidental entanglement in fishing nets, petroleum contamination and a change in abundance of prey species.

It is considered a species of conservation concern in both the USA and Russia. Guidelines to avoid disturbance of nesting birds have been drawn up in the USA.

The populations should be monitored and the effect of gill-net fishing and boat traffic evaluated. Legislation is required to avoid oil spills and pollution and global warming should be tackled through international agreements.

Chinese Crested Tern
Sterna bernsteini

Population: < 50 ▼	REASON FOR CR-LISTING		
	DECLINE	POPULATION	RANGE

THREATS
Disturbance, climate change

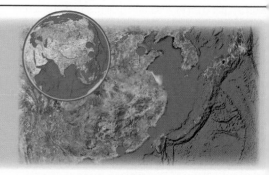

Photo: © Chen Lin

Changle City, Fujian Province, P.R.China, 2007

This poorly known species breeds on two islets off the Chinese eastern coast in Zhejiang and Fujian provinces (at least three chicks in 2008) and has been recorded on tidal mudflats or river deltas in South-East Asia outside the breeding season. A bird was photographed near Tianjin in September 2008 which gives hope for undiscovered breeding sites nearby. It is strictly coastal and pelagic and breeds among other

terns on small, uninhabited islets.

Coastal wetlands are altered for reclamation, shrimp farming and other uses in China and this constitutes a threat to this species along with pollution from domestic sewage, industrial effluent and plastic waste. Reclamation at the Minjiang estuary, where it occurs in April to September, was stopped in 2006 and it is now a county-level reserve. The Mazu islands were declared a reserve in 2000. An action plan is currently being drafted and all range countries need to conduct surveys at both its former localities and at other potentially suitable breeding sites in China and Taiwan.

Future conservation actions include monitoring known colonies without disturbance, including an enforced ban on landing on the breeding islands, survey and lobby for protection of wintering and migration sites, reduce the amount of pollution from industry, stop exploitation of eggs and embark on a profile-raising education/awareness campaign.

Chinese Crested Tern. Photo: © Chieh-Te Liang

Grenada Dove
Leptotila wellsi

Grenada, 2008

Population:	REASON FOR CR-LISTING		
66-120 ⬇	DECLINE	POPULATION	RANGE

THREATS
Infrastructure development, agriculture, disturbance, invasives

History

1884 – George Newbold Lawrence (1806-1895) describes the species in the first volume of The Auk.

1991 – the species is designated Grenada's national bird.

1998 – the population numbers 100 individuals, including 48 pairs.

2004 – the population has increased to 182 individuals but hurricane Ivan has a devastating effect and only 136 individuals remain.

2007 – a census in December produces 68 calling males.

2008 – the 1998 recovery plan is being updated to a 10-15 year conservation plan.

This small dove is endemic to Grenada in the Lesser Antilles where its population halved during 1987-1990. It occurs on the Mt Hartman Estate and National Park in the south-west part of the island and it was never common even if it was more widespread historically and may have occurred on offshore islands. There is another population at Perseverance on the west coast. Breeding is limited to the rainy season in the south-west but more extended on the west coast and it inhabits dry forest. It is thought to lay two eggs. Currently 28 territories are within protected areas, 11 on unprotected crown land and 29 on private land. Chronic and continuing habitat loss to enable the construction of small plantations and charcoal production is possibly being further compounded by introduced mammals predating fledglings. An increase in squatters and cattle in the 1990s resulted in more disturbance at one site. At Mt Hartman, a golf course, villas and roads are proposed adjacent to, and between, occupied habitats. The Government has recently amended the Grenada National Parks and Protected Areas Act to allow the sale of Mt Hartman National Park (created largely to conserve this species) for the development of a resort. Such a sale could result in extinction. Hurricanes pose a pertinent threat in that these can damage habitat structure and allow for the invasion of alien vines into suitable dove habitat which makes the small population vulnerable. The main conservation priorities are to continue protection and management of the existing populations and their habitats on both private and crown land and the establishment of a corridor between the Mount Hartman and Perseverence populations. There are no individuals in captivity.

Future measures include regular surveys to monitor population trends and rates of habitat loss and degradation. Mt. Hartman National Park should be protected and biological/ecological studies are required. The recovery plan should be implemented, habitat restored and two new subpopulations established.

Purple-winged Ground-dove
Claravis godefrida

Population: ↓ 50-249	REASON FOR CR-LISTING		
	DECLINE	POPULATION	RANGE

THREATS
Infrastructure development, agriculture

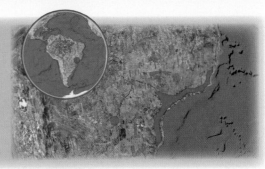

Photo: © Luiz Claudio Marigo

flowerings, but has been recorded eating other seeds (including those of sedges and grasses) and fruit. Records in Argentina 2007 were made in connection with flowering bamboo. Breeding apparently occurs in the austral summer, with birds calling from November to February. Historically it was reported in flocks of up to 100, but no recent records have involved more than five individuals.

Clearance and fragmentation of Atlantic forest for agricultural purposes may already have gone too far to ensure its long-term survival. It is traded uncommonly, but if taken this would have an effect on such a rare species.

his species was fairly common at the beginning of he 20th century in Brazil, Paraguay and Argentina. highly fragmented range, paucity of recent records nd its unobtrusiveness create uncertainties over s current status. It inhabits humid Atlantic forest ith records from near sea-level to 2,300 m. It may ndertake seasonal movements following bamboo

It is protected under Brazilian law and has been recorded in a number of protected reserves. A small captive population in Brazil has apparently died out. Future conservation actions include urgently surveying to find populations and document its calls which could then be used for surveys using playback. See also pp. 46-53.

Mindoro Bleeding-heart
Gallicolumba platenae

Population: ↓ 50-249	REASON FOR CR-LISTING		
	DECLINE	POPULATION	RANGE

THREATS
Persecution, logging

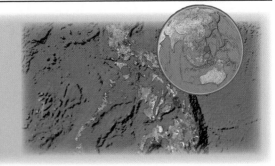

Sablayan Penal Colony, Mindoro, The Philippines, 2005

Photo: © Jon King

his small dove is endemic to the island of Mindoro, hilippines. It is known from only four sites within the ast thirty years; the site with most suitable habitat eing Mt. Siburan. Breeding has been recorded from ebruary to June and it inhabits closed-canopy and econdary lowland forest where it feeds on both nvertebrates and fruit.

Much of this bird's habitat has been eradicated y forest destruction. Rattan collection disturbs

undergrowth and on one site dynamiting forest to reach marble is also a threat. Hunting for food and the pet trade poses yet another threat, especially during the dry season in February – May.

A site support group has been established by Haribon (BirdLife in the Philippines) at the Siburan site. Accidental catching, especially using snares, of Mindoro Bleeding-hearts has not stopped but is deemed less now than five years ago. Ecotourists already visit the site and an ecotourism plan is being developed.

A detailed map of remaining forests on Mindoro has to be produced in order to start a systematic survey of the populations and to investigate its ecology. Tour guides will be trained as part of an ecotourism project and awareness campaigns planned. Hunting should be regulated.

HARIBON
FOUNDATION
protecting nature. preserving life.

Negros Bleeding-heart
Gallicolumba keayi

Dumaguete, Negros, Philippines, 2006

Population: ↓	REASON FOR CR-LISTING		
50-249	DECLINE	POPULATION	RANGE

THREATS
Agriculture, logging

History
1877 – the species is discovered by W. A. Keay, a sugar estate owner in Negros.

1900 – W. E. Clarke (1853-1938) describes the species in Ibis journal.

1997 – the species is discovered on the Philippine island of Panay.

2007 – two chicks hatch in captivity.

This dove breeds on the islands of Panay and Negros in the Philippines. As Panay has more forest than Negros, it is plausible that the population there is larger. It apparently prefers closed-canopy forests below 1,200 metres but on Panay it tolerates secondary habitats. Nesting is in May and June with fledging after only 12 days.

Destruction of primary forests is a major threat, on both Negros and Panay just a small percentage remain which are threatened by clearance for agriculture, timber and charcoal-burning. Trapping and hunting exacerbate the threats. Nest-predation has also been recorded but the animals responsible for it are unknown.

The only recent records are from a protected area on Negros while locals report it from the North Negros Forest Reserve (declared by Presidential decree in 2006), and another area where it was formerly recorded (Mt Talinis/Twin Lakes on Negros) has

been proposed for conservation-related funding. In the mid-1990s, the species featured on a bilingual environmental awareness poster as part of the "Only in the Philippines" series. A very small number of captive individuals have been bred at the A. Y. Reyes Zoological and Botanical Gardens. In 2007, two chicks hatched, though one died. Three birds salvaged from the illegal bird trade are in captivity and have produced eight young so far. In total the captive population is 17 birds.

More fieldwork should be conducted in all areas from which the species has been reported locally and all other sites where suitable habitat remains. Establishing the proposed 100 km² North-west Panay Peninsula National Park where the species has recently been discovered is important as is encouraging careful reforestation activities around remaining forests and law enforcement to stop small-scale yet rampant illegal logging.

Polynesian Ground-dove
Gallicolumba erythroptera

Tahiti, French Polynesia, 2007

Population:	REASON FOR CR-LISTING		
100-200 ⬇	DECLINE	POPULATION	RANGE

THREATS
Agriculture, invasives

History

1789 – German naturalist Johann Friedrich Gmelin (1748-1804) describes the species.

1987 – apparently survives on Matureivavao.

1990 and 1991 – all suitable islands in Rangiroa are visited and surveyed and a new population is discovered.

1999 – not found on Matureivavao but a small population is found on Teneraro.

2003 – an expedition finds a new population on Morane.

2005 – a female is taken into captivity on Tahiti.

2006 – nine doves in Rangiroa atoll, including one male on a rat-free island.

2007 – three birds are found on Vahanga, the atoll nearest to Morane, but no nests are found. Rat eradication takes place in Rangiroa.

2008 – a ten-day long expedition takes place in Rangiroa in August to survey ground-doves and evaluate rat eradication.

This species is now restricted to four small atolls (Teneraro, Morane, Rangiraoa and Vahanga) in French Polynesia. It was previously known to have occurred throughout the Tuamotu archipelago and the Society Islands. There were two subspecies apart from the nominate; *erythroptera* from Tahiti and Morrea but now extinct and *pectoralis* from central and northern Tuamotus but now probably extinct. It is found in primary forest on atolls with herbs, shrubs and ferns or dense shrubs and feeds on seeds, invertebrates, leaves, buds and fruit.

It was formerly caught by local people for consumption but it is more likely that the introduction of cats and rats, particularly Black Rat *Rattus rattus*, are the real reasons for its decline. Habitat loss is also likely to have been a factor as the largest atolls with the richest vegetation have been cleared for coconut plantations.

Rat eradication programmes and surveys have taken place. Only single birds exist in captivity on Tahiti and they are not deemed suitable for breeding. Further rat eradication programmes are planned by Société d'Ornithologie de Polynésie "Manu" in 2009 and more surveys should be made in the central Tuamotus and Acteon group to establish its population. In the latter group suitable islands for translocation could be identified. Locals can be involved by showing pictures when surveying and creating public awareness through schools and local press. Teneraro should be protected from introduction of predators and human disturbance.

Kakapo
Strigops habroptilus

Unusually for a parrot, the Kakapo has an elaborate lekking system when mating. The male makes several shallow depressions on the ground and utters a booming sound which can be heard for up to five kilometers to attract females.

Maud Island, New Zealand, 1995

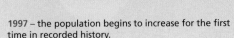

History

1845 – the first Kakapo is found by a European.

1894 – the first conservation attempt takes place when Richard Henry shifts several hundred birds from Fiordland to offshore islands. Stoats arrive and the effort fails.

1903 – three birds are transferred to Little Barrier Island, but disappear.

1912 – three birds are transferred to Kapiti Island.

1934 – the skin of a Kakapo is priced at 37 pence in the skin trade.

1936 – last sighting of a transferred bird on Kapiti Island.

1952 – New Zealand Department for Internal Affairs appeals for assistance in locating Kakapos.

1974 – helicopters are sent in to locate Kakapo, only eight birds are found.

1976 – the known population stands at 18 birds, all males, all in Fiordland.

1977 – a rapidly declining population of c.150 birds is discovered on Stewart Island including the first females seen in living memory.

1982-1992 – a total of 60 birds (22 females and 38 males) survive to be transferred from Stewart Island to offshore island refuges.

1997 – the population begins to increase for the first time in recorded history.

1998 – Polynesian Rat is eradicated from Codfish Island.

1999 – a female, missing for 13 years, is rediscovered on Little Barrier Island and incubating three fertile eggs.

2004 – seven juveniles die of septicaemia caused by a bacteria.

2006 – a survey of Fiordland fails to find any more Kakapo.

2007 – the Kakapo population stands at 55 adults (21 females and 34 males), and 31 juveniles (20 females and 11 males).

2008 – 7 chicks, 4 females and 3 males, hatched on Codfish island are transferred to specialised facilities to be hand-raised as rimu fruit did not ripen this year.

This nocturnal and flightless parrot occurred throughout North and South Island and Stewart Island, New Zealand but is now confined to Codfish and Anchor Islands to which it was transferred. It feeds on plant material and, especially, rimu fruit and breeds periodically every two to five years, coinciding with fruiting of key podocarp plant species. Females breed at six to eleven years of age and can reach 90 years of age. Males breed at five years and lek, using a bowl of c.50 cm diameter and a booming sound to attract females. The Stewart Island population met a serious threat in rats, with over 50% of monitored adults killed each year. Low egg fertility and low reproduction and recruitment rates are also of concern. Supplementary feeding has increased the success of breeding attempts and may actually stimulate breeding. All individuals are tagged and tracked throughout the year and nests are monitored using high-tech equipment and even heat pads when females are away from the nest foraging. There is much detailed research going on: refining methods of hand-rearing chicks, reducing supplementary feeding to produce more females and managing genetic diversity to improve hatching rates and its survival are good examples of how management of wild populations and captive-breeding can supplement each other.

Future conservation actions include more research into the key factors that limit breeding frequency and productivity. Key goals are to increase the number of females to 60 by 2016, increase genetic diversity, maintain or restore sufficient habitat to cater for the population increase and maintain public awareness and support.

Codfish Island, 2007

Photo: © Simon Fordham

Codfish Island, 2007

Photo: © Simon Fordham

Yellow-crested Cockatoo
Cacatua sulphurea

Komodo National Park,
Indonesia, 2006

Population: ↓	REASON FOR CR-LISTING		
2,500-9,999	DECLINE	POPULATION	RANGE

THREATS
Persecution, logging

History

1788 – the species is described by German zoologist Johann Friedrich Gmelin (1748-1804).

1981-1992 – CITES record 96,785 birds exported from Indonesia.

1989 – EU bans imports.

1992 – the US bans imports.

1993 – trade is stopped; before this an average of 1,600 birds a year were taken from Sumba.

1994 – a zero-quota for wild birds caught in Indonesia is established.

1996 – 2001 – 351 young are raised in a commercial breeding centre in the Philippines.

1997 – the species is protected in Indonesia.

2007 – Timor-Leste gets its first national park, which is hoped will benefit the survival of Yellow-crested Cockatoo.

2008 – another survey is planned for September.

This cockatoo is endemic to Timor-Leste and Indonesia, where it was formerly widespread from Bali to Timor, including Sulawesi. There are four subspecies, with *sulphurea* and *parvula* having a low long-term viability. There is also a long-established, viable population of several hundred birds in Hong Kong but it is unclear which subspecies are involved. It lives in forest, seemingly on some islands dependent on closed-canopy primary forest, while on others it survives despite total forest clearance, indicating that it has flexible requirements. It breeds in tree cavities between September and May (on Sumba) whilst on Komodo breeding occurs from October to May and it lives on seeds, nuts, berries and fruit.

Its decline can almost wholly be referred to exploitation for domestic and international trade, which has been exacerbated by forest clearance, with pesticides being thought to be an additional threat. In Komodo, where poaching and deforesting almost never occurs, the population still decreased by 60% between 2000 and 2005. It is believed that availability of nest sites there, due to wildfires, and seasonal availability of standing water are limiting factors. In Sumba, after a ban on capture, the population density has increased. The Komodo Dragon *Varanus komodoensis* preys on eggs and uses the nests of cockatoos.

Several national parks protect the species. Captive birds are bred for conservation purposes and a survey on Komodo is currently underway.

Further surveys are needed to establish sites for conservation actions and periodic surveillance of populations. More studies into its ecology need to be performed and nesting trees should be protected. Awareness of the species should be enhanced and creating artificial water holes near nests would be beneficial.

Philippine Cockatoo
Cacatua haematuropygia

Palawan, Philippines, 2008

Photo: © Stefan Behrens

Population: ↓ 1,000-2,700	REASON FOR CR-LISTING		
	DECLINE	POPULATION	RANGE
THREATS Agriculture, persecution, logging			

History

1776 – German Zoologist Philipp Ludwig Statius Müller (1725-1776) describes the species.

1990s – the population is estimated at between 1,000 and 4,000 in the early years of the decade.

2005 – drought on Rasa causes starvation and 12 chicks were hand-reared while a further 15 died in the wild.

2006 – Rasa Island is declared Wildlife Sanctuary by Presidential decree on February 15th.

2007 – the European studbook of the species holds 23 males, 13 females and three juveniles in June.

2008 – a very productive year on Rasa, where a record 49 hatchlings are banded as of May.

This cockatoo is endemic to the Philippines. It appears restricted to lowland primary and/or secondary forest in or adjacent to riverine or coastal areas with mangroves. Breeding takes place from July to December. It is partially nomadic, with birds flying from mainland to offshore islands as far as eight kilometres away.

Trapping is serious on Palawan, Polillo and Samar, and with birds fetching prices of up to $300, chicks are taken from virtually every known nest. Forest and mangrove destruction has affected it throughout its range and in some places it is considered an agricultural pest and therefore persecuted or hunted for food. Climatic factors such as typhoons and extremely dry breeding periods are also threats. There are six protected areas that harbour the species and another site that is proposed for funding. The Katala Foundation has run an intensive Philippine Cockatoo Conservation Programme for the last ten years. The population on Rasa Island, Palawan, went from 25 individuals to at least 180 birds thanks to conservation efforts which included retraining poachers as wildlife wardens thereby providing them with alternative sources of income, which was the single most efficient action. This is now being repeated at three other sites. Several awareness campaigns, including printing posters, have been launched. Release of captive birds is not on the cards now as their imprinting on humans has been too great, so currently the captive population is seen mostly as a safety-net and educational resource. Future measures include surveys and monitoring of population trends, levels of trapping, persecution and trade and designating further protected areas. Carefully prepared translocations into suitable lowland forest or mangrove habitats, preferably on smaller islands, should also be tried.

Malherbe's Parakeet
Cyanoramphus malherbi

Maud Island, New Zealand, March 2007

Population: 50-249 ⬇	REASON FOR CR-LISTING		
	DECLINE	POPULATION	RANGE
THREATS Invasives			

History

1857 – French naturalist Charles de Souancé (1823-1896) describes the species.

1999-2000 – the population crashes from 200-500 down to low tens due to rat predation during two consecutive summers.

2003 – the taxonomic status, which has been debated for over 100 years, is finally found to be specific after DNA studies by Jonathan Kearvell and Andrew Grant.

2008 – translocations are planned for a third island in Fiordland.

This parakeet, also known as Orange-fronted Parakeet, is known from three valleys in the South Island, New Zealand with sightings from four other sites in the 1990s and is the rarest parakeet in New Zealand. Its former range included North Island, most of South Island and Stewart Island. Birds have been translocated to Chalky Island in Fiordland and Maud Island where they are self-sustaining. Today it is restricted to beech forest and requires mature trees with hollows to nest in. It feeds in low-growing shrubs and in lower forest level on seeds, fruits, leaves, flowers and invertebrates and breeding is linked with the irregular seeding of *Nothofagus* beech. It breeds from December and January, but can extend into the winter if seeding is good, and lays five to eight eggs.

The primary cause of decline can probably be attributed to introduced rats and stoat. As predation occurs on the nest, the female-ratio is skewed and managed beech forests are unlikely to have trees with hollows which cause lack of nesting sites. Browsing by cattle, deer and possums alter the forest structure and have an impact on feeding.

The species is difficult to separate from Yellow-crowned Parakeet *Cyanoramphus auriceps*, which hampers monitoring and conservation. The two river valleys where it breeds are to be restored and protected through pest management, including culling stoat. There is on-going work to establish populations on predator-free islands, and unbanded birds, i. e. birds that are born and raised there, have been observed breeding. Breeding trees that are found on the mainland receive individual predator-protection and Operation Ark is aiming to rid South Island beech forests of rats and stoats.

A complete survey of current and previous populations should be performed as well as detailed studies on its breeding biology and ecology. People should be trained in identifying the species and further attempts of introduction to predator-free islands should be made.

Orange-bellied Parrot
Neophema chrysogaster

Melaleuca, Tasmania, 2007

Photo: © Chris Tzaros

Population: ↓ 150	REASON FOR CR-LISTING		
	DECLINE	POPULATION	RANGE

THREATS
Infrastructure development, agriculture, altered fire regimes, invasives, climate change

History

1790 – British ornithologist John Latham (1740-1837) describes the species.

1984 – a recovery plan is established.

2006 – 40 young captive birds die of an unknown reason, virus is suspected.

2007 – 70 birds are released into the wild in spring.

This parrot breeds in probably only two sites in south-west Tasmania, Australia. After breeding it migrates to mainland Australia, stopping on King Island and wintering at various sites from south-eastern South Australia to south-eastern New South Wales. Wintering counts on the mainland have produced declining numbers, but breeding counts show fairly stable numbers even if minor declines in winter survival have led to a decreasing population.

It breeds in Eucalyptus forest and rainforest bordering moorland plains, where it feeds on grass and sedge seeds. The nest is in a hollow and dispersal after breeding takes it to beaches, saltmarshes, dunes, and coastal pastures and shrublands. The pair remains together for life.

The main threat is thought to be habitat change in wintering sites, such as overgrazing, conversion into agriculture, urban and industrial development. The degradation of remaining saltmarshes is a major threat. Competition with introduced seed-eating finches may take place on the wintering grounds. At the breeding sites, introduced starlings *Sturnus vulgaris* fill nest hollows with material which renders them useless for parrots and changes in fire regimes may have altered habitat. Random events, such as predation by foxes or cats and climatological factors can have a substantial effect on such a small population. An application of a mining exploration license may threaten one of the breeding areas. A recovery team was founded in 1980 and a captive-breeding programme has been established with the main centre at Healesville Sanctuary, Victoria, from which c.75 birds are released annually. There are about 150 birds in captivity. Awareness-raising and education programmes are conducted and effort is put into habitat management, re-establishing salt marshes, maintaining breeding habitat through burning, reserving and/or managing feeding habitat in Tasmania, Victoria and King Island. Breeding, migration and winter counts are made annually and several research projects are ongoing.

Future actions include surveying all salt marshes in the wintering range, taking human disturbance and predator control measures and protecting and creating wintering habitat. The captive population's Psittacine Circoviral Disease should be monitored and managed.

Spix´s Macaw
Cyanopsitta spixii

This species is best considered extinct in the wild, but with over 70 birds in captivity there is hope that it can be reintroduced to Brazil in the future.

Young birds at Al Wabra Wildlife Preservation, Qatar

Photo: © Cató Kammammel/Al Wabra Wildlife Preservation

History

1817 – German Naturalist Johann Baptist von Spix (1781 – 1821) collects the first individual, thinking it is a Hyacinth Macaw *Anodorhynchus hyacinthus*.

1832 – German naturalist Johann Georg Wagler (1800-1832) discovers that Spix's bird is a new species, and names it in honour of him.

1985 – five birds are rediscovered at Bahia

2000 – the remaining wild male was seen on 5th October for the last time. 60 birds, of which 54 captive-bred, are officially held in captivity.

2004 – Loro Parque raises two chicks. The working group for the "Recovery of Spix's Macaw" is formed.

2006 – Al Wabra Wildlife Preservation raises seven chicks. The known captive population is 67-68.

2008 – 78 individuals are held in captivity for breeding, out of a total of 120 individuals, most of these in Al Wabra Wildlife Preservation in Qatar.

Despite being known to science since the early 1800s, the species was largely ignored by the authorities and biologists until the 1980s when it was realized that it could be extinct. An extensive search in 1985 revealed only five birds left and by 1988 it appeared there were none. A subsequent search undertaken in 1990 succeeded in locating the last wild Spix's Macaw, a male. His innate drive to reproduce led to him to form an extraordinary pair bond with a female Blue-winged Macaw *Prophyrrura maracana*, which culminated in several unsuccessful breeding events despite fertile eggs being laid. In 1995, a captive Spix's Macaw female thought to be the former partner of the last wild male was released at a site frequented by the male but tragically she disappeared after seven weeks, possibly having collided with a power line. There have been occasional reports of the species up until fairly recently, giving a glimmer of hope that some individuals may remain. They can live 20-30 years in the wild and 20-40 years in captivity. Gallery woodland habitat dominated by caraiba trees for nesting is required and it feeds mainly on fruit from two regionally characteristic *Euphoribiacae* plant species. Breeding occurs during the austral summer with two or three eggs being laid. In captivity it is not uncommon for the species to lay up to five eggs per clutch. There are two principal factors for this species's decline; the destruction of the woodland gallery habitat it prefers and human colonisation and exploitation with subsequent trapping for the illegal bird trade. The colonisation of aggressive African bees and the construction of a hydroelectric dam may also have contributed. Brazilian law protects this species and there are several local community conservation programmes that pave the way for reintroductions. A working group for the species's recovery has been established and state-of-the-art breeding facilities are in place. A handbook on captive management and species recovery is in preparation, and all young captive-bred chicks are leg-banded and micro-chipped. Chicks are hand-reared as this is considered a safer option, but parent-rearing will take place when the numbers are more stable. The international studbook managing the birds participating in the official captive breeding program includes 76 (33 male, 41 female, 2 sex unknown) individuals.

Future conservation measures include identifying a suitable release site for planned releases between 2013-2030, continuing ecological studies, securing habitat of known historical importance and continuing community awareness and education programmes.

Young birds at Al Wabra Wildlife Preservation

Photo: © Sven Hammer/ Al Wabra Wildlife Preservation

Lear's Macaw
Anodorhynchus leari

Population: 249-500 ↓	REASON FOR CR-LISTING		
	DECLINE	POPULATION	RANGE

THREATS
Agriculture, persecution, altered fire regimes

Brazil, 2008

Photo: © Andy & Gill Swash/www.worldwildlifeimages.com

This macaw was not seen in the wild by ornithologists for over 150 years, before it was rediscovered in Brazil in 1978. Its numbers have increased, but this may be due to better survey methods rather than a genuine increase. As subadults form pairs and behave as if nesting, it is not certain how many birds there are that are actually in a reproductive state. It occurs in catinga with sandstone cliffs. Licurí palm nuts, maize, agave flowers and plants provide food. It breeds from February to April with two young often fledging. Illegal capture for the bird trade and smuggling are the main threats. Licurí palms have been much reduced to give way to livestock grazing.
The species is protected under Brazilian law. A management agreement has been made with landowners and in 2007 a corn replacement scheme was begun by Parrots International and the Lymington Foundation. American Bird Conservancy provided support to in-country partner Fundação Biodiversitas in 2007, to acquire nine additional properties totalling 1,300 hectares to expand the Canudos Biological Station and to establish a protected area.
Legal measures should be enforced and compensation to farmers should be continued. Licurí-planting should be developed systematically and more studies made into this macaw's ecology.

Yellow-eared Parrot
Ognorhynchus icterotis

Population: 600 ↑	REASON FOR CR-LISTING		
	DECLINE	POPULATION	RANGE

THREATS
Agriculture

Roncesvalles, Tolima, 2005

Photo: © Alonso Quevedo

This parrot occurs in the Andean ranges of Colombia and Ecuador. When rediscovered in Colombia in 1999 there were only 81 birds and reports of flocks of about 20 birds have since come from the Intag Valley, Ecuador. It favours wax palms for roosting, nesting and feeding and occurs in humid montane forest, elfin forest and partly cleared terrain. It breeds from April to November and breeding pairs enlist helpers during the chick-rearing stage.
Considerable habitat loss and fragmentation has occurred in Colombia. The decline of wax palms has certainly had an effect. Trapping has had some impact in Colombia and hunting for food was prolific in Ecuador. In April 2007, 52 nests were found, which contained 132 chicks in May and June.
A traditional roosting site in Ecuador has been purchased and is being reforested, and surveys will take place there in 2008 to determine its status. An awareness campaign among locals has hopefully stopped its persecution at that site. A proactive approach in Colombia, involving awareness, habitat restoration, fencing of wax palm sites and nest boxes has increased the size of this population.
Searches should be made for additional populations, especially in the Intag Valley of Ecuador. Further habitat should be acquired and protected.

Blue-throated Macaw
Ara glaucogularis

Loreto, Beni, 2005

Photo: © Joe Tobias

Population:	REASON FOR CR-LISTING		
50-249	DECLINE	POPULATION	RANGE

THREATS
Persecution

History

1921 – Roberto Dabbene (1864-1938) describes the species.

1984 – live exports of Blue-throated Macaws are banned in Bolivia.

1992 – a wild population is discovered in Bolivia.

1993 – a survey estimates 54 individuals.

2006 – a new population numbering 100 is discovered.

2007-2008 – fifty nest boxes are installed and result in

four chicks fledging.

2008 – twenty Blue-throated Macaws are protected by a private reserve acquired by Armonia and Loro Parque Foundation.

This macaw is known from 4,000 km² of the Beni department in northern Bolivia where it was discovered in the wild in 1992. It inhabits forest islands and gallery forest and lays its nest in a hollow where one to three eggs are hatched. The species is usually found in solitary pairs, but in a recently discovered site, birds are highly gregarious, with a dry season roosting site containing over 70 individuals. The facial lines are unique which allows for individual identification in the field.

Exploitation for the trade has reduced since 2000 but is still a serious threat. A nest box program by Armonia/Loro Parque Fundacion has found that there is a great demand for nesting cavities - probably due to years of burning and habitat destruction. As a

consequence, they plan to continue nest box work with over 100 nest boxes for the breeding season of 2008/2009. Hunting for food, fish bait and feathers probably has only a small impact in certain areas. Live export from Bolivia was banned already in 1984, but illegal export continues. Nest boxes have been built and widespread education through campaigns has taken place as well as ongoing surveys. The World Parrot Trust is involved in nest protection, feeding chicks and manipulation.

Future actions include setting up more nest boxes, studying its ecology and stopping illegal trade. Land acquisition is a key issue and could be used for tourism and awareness purposes. More field research of e. g. health threats to the population is also required.

Grey-breasted Parakeet

Pyrrhura griseipectus

This species is also known as the Grey-breasted Conure and is an endemic of high-altitude forest enclaves in north-east Brazil. A captive population, if managed well, could be crucial to its survival.

Brazil, 2008

Population: ↓ 50-249	REASON FOR CR-LISTING		
	DECLINE	POPULATION	RANGE

THREATS
Agriculture, persecution

History

1900 – Italian zoologist Tommasi Salvadori (1835-1923) describes the species from a type specimen from the cage-bird trade.

1972-74 – the Brazilian Coffee Institute attempts to eradicate shade coffee plantations and replace them with sun-grown coffee, with disastrous economic results and deforestation.

1990 – the Serra de Baturité Environmental Protection Area (APA) is created covering 32,690 ha in seven municipalities.

2005 – the species is recognised as valid by the international scientific community, previously it has been treated as belonging to the Maroon-faced Parakeet *Pyrrhura leucotis*.

2006 – the species is recognised as Critically Endangered by international conservation groups.

2007 – two conservation projects sponsored by the Brazilian "Fundação O Boticário de Proteção à Natureza" and the Loro Parque Fundacion are conducted by the Brazilian NGO Aquasis.

2008 – eleven private reserves are under establishment in the Baturité. A one-year project of installing nest boxes in these reserves commences in July, sponsored by the Loro Parque Foundation.

his species is known, based on skins, from four areas north-eastern Brazil, but currently occurs in only in ne of these, the Serra do Baturité in Ceará. There is, owever, strong evidence (reports from locals) that it as occurred in the near past at least near Quixada, eará state and in Serra Negra Biological Reserve, ernambuco state. Recent fieldwork indicate that it as occurred in almost all small mountains with sub-umid and humid forest known locally as "brejos" oove 500 meters and feeds on fruits and seeds in the anopy. It nests in a hole from February to May and ys a clutch of two to four eggs. The young attain dult plumage after their second year.

uch of the forests of the Baturité have been emoved to allow for sun and shade grown coffee, nd this habitat destruction has had a considerable ffect. The principal threat though, is believed to be apping for the illegal local and national trade, and also features in the international cage bird trade. ecent field work in the Serra Negra Biological Station iled to find the species, although locals' opinion oout its occurrence is contradicting. The forest is itable, but if it still occurs numbers are likely to e low and the population probably not viable. arijuana cultivation and hostile local culture make eld work difficult.

occurs in the Baturité Mountains Environmental rotection Area which is designated for sustainable se and is not managed for conservation. A private ndowner in the area has managed to increase the opulation by managing his lands. The Brazilian GO Aquasis has run two projects since 2007; one onitoring the Baturité population, and researching s biology, one to survey for further populations. urthermore, several private reserves are under eation in the Baturité and Aquasis are trying to volve more landowners in the area. A massive vareness campaign aiming to involve locals in this pecies's conservation will take place simultaneously ith nest box installations. It breeds well in captivity nd populations are held both in Brazil and abroad. rovided these are well managed and coordinated

they could be used for reintroductions. Areas similar to the Baturité mountains have been surveyed and found to have probably held the species and could therefore be suitable for reintroductions. Incitements should be available for landowners to establish a network of private reserves and develop tools and strategies to improve conservation management in the Baturité Mountains Protected Area. Awareness campaigns and investigations into the feasibility of using artificial nests should also be carried out.

Serra de Baturitá, State of Ceará, NE Brazil, 2006

Photo: © Ciro Albano

Puerto Rican Amazon

Amazona vittata

A hurricane halved the wild population 20 years ago but with the help of released and captive birds and careful conservation management there is now more hope for this species.

Rio Abajo Forest, Utuado, Puerto Rico, 2008

Population: 30-35 ⟷	REASON FOR CR-LISTING		
	DECLINE	POPULATION	RANGE

THREATS
Invasives, climate change

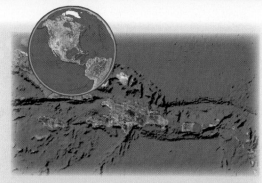

History

1783 – Dutch zoologist Pieter Boddaert (c.1730-1795) describes the species.

1930s – the population is reduced to 2,000.

1968 – a recovery plan is implemented.

1973 – a first captive population is established.

1975 – 13 birds remain.

1989 – Hurricane Hugo reduces the 47 wild birds to about 23.

1992 – 22-23 parrots are in the wild and 58 in captivity. Record fledging increases the wild population to 39 or 40.

1993 – a second captive population is established.

2000 – there are 40 wild birds, another nine introduced to the wild and 100 in captivity in two aviaries.

2004 – thieves break into an aviary and steal captive adults. The wild population stands at 30-35 individuals.

2006 – 20 birds are released into the Rio Abaja State Forest marking the start of a second population in the wild.

2007 – more birds are released and the total of released birds is now 46, with a 55% survival.

2008 – four active nests are found in the wild resulting in six fledged birds. Eight birds are released using a precision release method. Two fledged and two released birds are predated by Red-tailed Hawks.

his amazon is endemic to Puerto Rico and once ccurred throughout the forested areas of the island. istorically it occurred in forest and mangroves but)day it is restricted to forest at approximately 200-)0 metres. It lays three to four eggs in deep tree vities and nests from February to June. It mates for fe and starts breeding at four years of age.

here has been an almost total loss of suitable forest abitat and hunting for food and pest control, and he cage-bird trade, has had crippling effects. The rincipal threats are now competition for nest-sites,)ss of young to parasitic botflies, predation and atural disasters such as hurricanes. Predation by ien invasive mammals is also having a serious impact n productivity. Red-tailed Hawks *Buteo jamaicensis* redate parrots and hamper releases of captive-bred dividuals while predator-aversion training before leasing has improved the survival of captive-reared rds after release into the wild. Between 2000 and)02 raptor predation claimed 21% of all released dividuals.

iajor intervention, involving artificial nest-sites, ntrol of nest predators and competitors and ptive-breeding to preserve this species commenced irty years ago, but on average the population as so far only increased by one bird a year. There e over 200 birds in two captive-breeding centres. he aim is to have it downlisted by 2020, with two able, wild populations numbering over 500, that ave been established for more than five years. The iccess of newly fledged parrots is monitored using dio-telemetry and nests are monitored by infra-red imeras. Trapping of exotic mammalian predators as been shown to be a highly cost-effective way of mserving Puerto Rican Parrots. From 2008 "precision leases", entailing releasing a sub-adult bird at a ild nest just after fledging of the chicks to promote termediate and close interaction between wild and ptive-bred birds, are taking place.

)pulation trends need to be continually monitored,

and the fate of released birds tracked. The integrated conservation management programme should be maintained and synchronisation (due to the low number of wild nests) of breeding of wild and captive birds to increase the number of captive-bred chicks that can be fostered by wild parents improved. Predator trapping should be integrated into the existing conservation management programme.

Rio Abajo Forest, Utuado, Puerto Rico, 2008

Photo: © Jonathan M Morel

Indigo-winged Parrot
Hapalopsittaca fuertesi

*Reserva Natural
Colibri del Sol, 2006*

Population: 50-249 ↓	REASON FOR CR-LISTING		
	DECLINE	POPULATION	RANGE
	THREATS		
	Agriculture, logging		

History

1911 – the first specimens are obtained at Laguneta and Santa Isabel.

1912 – American ornithologist Frank M. Chapman (1864-1945) describes the species. It is named after the famous American ornithologist and painter Louis Agassiz Fuertes (1874-1929).

1989 – an unconfirmed sighting is made.

2002 – the first confirmed sighting is made in July at 10,000 feet in the central Andes, close to Los Nevados National Park, by Jorge Velasquez and Alonso Quevedo when 14 birds are located in a small area of forest.

2003 – the first active nest is found in February.

2008 – the Fuerte's Parrot Species Conservation Plan is published in the early year. The first private reserve, named Loro Coroniazul Bird Reserve after the bird, and encompassing 5,000 acres is established through a joint project by American Bird Conservancy, ProAves and IUCN Netherlands.

This species, also known as Fuerte's Parrot, is localised to the western slopes of the Central Andes, Colombia where it was rediscovered in 2002. It lives in cloud-forest around 3,000 metres with a high occurrence of mistletoe, its staple diet. It nests from January to May, laying three eggs.

Very little of the type-locality forest exists now and selective logging of mature trees with cavities has led to a dearth of nest sites. It is protected in two reserves and Fundación ProAves supported by Fundacion Loro Parque and the American Bird Conservancy are protecting one stronghold of the species. A `parrot bus´ is used to spread awareness of this species among local people and has been able to reach 70,000 people in Colombia. Artificial nestboxes are also being used by the Vulnerable Golden-plumed Parakeet *Leptosittaca branickii* and these are being increased

to deal with an increase in intraspecific competition for them. Breeding success is apparently higher when the parrots use the nest boxes. There is no captive population.

Future actions include investigating the possibility that it occurs in another National Park and in an adjacent Nature Reserve, researching ecological requirements to enable effective management of remaining habitat, working with the local community in raising awareness, avoiding possible trade of the species, reforesting 250 acres of nature pastureland with suitable trees and expanding the Loro Coroniazul Bird Reserve through land acquisitions.

ProAves
www.proaves.org

Sumatran Ground-cuckoo
Carpococcyx viridis

Population: ↓	REASON FOR CR-LISTING		
50-249	DECLINE	POPULATION	RANGE

THREATS
Logging

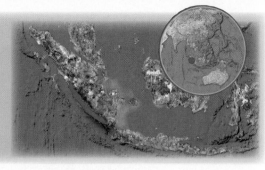

Sumatra, 2006

Photo: © WCS/Nick Brickle

There are protected areas within its known range in the Barisan Mountains. Survey effort is likely to increase following the recent recording of its call (although this possibly captured an alarm/distress call rather than the usual call) as knowledge of ground-cuckoo calls has facilitated study of two other Asian species in the past. Efforts to protect habitat and promote tourism are being developed. The local hunters that first reported the birds have now become ecotourist guides.

This ground-cuckoo is endemic to the island of
Sumatra, Indonesia where it is probably rare and
local. Recent records have been made in Bukit Barisan
Selatan National Park and near Kerinci Seblat National
Park where four or five birds are regularly seen by
ecotourists. It apparently inhabits lower montane
forests and foothills with all recent records from
00 metres. It is terrestrial, feeding on invertebrates
in the forest floor. Nothing else is known about its
ecology.

Future actions include choosing potential survey areas by identifying remaining habitat tracts in the Barisan Mountains, particularly near historical localities, and conducting village interviews. Extensive surveys (utilising recordings of the species's call) could be performed to establish its true range, current distribution and population, and assess its habitat requirements, threats and conservation needs. The species should be fully protected under Indonesian law.

Black-hooded Coucal
Centropus steerii

Population: ↓	REASON FOR CR-LISTING		
50-249	DECLINE	POPULATION	RANGE

THREATS
Agriculture, logging

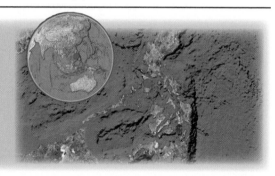

Painting: © Hilary Burn/HBW4 (Lynx Edicions)

This coucal is endemic to Mindoro,
Philippines where its population is
now small and fragmented with known
occurrences in just three locations. It is
found in primary lowland and transitional
dipterocarp forest where it occurs in dense
tangled thickets, vine-covered shrubs and
bamboo. It seems to have been replaced
in forest edge and secondary growth by
Philippine Coucal *C. viridis*.
Forests have been much reduced on Mindoro, and it

is believed that at the current rate of deforestation all forest may have disappeared by 2020-2030. The genetic viability is also believed to be a risk as the numbers are small and the population fragmented. It occurs in the forest patch at Siburan which is effectively part of the Sablayan Penal Colony, from where the Mindoro Bleeding-heart is also known. A management plan for the forest at Siburan that reconciles biodiversity with its role as a prison has been started.

Future actions include identifying remaining suitable habitat and surveying it to clarify its current status. Formal, managed protected areas to conserve remnant forest at two sites should be established. Mt Iglit-Baco National Park should be extended to encompass remaining lowland forest tracts. Public awareness about the status and importance of this species should be increased.

Puerto Rican Nightjar
Caprimulgus noctitherus

Guanica State Forest, 2008

Population:	REASON FOR CR-LISTING		
1,400-2,000 ⟷	DECLINE	POPULATION	RANGE

THREATS
No high/medium-impact threats

History

1888 – the species is discovered on 29th October near Bayamon, but thought to be a migrant Whip-poor-will *Caprimulgus vociferus*.

1919 – American biologist Alexander Wetmore (1886-1978) describes the species.

1961 – the second specimen is collected by Ricardo Cotte and William Blasini at Guanica Forest.

1984 – a population estimate gives 670 – 800 pairs.

2004 – 1,400 to 2,000 pairs are estimated to occur.

This nightjar occurs in three populations spread in south-west Puerto Rico. It is found in closed-canopy dry forest on limestone soils and in open under-storey, but also in drier, open areas and Eucalyptus plantations and ranges mainly between altitudes of 75 and 300 metres. Undisturbed forest with high insect numbers are a prerequisite. Breeding takes place from late February to early July, but mainly in April-June with the eggs laid directly on the ground on leaf litter between four and six metres below the forest canopy. Birds exhibit strong site fidelity and males can be heard calling all year round. It feeds on beetles, moths and other insects which are taken in flight, often fly-catching from a vantage point, and almost always below the canopy.

Degradation and loss of habitat, especially from residential, industrial and recreational expansion, has a significant impact. A proposed wind-farm development in one IBA has the potential to wipe ou 5% of the total breeding population.

It is legally protected with some sites being public lands designated as state forests or a biosphere reserve. The Conservation Trust of Puerto Rico has acquired lands where nightjars are abundant, and have the only protected nightjar habitat in that portion of their range. The population is surveyed regularly and spatial analysis is being used to identify areas of potentially suitable habitat for protection and to examine changes in habitat cover over time. Future conservation actions include surveys and monitoring of population trends and awareness campaigns. Disturbed areas could be reforested with native and selected plantation species and privately owned habitat could be acquired.

Forest Owlet
Heteroglaux blewitti

Population: ↓ 50-249	REASON FOR CR-LISTING
	DECLINE · **POPULATION** · RANGE

THREATS
Agriculture, logging, invasives

Melghat, 2008

Photo: © James Eaton/www.birdtourasia.com

...is diurnal owlet is restricted to Maharashtra and ...adhya Pradesh where two new sites have been ...scovered, with historical records in Orissa, India. The ...elghat Tiger reserve is considered its stronghold ...d in May 2008 a warden, Mr. Abhishek Wakode ...otographed a bird 40 km outside of the reserve. ...cent sightings are from fairly open deciduous forest ...minated by Teak *Tectona grandis* while historical ...cords came from moist deciduous forest or dense jungle. It feeds on lizards, small rodents, grasshoppers and nestlings of other birds. Breeding takes place between October and May when two eggs are laid in a hole in a softwood tree.

Depletion of forest and intense pressure from local people (irrigation projects, hunting) on remaining forest are likely threats. There is competition for a limited number of nesting cavities.

Since its rediscovery in 1997, fieldwork has been conducted into its status, ecology and threats. Interventions have been made to seek the prevention of further forest losses at the site of rediscovery. An education and awareness programme has been initiated.

Future conservation measures include preventing illicit wood-cutting and hunting of wildlife in forests within the species's range, surveying suitable habitat, controlling the use of pesticides and rodenticides and protecting nest sites to avoid destruction of nests.

Chestnut-bellied Hummingbird
Amazilia castaneiventris

Population: ↓ 250-999	REASON FOR CR-LISTING
	DECLINE · POPULATION · **RANGE**

THREATS
Agriculture, energy, logging

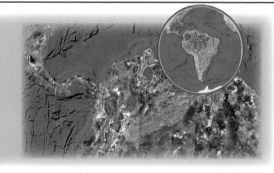

Soata Boyaca, 2006

Photo: © Giovanni Alberto Chaves Portilla

...is hummingbird, known as Quincha de Soata in ...anish, is only found on the slopes of Serranía de San ...cas and the east Andes, Colombia. A recent survey ...oduced records from 15 sites in the department of ...yaca. It lives in humid forest and is found mostly ...an altitude of 1,500–2,200 metres. The breeding ...ason is between December and February and the ...st is in the form of a cup, made with lichens and ...iders' webs. Its main feeding plant is *Tricanthera ...gantea* and it benefits from a number of cultivated crops such as Guamo (*Inga sp*), Banana (*Musa sp*), Coffee and Yatago (*Trichanthera gigantea*) flowers. Its natural habitat has been severely fragmented and replaced by coffee plantations and light woodland. The semi-arid habitats are less threatened, but affected by livestock-grazing and seasonal burning. Local NGOs Fundacion Colibri, Organizacion Ambiental Ocotea and Fundacion Ecodiversidad have established a reserve in cooperation with local communities since 2005 and they started a banding and nest monitoring scheme in 2008. Awareness campaigns involving school children have also taken place.

Conservation actions to take in the future include studying reproductive biology, population movements in relation to the floral phenology of *Tricanthera gigantea*, protect areas of suitable habitat found to hold the species and continue encouraging awareness of conservation issues.

161

Honduran Emerald

Amazilia luciae

Aguan Valley, Honduras, 2005

Population: 250-999 ↓

REASON FOR CR-LISTING		
DECLINE	POPULATION	RANGE

THREATS
Agriculture, transport

History

1867 – American ornithologist and businessman Georg Newbold Lawrence (1806-1895) describes the species.

1950 – last record for three decades.

1988 – it is found to be common at two sites 16 km apart near Olanchito and Coyoles in the upper río Aguán valley, Yoro.

1991 – 22-28 birds were found in 2.5 ha of habitat near Olanchito.

2007 – an expedition using light aircraft to identify habitats find new populations in Olancho in February.

This species is restricted to arid interior valleys of Honduras with three known sites today and eleven historical sites. It inhabits arid thorn-forest and scrub apparently at elevations up to 1,220 m. Feeding has been observed at several flowering plants and a conspicuous orangepipe cactus but it has also been recorded catching insects. The species is thought to undertake seasonal movements in search of food. Much thorn-forest has been cleared for grazing and agriculture and what little remains is extremely dry with few birds of any species present. Perhaps most concerning are plans to pave and extend a road through the range of this species, which would presumably lead to further habitat loss.

The Honduran Air Force property known as Polígono in the río Aguán valley is now managed by the American Bird Conservancy and the Fundación Parque Nacional Pico Bonito as a core area for a proposed thorn forest reserve. An impact assessment of the proposed road is planned. The species is a conservation target of the Hummingbird Society. A survey using aircraft and land-based observers in 2007 found a new population.

Required conservation actions include establishing a system of core protected areas and work with the neighbouring ranches to ensure that adjacent land is appropriately managed, such as for example fencing thorn forest to exclude cattle. The Sierra de Agalta National Park could be expanded to encompass suitable habitat within the valley and surveys to locate additional populations are required. The species could be promoted as a flagship for local and national conservation and fencing the thorn forest around Polígono to exclude cattle should be completed.

Black-breasted Puffleg
Eriocnemis nigrivestis

Yanacocha, Ecuador, 2005

Population: ⬇
208-268

REASON FOR CR-LISTING		
DECLINE	POPULATION	RANGE

THREATS
Energy, logging, geological events, climate change

History

1852 – French naturalists Jules Bourcier (1797-1873) and Étienne Mulsant (1797-1880) describe the species. More than 100 specimens are known.

1983 – a possible sighting is made at Volcán Atacazo.

2005 – the species is adopted as the official emblem of Ecuador's capital Quito.

2006 – a new population on Cordillera de Toisán is discovered by Olaf Jahn on 19th August. Population estimate 48-108 birds.

2007 – a standardised population monitoring study and community outreach program is initiated on the north-western slopes of Volcán Pichincha.

2008 – the first Species Action Plan is published.

This species is found seasonally and locally in mountain slopes in north-western Ecuador on the Pichincha volcano and the Cordillera de Toisán and, at least formerly, Atacazo volcano. The known area with suitable habitat encompasses only about 68 km². It inhabits humid and wet high-Andean montane forest, occurring along forest edges by roadsides, steep slopes with stunted vegetation, and the forest interior. Dispersal is poorly known but possibly linked to staggered flowering of at least 29 food plants, and in recent years it has been most numerous between 2,850 and 3,500m. Breeding is presumed to take place between October and March.

The key threat is felling of forest for timber and charcoal. The forest cover on the Cordillera de Toisán is, however, still intact, while almost 97% of the habitat on the north-western slopes of Pichincha volcano has been destroyed. Global warming may be a serious and growing threat in the medium term. Media coverage of recent research on the species

and threats to its habitat has encouraged the authorities to control access to remaining habitat at the Pichincha. The Jocotoco and Nubesierra Foundations have acquired and now protect 2,000 ha of key habitat while a third area is within the Bosque Protector Mindo-Nambillo.

Conservation measures to be taken are to survey unexplored forest tracts, especially at Atacazo and the main massif of the Toisán, implement long-term population monitoring at known sites, restore native vegetation in current grasslands near sites, consolidate protection of existing governmental reserves, provide economic incentives for the establishment of community reserves, provide local people with alternative incomes that to do not damage habitat, engage the government in the creation of protected areas on state owned lands, lobby for legislation prohibiting mining within its distribution and reforest corridors to link suitable habitat fragments.

Juan Fernández Firecrown
Sephanoides fernandensis

Juan Fernández Islands, 2006

Population: ↓ 2,500-3,000	REASON FOR CR-LISTING		
	DECLINE	POPULATION	RANGE
	THREATS Invasives		

1831 – the species is described by Captain Phillip Parker King (1791-1856).

1908 – the race *leyboldi* is recorded for the last time on Isla Alejandro Selkirk.

1935 – the Juan Fernández Islands are designated a Chilean National Park.

2002 – a direct count reveals 200 birds, of which only 60 are females.

2007 – a citizen's science project involving island residents in counts is performed.

2008 – two island residents are hired as coordinators for conservation activities.

This species is endemic to the Juan Fernández islands, sometimes called Little Galapagos, off Chile. The male and female differ much more than other hummingbirds do so they were initially thought to be different species. It feeds on nectar and, especially during the chick-rearing period, small insects. Breeding takes place mainly from August to October and two eggs are laid in up to two clutches per season.

The habitat quality has been degraded by humans, rabbits and invasive plants. Introduced predators may also share responsibility for declines and there may be competition with the self-introduced Green-backed Firecrown *Sephanoides sephanoides* which arrived in the early 19th century. Invasive plants, especially Elm-leaf Blackberry and Maqui, are thought to have a negative effect while others, such as Eucalyptus, are thought to have a positive impact on feeding opportunities. Nests are virtually always placed in native, largely undisturbed, forest.

The Juan Fernández Islands were designated a national park 70 years ago and were nominated for World Heritage listing. In 2008 a number of conservation activities took place including employing two islanders as coordinators of invasive plant control in critical breeding habitat, habitat restoration in native forest, volunteer programmes for islanders to control alien plants, monitoring breeding success, mapping phenology of important flowering plants, cat control in the town of Robinson Crusoe and environmental education programs of residents in schools emphasising on children up to the age of 12. Conservation measures to be taken in the future include replanting native flora, enforce grazing restrictions, evaluate feasibility of establishing feeding stations in native forest, replant fast-growing soil-binding trees along highly eroded slopes and increasing awareness. It is also essential to research female Juan Fernández Firecrown's survival and further in-depth study of the competition it faces from conspecific males (which number three to one female) as well as its relations with Green-backed Firecrown.

Tuamotu Kingfisher
Todiramphus gambieri

French Polynesia, 2006

Population: ↓	REASON FOR CR-LISTING		
125	DECLINE	POPULATION	RANGE

THREATS
No high/medium-impact threats

History

1895 – French zoologist Jean Frédéric Émile Oustalet (1844-1905) describes the species.

1922 – the nominate subspecies *gambieri*, which occurred on Mangareva, Gambier Islands becomes extinct.

1974 – between 400 and 600 individuals are thought to exist.

2003 – surveys estimate the population is down to 40 individuals.

2008 – extensive field work takes place in September-November.

This kingfisher only occurs on the small (21 km²) French Polynesian island of Niau, in the Tuamotu archipelago. The remaining population belongs to the subspecies *niauensis*, the nominate race from the island of Mangareva being extinct. It prefers semi-open coconut plantation habitats, limestone forests, and cultivated areas around villages. The birds readily use Niau's ephemeral wetlands and ocean coasts for foraging on insects and lizards. They breed from September to January in nest cavities excavated from dead and decaying coconut palms.

The main threat to the Tuamotu Kingfisher is thought to be limited nesting resources and predation on young birds from cats. Introduced rats may also compete with the birds for food, and nest sites may have been lost during recent tropical hurricanes. Niau is included in the Fakarava Man and Biosphere Protected Area. A field investigation studying the species's ecology, behaviour and movements took place in 2006, 2007, and again in September-November 2008. The entire island was thoroughly surveyed. Tuamotu Kingfishers were also ringed with small plastic leg bands, and tagged with miniature radio transmitters to track movements, nesting success, and survival. Additional genetic studies are underway to evaluate heritage and genetic variability that may impact survival.

Conservation measures to be taken include further fieldwork to validate population estimates, an assessment of forest resources needed by the birds, and a study of the impact of rats on kingfisher survival and reproduction. Additionally, a cooperative program to protect nesting habitat was started involving resident coconut farmers and an endangered species education program was initiated in the Niau primary school. Consideration is being given in reintroducing Tuamotu Kingfishers to their former range on Manga-reva island, or in establishing a second supplementary population elsewhere.

Rufous-headed Hornbill
Aceros waldeni

Panay, 1996

Population: 120-160 ⬇	REASON FOR CR-LISTING		
	DECLINE	POPULATION	RANGE

THREATS
Persecution

History

1874 – the first specimen is collected on Panay.

1877 – British ornithologist Richard Bowdler Sharpe (1847-1909) describes the species.

2005 – the first successful captive breeding takes place in the Mariit Conservation Park.

2006 – the population in the Central Panay Mountains range is 502 breeding pairs.

2008 – seven breeding pairs in captivity, with five pairs producing one chick each.

This species, also known as Visayan Wrinkled Hornbill, is endemic to the Philippines where it occurs on Panay and possibly Negros. It is extinct from Guimaras. It lives in canopy forests, frequenting logged areas and occasionally isolated trees in clearings and is probably adapted to lower or mid-elevation forest where it feeds on both animal matter and on figs and other fruits. It may make local nomadic movements in response to food availability and nests in large trees. At least temporally it feeds on forest fruits which make it adversely affected by deforestation and severe deforestation led to its extinction from Guimaras and its scarcity elsewhere. Hunting has also had a severe impact. Nest poaching, after which females and their young are sold for food or to the local bird trade, is still a serious threat and consequently affected half of all broods before a nest-protection scheme was implemented.

It occurs in some protected areas and awareness campaigns have been carried out. A nest-guarding scheme led to a 95% reduction in nest poaching in Panay and that population can be stabilised if small-scale logging in the forest can be stopped. Hornbills confiscated from hunter/traders are rehabilitated and then released into the wild and captive breeding of the species takes place although it is not known whether birds have actually been released back into the wild yet.

Conservation measures required include continuing Phil Conserve's guarding scheme, disseminating and acting upon results from recent island-wide surveys, continuing community awareness programmes to reduce hunting and illegal logging and working in partnership at government level to strengthen protected area legislation and improving the network in the long-term.

Kaempfer's Woodpecker
Celeus obrieni

Pium, State of Tocantins, Brazil, 2008

Photo: © Ciro Albano

Population: < 50-249 ↓	REASON FOR CR-LISTING		
	DECLINE	POPULATION	RANGE

THREATS
Agriculture, transport, logging

History

1926 – a female is collected by Emil Kaempfer in Uruçuí, north-east Brazil on 16th August.

1973 – Short describes it as a new subspecies of Rufous-headed Woodpecker *Celeus spectabilis*.

1980 – a search is made for the taxon but it is not found.

2004 – Marcelo Ferreira de Vasconcelos tape-record a Kaempfer's Woodpecker on the right bank of Rio Tocantins, Maranhão state.

2006 – Advaldo Dias do Prado and his team net and photograph an individual on 21st October, 400 km south-west of the type locality.

2007 – a total of 23 different individuals are now known. The species is changed from Not Evaluated to Critically Endangered.

2008 – research is undertaken focusing on home range, a total population estimate and range and availability of suitable habitats.

This species is also known as Caatinga Woodpecker. Rediscovered in 2006 after a gap of 80 years, this woodpecker has been found to occur in several states in central Brazil including Tocantins and Maranhão but not in the type locality in Piauí. In 2007, more individuals were found at sites fairly far apart. The range in which it could occur comprises approximately 10,000 km², and as it is an under-watched area it is not too surprising that the species has eluded detection. Its habits are unknown and it seems to occupy rather different habitat (cerrado bamboo patches) than its sister-species Rufous-headed Woodpecker *Celeus spectabilis*. There is a possibility, however, that it might not be bamboo-dependent as one of the 2007 records was from a site where bamboo is absent.

The main threats to the species are probably habitat-related; conversion through soya crops and fires and infrastructure development (building of a highway). Its rediscovery was made during surveys prior to the building of a new section of a highway which probably will facilitate access to the area and expansion of cultivation. The preferred habitat is frequently burned for cattle ranching; whether this practice destroys habitat or helps to maintain it remains poorly understood.

The company responsible for the construction of the highway are supporting a monitoring study. Required conservation actions include further surveys to determine range, numbers, population trends and threats.

Araripe Manakin
Antilophia bokermanni

Brazil, 2008

Population: ↓
250-999

REASON FOR CR-LISTING		
DECLINE	POPULATION	RANGE

THREATS
Infrastructure development, agriculture,
dams & water use

History

1996 – Araripe Manakin is discovered.

1998 – the species is described by Galileu Coelho and
Weber Girão Silva.

2002 – first population assessments and genetic studies
conducted, with a grant from the Brazilian "Fundação
O Boticário de Proteção à Natureza".

2004 – the BP Conservation Leadership Programme and
the Brazilian Ministry of Environment co-sponsor an
extensive field effort to determine the population size,
present range, reproductive biology, and major threats
to the Araripe Manakin, conducted by the Brazilian
NGO Aquasis.

2005 – team members of the conservation project

become fire fighters to protect nests from a blazing
forest fire.

2006 – a Conservation Plan is published (Aquasis, 2006).

2007 – a new award is granted by the BP Conservation
Leadership Programme to establish a Wildlife Refuge
for the Araripe Manakin.

2008 – world-famous broadcaster Sir David
Attenborough becomes Species Champion for Araripe
Manakin in August.

This species occurs in a small area on the north-eastern
slope of Chapada do Araripe, Ceará, Brazil where it
is known from approximately 40 localities. It lives in
vine-abundant lower and middle storey of tall, second
growth forest, edge and adjacent clearings, preferring
more humid areas of moist forest near springs and
streams. Food is thought to consist of small fruits and
plants. All nests that have been found so far have
been in vegetation overhanging streams.

The main threats are agriculture, cattle-raising and
exploitation for holiday homes and recreational
facilities. A water park was constructed in 2006 with
a small patch of habitat conserved where Araripe
Manakins persist despite the disturbance. It is not
known to be trapped or kept as a pet.

The type-locality is within the Chapada do Araripe
Environmental Protection Area, which is adjacent

to Araripe National Forest, but both are designated
"sustainable use" and consequently fail to prevent
exploitation or disturbance of habitat. However, the
owner of the land adjacent to the type-locality has
decided to protect the forest following the discovery
of this species. Local NGO Aquasis supported by British
Petroleum has run a conservation project there for the
last few years.

Future conservation actions include surveying similar
habitats throughout north-east Brazil to locate
additional populations, formally protect remaining
habitat, provide incentives for landowners to establish
a network of private reserves as buffer zones,
work with environmental and water management
authorities to protect springs and streams along
the slopes of the Chapada and conduct awareness
campaigns.

Kaempfer's Tody-tyrant
Hemitriccus kaempferi

Salto do Piraí, Joinville, Santa Catarina, Brazil, 2006

Photo: © Vítor de Q. Piacentini

Population: 9,000-18,500 ▼	REASON FOR CR-LISTING		
	DECLINE	POPULATION	RANGE

THREATS
Infrastructure development, agriculture

History

1929 – one specimen is collected at Salto do Piraí, Joinville, Santa Catarina.

1950 – a second specimen, which remained unnoticed until 1991, is collected at Brusque, Santa Catarina.

1953 – John Zimmer describes the species.

1991 – the species is rediscovered at the type-locality.

1998 – a new population is found in a private-owned Reserve in Itapoá, Santa Catarina.

2004 – the first mentions of its occurrence in Paraná are published.

2008 – new sites are published in the Brazilian Red Book of Threatened Species.

This species is known only from six localities in southeastern Brazil, in the States of Santa Catarina and Paraná. Its occurrence is very fragmented within its range and it is rare. The Environmental Protection Area of Guaratuba shelters the largest known population. It inhabits humid, heterogeneous, lowland evergreen Atlantic Forest and secondary growth, feeding predominantly in the mid-storey, hover-gleaning and sallying during flights and also gleaning and reaching. At some sites it forages in dense tangles of lianas, often over small rivers. It does not join mixed-species flocks; instead, pairs appear to remain in well-defined territories. A nest under construction was found in October 1998, at a height of six metres above ground-level, two to three metres inside primary forest at an elevation of 250 metres. The main threats are banana, rice and timber plantations and urbanisation of the coastal plain. It is protected under Brazilian law and occurs within one protected area in Paraná and one small reserve in Santa Catarina. Future conservation actions include slowing rates of deforestation, survey remaining patches of lowland forest to clarify distribution and status and survey forest within the vicinity of the type-locality Brusque, investigate ecological requirements of the species at current localities, and expand protected areas to incorporate adjacent patches of the species's lowland forest habitat.

169

Restinga Antwren
Formicivora littoralis

Ponta da Farinha, Iguaba Grande, Brazil, 2008

Population: ↓ 250-999	REASON FOR CR-LISTING		
	DECLINE	POPULATION	RANGE

THREATS
Infrastructure development, energy

History

1990 – Luis A. Pedreira Gonzaga and José Fernando Pacheco describe the form.

1992 – it is considered a species.

2008 – an Action Plan workshop in partnership with the National Environmental Agency IBAMA takes place in May. In July, an awareness workshop targeting teachers is held while field work involving nest mapping commences in August.

This species has a very restricted range on the coast of Rio de Janeiro State, Brazil, between the municipalities of Saquarema and Armação dos Búzios and is the only bird species endemic to restinga habitats. It is found in high densities occupying sandy coastal plain vegetation associated with Atlantic Forest. It lives in pairs in areas included in a mosaic of habitats, such as patches of vegetation, which seem naturally fragmented. The diet consists mainly of invertebrates. It forages in pairs into the almost impenetrable vegetation that also provides the birds with protection from environmental factors including predation. Breeding appears to be almost year-round, from May to February. The nest is constructed from fibres attached to horizontal branch forks. The clutch-size is two with both sexes sharing parental duties. The main, current threats are urbanisation and the consequent fragmentation and degradation of natural areas. The region faces a high density and growth rate of human population and is facing pressure from unsustainable tourism.

It is found in three State Environment Protections Areas: APA Massambaba, APA Sapiatiba (Ponta da Farinha / Morro do Governo) and APA Pau Brasil. Research into ecology (reproduction rates, home range and foraging behaviour in particular) is underway and a land ownership assessment has commenced, which should result in creating new public protected areas. Awareness campaigns include printing t-shirts and posters and arranging workshops directed at local school teachers. Ecological studies and growing and restituting restinga plants has been initiated in the area of Federal Fluminense University (Ponta da Farinha).

Other conservation actions that need to be taken include surveys, ensure continued support for the protected areas where it occurs and conduct impact assessments prior to real-estate projects.

Stresemann's Bristlefront
Merulaxis stresemanni

Painting: © Tomasz Cofta

Population: 50-249 ⬇	REASON FOR CR-LISTING		
	DECLINE	POPULATION	RANGE
THREATS Agriculture			

History

1945 – a specimen is taken in near Ilhéus, Bahia state, Brazil.

1960 – Helmut Sick (1910-1991) describes the species.

1995 – a male is found and tape-recorded at privately-owned Fazenda Jueirana, Bahia.

2006 – several birds are found in Minas Gerais.

2007 – local NGO Fundação Biodiversitas buys an area of 392 hectars at Bandeira city, in the Jequitinhonha valley, Minas Gerais state.

This species was "lost" for over 100 years when a specimen was taken in 1945 in Bahia, Brazil. Fifty years later it was rediscovered again and it is since also found in Minas Gerais. Very little is known about it but it has been seen foraging on the ground and on fallen tree trunks in an area of drier forest between two humid valleys and has been found in humid forest at 700-800 metres. Birds are very responsive to play-back, approaching the observer to within two metres. A great threat is that much humid forest has given place to cacao plantations and forest is being cleared for cattle-ranching, logging or by accidental or intentional forest fires.

It has protection from Brazilian law. A reforestation project aiming at creating a biological corridor between two areas is planned, and a local NGO and the American Bird Conservancy has acquired land, but thousands of hectares of forest remains unprotected. Conservation measures to be taken include surveying using playback, searching for additional populations in all fragments of lowland forests in and around Bahia, determining the size and status of the remaining population, safeguarding remaining unprotected forest and creating corridors to connect small tracts of pristine forest.

Minas Gerais Tyrannulet
Phylloscartes roquettei

Population:	REASON FOR CR-LISTING		
50-249 ↓	DECLINE	POPULATION	RANGE

THREATS
Agriculture, energy, logging

Parque Nacional Cavernas do Peruaçu, Brazil, 2003

Photo: © Dante Buzzetti

This species occurs in central Minas Gerais, east-central Brazil where the type specimen was collected in 1926. Several new occurrences have been found along the São Francisco and Jequitinhonha river valleys. Not much is known about its ecology, but nest building has been observed in October. In both dry and gallery forests, it appears to prefer the upper branches of taller, emergent trees, where it finds insect prey.

Its habitat is probably the most threatened in central Brazil. Charcoal-burners were fully active at the type-locality twenty years ago, where there was also extensive forest cutting for pasture and agricultural development. The São Francisco basin is also threatened by limestone quarrying and a large-scale irrigation. These same threats are impacting upon recently discovered locations and are exacerbated when remaining forest is highly fragmented.
The only conservation measure known is protection under Brazilian law. One record is from a National Park, Cavernas do Peruaçu National Park.
Conservation measures to be taken include surveys to locate additional populations, urgently protect known areas, as well as other suitable habitat patches conduct an environmental awareness campaign directed at landowners, local communities and school and reinforce the protection of the region's gallery forests.

Royal Cinclodes
Cinclodes aricomae

Population:	REASON FOR CR-LISTING		
50-249 ↓	DECLINE	POPULATION	RANGE

THREATS
Agriculture, altered fire regimes

Apurimac, Peru, May 2006

Photo: © Valère Claverie

This species occurs in south-west Peru and adjacent Bolivia. It was thought to be confined to tiny, humid patches of *Polylepis* woodland and montane scrub, but was found in June 2008 in *Gynoxis* shrubland several hundred kilometres northwest of the current known range indicating that it may be more wide-spread and less specialised in habitat than previously thought. It occurs at 3,500-4,800 m and feeds in moss, leaf-litter and decaying wood, descending temporarily to lower elevations during periods of snow.

The breeding season probably begins in December. The greatest identified threats are uncontrolled use of heavy fire and grazing, which prevent *Polylepis* regeneration. Cutting for timber, firewood and charcoal occurs locally and can probably be sustainable provided regeneration is allowed for.
It already occurs in protected areas and awareness campaigns have been conducted.
Conservation measures to be taken include surveys until November 2008 to determine its distribution and ecology, protection, mapping and restoration of *Polylepis* habitat, improving traditional land-use management by segregating agricultural, grazing and forest areas, encourage local people to develop land-use management and restoration schemes, establish private nature reserves in key sites and encourage creation and participation of PES (Payment for Environmental Systems) schemes with local hotel owners/Tour Companies in Yanahuara/Urubamaba.

Bahia Tapaculo
Scytalopus psychopompus

Population: 50-249 ⬇	REASON FOR CR-LISTING		
	DECLINE	POPULATION	RANGE

THREATS
No high/medium-impact threats

Michelin Forest, Ituberá, Bahia, Brazil, 2008

Photo: © Ciro Albano

This species no longer exists in the two localities in which it was first collected in 1944 and 1983, but occurs in six municipalities in Bahia. It is extremely shy and difficult to detect in surveys. It seems that mature wet lowland forests are necessary for it to be present. It is restricted to patches in river and stream valleys with small swamps around the main river course or swampy parts of the river itself, up to a maximum of approximately 50 metres from the river channel. Its preferred micro-habitat appears to be areas with dense agglomerates of vines and shrubs covered by trunks and branches of fallen trees.

The forest destruction has been intensive in the Atlantic Forest south of Salvador in Bahia, and only 10% remains.

It occurs in one biological reserve, Una, which was expanded to comprise 7,100 ha in 2008. No other conservation actions have been taken.

Future conservation actions include continued studies of known populations, searching for the species in other habitat fragments, determine its status and population size, study its ecology and habitat requirements and initiate sustainable development projects within its range.

Tachira Antpitta
Grallaria chthonia

Population: < 50 ⬇	REASON FOR CR-LISTING		
	DECLINE	POPULATION	RANGE

THREATS
Agriculture

Painting: © Lyn Wells/BirdLife

This species is only known from the type-locality Hacienda la Providencia on the río Chiquita in south-west Táchira, west Venezuela. Ornithologists William Henry Phelps (1875-1965) and Alexander Wetmore (1886-1978) collected four individuals in 1955 and 1956 and it has not been seen since. In September 1990 another search was made without results and a third search took place in December 1996.

The specimens were collected in dense cloud-forest at 1,800-2,100 metres.

The type locality has been deforested, but habitat remains in the vicinity. In 1990, forest above 1,500 m was considered undisturbed but deforestation was taking place rapidly.

The type-locality is situated within a National Park. Future conservation actions include further surveys (especially in May-June when it should be most vocal) to assess its current status and ecological requirements in the vicinity of the type-locality, reassessment of the potential impact of deforestation, ensure the de facto protection of El Tamá National Park and determine its taxonomic status.

Masafuera Rayadito
Aphrastura masafuerae

Masafuera Island , 2006

Population:	REASON FOR CR-LISTING		
250-999 ↓	DECLINE	POPULATION	RANGE

THREATS
No high/medium-impact threats

History

1866 – German-Chilean zoologist Rodolfo Armando Philippi (1808-1904) and German ornithologist Christian Ludwig Landbeck (1807-1890) describe the species.

1935 – the Juan Fernández Islands are designated a national park.

1967 – the Corporación Nacional Forestal (CONAF), the Chilean agency responsible for administering national parks, establishes an administrative office in the islands and begins to enforce park regulations.

1977 – UNESCO establishes the archipelago as an International Biosphere Reserve.

1986 – surveys by Dr Michael Brooke result in a population estimate of 500 individuals.

2001-2002 – c.140 individuals.

2006-2007 – surveys by Tomasevic *et al.* result in a population estimate of 248 individuals in an area representing 1/3 – 1/4 of the total potential habitat.

2006 – 81 nest boxes are installed in potential breeding habitat.

2007 – evidence of nesting/attempted nesting in three of the installed nest boxes.

2008 – no work conducted on the species.

This species, belonging to the ovenbird family, is endemic to Alejandro Selkirk Island, Juan Fernández Islands, Chile. It is found primarily in *Dicksonia externa* fern forest in the upper elevations of the island, and has a strong association with Canelo *Drimys confertifolia*. Birds breed during October to February. The nest is placed in natural cavities in both rocks and trees and it feeds on insects.

Many natural vegetation communities on Alejandro Selkirk have been degraded and fragmented but probably remain secure for as long as mature tracts of tree fern-canelo assemblages which are used for foraging, roosting and nesting cavities remain. Introduced mammalian predators are thought to have a significant impact on the population. Native Red-backed Hawks *Buteo polyosoma exsul* have increased during the last decade as illegal hunting of this species

by fishermen has ceased and the hawk population has benefited from predating introduced mammals. There are several documented cases of hawks preying on rayaditos.

The Chilean government ran a habitat restoration programme 1997-2003. There is one park ranger posted on Alejandro Selkirk for eight months per year. At least three nest boxes, installed in February to March 2006, were used during the 2006-2007 breeding season.

Conservation measures for the future are eradication of introduced mammals from the island. Employing a second ranger on Alejandro Selkirk would allow for more monitoring and additional habitat restoration activities. A continuous monitoring scheme and eradication of three invasive plant species are also priority conservation actions.

Alagoas Foliage-gleaner
Philydor novaesi

Brazil, 2008

Photo: © Andy & Gill Swash / www.worldwildlifeimages.com

Population: ↓	REASON FOR CR-LISTING		
50-249	DECLINE	POPULATION	RANGE

THREATS
Infrastructure development, agriculture, logging, altered fire regimes

History

1979 – discovered in Murici, Alagoas and considered as easy to locate.

1983 – Dante Martins Teixeira and Luis Pedreira Gonzaga describe the species.

1992 – last record for six years.

1998 – it is rediscovered.

2001 – the Murici Ecological Station is established protecting 6,116 ha of habitat.

2003 – the species is rediscovered at the Frei Caneca Private Reserve in Pernambuco.

2007-2008 – bird monitoring in SAVE Brasil property records the species on four occasions. It is found in both primary and secondary forests.

2008 – a census is planned at Serra do Urubu.

This species has only been recorded at two sites in Alagoas and Pernambuco, north-eastern Brazil. It inhabits the edges of clearings in interior upland forest at 400-550 m, from the understorey to the subcanopy, and has been observed in selectively logged and old secondary forests. Birds have often been found in mixed-species flocks, but also as singles and in small groups. Food is gleaned from leaves, bark, crevices and debris, and consists of insects (including larvae taken from dead wood), beetles, grasshoppers and ants. There is little breeding information, but an immature was collected in January and birds were moulting in February. The destruction of Atlantic Forests is the main conservation issue, leading to fragmentation and conversion to sugarcane plantations and pastureland. Logging roads create access and remaining forest fragments are severely threatened by fires spreading from adjacent plantations. The Feri Caneca private

reserve and adjacent SAVE Brasil protected area are still suffering from ongoing illegal charcoal exploitation. The massive clearance of Atlantic Forest in Alagoas and Pernambuco has left few other sites likely to support populations of this species.

It is protected under Brazilian law and occurs in Murici Ecological Station habitat, as well as in a private reserve in Pernambuco and adjacent lands that have been purchased by SAVE Brasil.

Future conservation measures include surveys of remaining patches of upland Atlantic Forest in Alagoas and Pernambuco, ensure the de facto protection of Murici Ecological Station and forest on the Serra do Urubu, provide local people with a viable alternative to charcoal production, study the species's ecology and breeding biology, implement environmental education programmes and monitor population trends at known sites.

Réunion Cuckooshrike
Coracina newtoni

There are two males to each female of this species that has been upgraded to Critically Endangered in 2008. This could be explained by females being susceptible to predation from mammals as they tend to the nests at night.

Réunion, 2008

Photo: © F. Théron-SEOR.

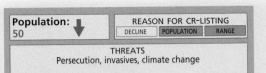

Population: ↓ 50	REASON FOR CR-LISTING
	DECLINE	POPULATION	RANGE

THREATS
Persecution, invasives, climate change

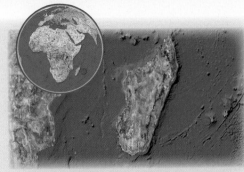

History

1866 – Francois P. L. Pollen (1842-1866) describes the species.

1991 – 120 pairs estimated which indicates stable numbers since 1974.

1999 – the reserve of Roche Ecrite is established, incorporating 95% of the current range.

2003-2004 – 100 singing males estimated. 27% of the males were unpaired, and only a third of females produced young.

2004 – an Action Plan is published.

2004-05 – 48% of surveyed males lacked partners.

2005-06 – 57% of males without partners. Five fledglings produced.

2006-07 – 64% of males lacked mates. Eight fledglings produced.

2007 – only 25 breeding pairs estimated but produce 22 fledglings.

This cuckooshrike is endemic to Réunion (to France) and occurs in two small areas. It is now found between 1,000 and 1,800 m, and is strictly associated with closed-canopy natural forest, occurring in mixed evergreen subtropical forest that also often includes areas of heath *Philippia montana* and tamarin *Acacia heterophylla*. It is chiefly insectivorous but also eats the fruits of some native trees. Breeding occurs between September and February, and it has an incubation period of 15-17 days and a fledging period of 17-23 days.

Nest-predation by rats and feral cats appears to be the primary reason for poor reproductive success; as only females incubate during the night this could explain the skewed sex ratio which currently is two males to one female. Disturbance from recreational activities and littering, which feeds predating rats, are threats. Fire, cyclones, alien vegetation and habitat degradation caused by deer also affects it. More uncertain threats may be limitation by habitat quality and deterioration, and available food. It is apparently unable to colonise new areas which makes it especially vulnerable to habitat changes.

Habitat management involves a logging ban, control of exotic plants, fire breaks, better control of hunting, curbing of tourism activities such as hiking in the mountains, and action to reduce deer numbers. The Species Action Plan has an aim to reverse the trend towards extinction by increasing the numbers of females in the population, eventually doubling the number of females over the course of ten years and achieving a viable population of 125 pairs. Experimental rat and cat control was started prior to the 2003-2004 breeding season; four out of five pairs in sites with predator control then raised young, compared with two out of six pairs in uncontrolled sites. In 2007, the breeding success was 91% in pairs with predator control, compared to 30% for those without. An awareness campaign to reduce littering and promote recycling is planned.

Future conservation measures include research the ecology of this species, protection from and control of predators, assess the conditions needed for successful establishment of new populations in suitable habitat within other areas, ensure that the action plans for the nature reserve and conservation of the species are consistent and compatible, study the species's genetics and demography, combat poaching, prevent actions by people that exacerbate the predator problem, protect additional habitat both presently and potentially occupied by the species, carry out research into the threat of disease, consider supplementary feeding trials, control invasive plants, restore burnt areas and take measures to reduce disturbance.

Réunion, 2004

Photo: © T. Ghestemme-SEOR

Rio de Janeiro Antwren
Myrmotherula fluminensis

Population: ↓ 50-249	REASON FOR CR-LISTING		
	DECLINE	POPULATION	RANGE

THREATS
Infrastructure development, agriculture, logging

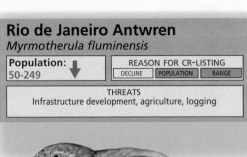

Painting: © Carl Christian Tofte

This species was discovered in 1982 in Santo Aleixo, Majé, in central Rio de Janeiro State, Brazil. Unconfirmed reports then came from the Guapi Açu Ecological Reserve from 1994 onwards. Birds matching Rio de Janeiro Antwren in characters are indistinguishable vocally from the *luctuosa* subspecies of White-flanked Antwren *M. axillaris*. The subsequent possible sightings have typically been in young secondary forest adjacent to old clearings, at elevations of 35-200 m.

The virtually complete loss of all lowland forest on the coastal plain south of the Serra dos Órgãos has most likely deprived this species of suitable habitat. At the Guapi Açu Ecological Reserve, there is a maximum of only 10 km² of suitable habitat within the species's known elevational range.

Guapi Açu Ecological Reserve encompasses 74 km² of privately-owned land at an altitudinal range of 35-2,000 m. The 20 km² Fazenda Serra do Mar forms the core of this reserve. There is an ongoing project analysing whether Rio de Janeiro Antwren represents a hybrid between White-flanked and Unicoloured Antwren *M. unicolor*.

Future conservation measures include determining the taxonomic validity of Rio de Janeiro Antwren. Its status at Guapi Açu must be assessed, suitable habitat in the surrounding areas surveyed and ecological studies conducted to determine habitat requirements.

Uluguru Bush-shrike
Malaconotus allius

Population: ↓ 2,400	REASON FOR CR-LISTING		
	DECLINE	POPULATION	RANGE

THREATS
Logging

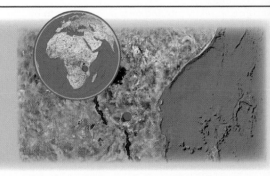

Painting: © Kim Franklin

This bush-shrike occurs only in the Uluguru mountains, Tanzania where it is found in both the Uluguru North Forest Reserve and the Uluguru South where two pairs were seen in 2007. It inhabits the canopy of moist sub-montane and montane forest, but has also been found in degraded forest. It possibly joins mixed-species flocks and feeds on large arthropods. Nothing is known of its breeding ecology but breeding has been suspected in Uluguru South in March.

The disappearance of forest is a major threat even if much of the terrain on the main mountain is too steep for cultivation and thereby exploitation by the increasing human population. Cutting for firewood and some timber leads to loss of tree cover and consequent increases of thicket tangles and invasive brambles.

The remaining forest is mainly within the central government protection Forest Reserves, which are managed for the catchment of rivers providing water for the inhabitants of Dar-es-Salaam. Conservation action in the Ulugurus focuses on assisting local initiatives and increasing the involvement of local communities in forest management. The area is also proposed as a Nature Reserve.

Future conservation measures include clarification of preferred habitat-types, efforts to reduce firewood collecting in the reserve and estimation of actual numbers.

Isabela Oriole
Oriolus isabellae

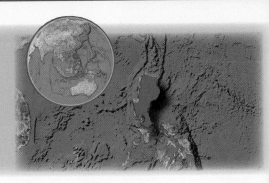

Population: 50-249 ▼	REASON FOR CR-LISTING
	DECLINE / **POPULATION** / RANGE

THREATS
Logging

Ambabok, San Mariano, 2004

This oriole is endemic to Luzon island, Philippines where its distribution is patchy at best. It frequents the canopy and middle storeys of forests, especially thick bamboo forest, but also forest edge, from 50-440 m. Constraints on its distribution and relative abundance are unknown, but it appears to tolerate secondary growth. It has recently been observed in mixed-species flocks in fruiting trees. Since the 1930s, forest cover in the Sierra Madre has declined by 83% and, by the late 1980s, only 24% of Luzon was estimated to remain forested, with most remaining areas under logging concession. There is virtually no forest left near Disulap, a key historical site, and one of the recent records was from a degraded forest tract, isolated from the Sierra Madre forests offering no long-term prospects for the species. Small-scale illegal logging has been observed in 2003-2004 adjacent to the Northern Sierra Madre National Park. Ambabok, where the species was recorded in 2003 and 2004, is located within the Northern Sierra Madre Natural Park though there is no active law enforcement in this area. The Bataan Natural Park/Subic Bay protected area, which supports up to 50 km² of forest, probably encompasses one of the historical localities. Future conservation measures include surveys, proposed key sites found for formal protection, lobby for active on-the-ground protection of the Northern Sierra Madre National Park and raise awareness among people and government about the species in an effort to implement conservation measures.

Photo: © Merlijn van Weerd

São Tomé Fiscal
Lanius newtoni

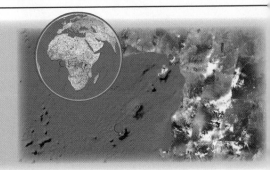

Population: < 50 ?	REASON FOR CR-LISTING
	DECLINE / **POPULATION** / RANGE

THREATS
No high/medium-impact threats

São Tome, 2006

This shrike is endemic to the island of São Tomé e Principe in the Gulf of Guinea. The population is tiny but new sites holding the species were discovered in 2007. All records are from primary lowland and mid-altitude forest. It moves alone or in pairs, coming down to understorey (below two metres) where it has been observed feeding on seeds of fruit which it crushes with its bill. Breeding may take place prior to the dry season but this needs confirmation.

Historically, large areas of lowland and mid-altitude forest were cleared for cocoa and coffee plantations. Road developments are facilitating the spread of potential predators. Birds may have declined in the Bombaim area as disturbance has increased owing to people harvesting for palm-wine.

Primary forest is protected, though there is no law enforcement within these areas. In 2008, a training programme with NGOs Associação de Biólogos Saotomenses and Monte Pico will aim to involve local to study and conserve São Tomean species.

Future conservation actions include researching its population, ecology and key threats, including possible predation by introduced mammals and listing it as a protected species under National law. Management and protection of the recently gazetted protected areas is required.

Photo: © Jonathan Rossouw

Sangihe Shrike-thrush
Colluricincla sanghirensis

Population: ↓ 50-249	REASON FOR CR-LISTING		
	DECLINE	POPULATION	RANGE

THREATS
Agriculture

Mount Sahengbalira, Sangihe, Indonesia, 1999

Photo: © Jon Riley

This species is endemic to the island of Sangihe, north of Sulawesi, Indonesia where it occurs on two mountains, Gunung Sahendaruman and Gunung Sahengbalira. It is resident in lower montane forest between 600 and 750 m, occurring singly and, perhaps more frequently, in small groups in the middle and upper forest storeys but also in dense rattan undergrowth.
The largest single patch of remaining habitat where it has been found totals 225-349 ha in size, but is under pressure from shifting farmers.

The "Action Sampiri" project works with biodiversity conservation in Sangihe. An outcome of this work includes plans to reclassify the existing four km² of "protection forest" on Gunung Sahengbalira as a wildlife reserve. In 2007 the Wildlife Conservation Society began four years of work in Sangihe which will provide opportunities to protect remaining habitat and form a basis for further activities.
Conservation measures to be taken in the future include further surveys, support proposals for the rapid gazettement of remaining forest on Gunung Sahengbalira as a strict nature reserve, continue education programmes emphasising the value of forest cover to water retention and the benefits of sound farming practices on already cleared slopes and also encourage forestry staff to establish a permanent presence on the island.

Caerulean Paradise-flycatcher
Eutrichomyias rowleyi

Population: ↓ 19-135	REASON FOR CR-LISTING		
	DECLINE	POPULATION	RANGE

THREATS
Agriculture, persecution

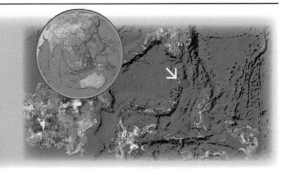

Mount Sahengbalira, Sangihe, Indonesia, 1998

Photo: © Jon Riley

This flycatcher is endemic to Sangihe island, north of Sulawesi, Indonesia. It was lost for over a century, having been discovered in 1873, until it was seen again in 1998. It occurs around the base of the mountain Gunung Sahendaruman where it is sedentary, resident in primary forest (less often in old secondary growth) on steep-sided valley slopes and valley bottoms with streams. Observations have also been made in ridge-top scrub close to a steep, forested gully. Prey is taken in active flight, perch-gleaning, by undertaking looping sallies and by descending to the ground and it often associates with other bird species and a particular squirrel species when feeding.
Virtually the entire island of Sangihe has been deforested leaving very little suitable habitat (thought not to encompass more than 18 km²).
As an outcome of work by "Action Sampiri" plans are afoot to reclassify the existing four km² of "protection forest" on Gunung Sahengbalira as a wildlife reserve. In 2007 the Wildlife Conservation Society began four years of work in Sangihe.
Future conservation measures include further surveys, continue education programmes emphasising the value of forest-cover to water retention and the benefits of sound farming practices and encourage forestry staff to establish a permanent presence on the island.

Seychelles Paradise-flycatcher
Terpsiphone corvina

Once found on many islands in the Seychelles archipelago, it now only exists on La Digue where developments are putting increasing pressure on it. It only lays one egg.

Photo: © Christer Sundström

La Digue, Seychelles, 2006

Population: 208-278 ⟷	REASON FOR CR-LISTING

| | DECLINE | POPULATION | RANGE |

| THREATS |
| Invasives |

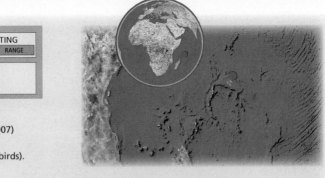

History

1867 – British zoologist Alfred Newton (1829-1907) describes the species.

1995/1996 – surveys find 69-83 pairs (c.150-200 birds).

1991 – a small area of woodland on La Digue is established as a Nature Reserve.

2000 – surveys find 104-139 pairs in 2000.

2002 – 21 ha of marshland adjacent to the Nature

Reserve on La Digue are purchased.

2008 – a translocation programme to Denis Island begins.

This paradise-flycatcher is endemic to the Seychelles, with its main occurrence on La Digue. It used to be widespread on Praslin and all surrounding islands. Small numbers are seen on Marianne but it seems that it cannot establish itself there. It requires mature stands of indigenous trees but has been observed utilising forest fragments and forest-edge habitat as well. Its nest is a cup of fibre and spider webs and it lays one egg; the main nesting period is in December to April but it can breed all year round.

Alarming rates of habitat loss and fragmentation, due to tourism and private housing developments, may be the greatest threats on La Digue and a wilting disease affecting Takamaka trees has lead to increased woodland clearance on the La Digue Plateau. Alien mammals and also some endemic bird species have recently been shown to be nest predators. The level of nest predation is highest at the forest edge compounding the already negative impact of habitat fragmentation. Adult birds appear to have lower survival rates in areas with more alien species. Introduced plants in La Digue's marshes, such as water lettuce, may possibly have reduced favoured invertebrate prey, although this is unproven.

A small area of mature woodland has been established as a Nature Reserve on La Digue. Warden staff has been recruited, some pools have been established to increase standing water, an education centre constructed, and public awareness programmes initiated. This population was surveyed in 2007 and productivity is routinely monitored. A Rare Pride Social Marketing campaign by Nature Seychelles among locals of La Digue has taken place to raise the profile and raise awareness of the threats and actions needed to save the species. A programme has been completed to assess the best islands to which future translocations could be considered. Habitat restoration is ongoing on the now predator-free Denis Island in preparation for translocation in the near future. All these efforts will be coordinated by a new three-year project funded by the Darwin Initiative and implemented by a partnership of NGOs and the Ministry of Environment and Natural Resources. Future conservation actions include translocation programmes to increase the number of populations to at least three, conserve woodland habitat on La Digue and consider replanting native forest, continue

population and nest monitoring and research into territory quality and food requirements, assess the impact of habitat loss, predation and historical changes in land-use, encourage placement of new development away from the Western Plateau or in areas with no existing woodland, continue removal of invasive water plants on La Digue, conduct field surveys to clarify the status of this species on Marianne, Félicité and Praslin and clarify its existence on Grand Soeur.

La Digue, Seychelles, 2004

Photo: © Jon Hornbuckle

Tahiti Monarch

Pomarea nigra

Papehue Valley, Tahiti, 2005

Population: ↑ 40-45	REASON FOR CR-LISTING		
	DECLINE	POPULATION	RANGE
THREATS Invasives, climate change			

History

1786 – Swedish naturalist and disciple to Carolus Linnaeus, Anders Sparrman (1748-1820), describes the species.

1937 – the tree *Miconia calvescens* is introduced.

1983 – a hurricane facilitates the spread of *Miconia calvescens*.

1998 – 12 pairs, 27 birds, are located in four sites in September. Rat control around nests is initiated by Société d'Ornithologie de Polynésie MANU.

2006 – 12 territories are occupied by 19 adult or subadult birds in accessible parts of its range.

2007 – 19 individuals are known, among them seven pairs and four fledged juveniles.

2008 – possible predation from Common Myna and Red-vented Bulbul is studied in detail.

One of four endemic Critically Endangered species in French Polynesia, this Monarch is found on Tahiti, Society Islands where it occurs in four valleys. It is only found in deep valleys where the tree "mara" *Neonauclea forsteri* is a common feature. It is highly territorial, foraging both in the canopy and the undergrowth for insects and breeds in July to October. A deterioration of habitat quality is a likely threat, as the forest is largely composed of introduced invasive species from South America and Africa. Predation by rats is also an important factor. A three-year study showed that significantly more Red-vented Bulbul *Pycnonotus cafer* and Common Myna *Acridotheres tristis* were present in territories that experienced nest failure or early fledgling death.

Rat control has been successful if conducted through-out the year and over the entire valley. However, if control is confined to monarch territories only, re-invasions from adjacent areas will occur on a regular basis. An action plan has also been produced, and the feasibility of translocation is being assessed with possible receiving islands identified.

Future conservation actions include regularly monitor known territories, continue rat control using a combination of poisoning and tree-banding with aluminium sheets, conduct experiments to improve the quality of the habitat by encouraging the growth of young mara trees and removing African Tulip Trees, confirm the impact of introduced birds and investigate their control. If considered essential, take surviving birds into captivity and increase this population through captive breeding and release them once a suitable site or island has been identified or restored. The aim for the end of 2008 is that all known breeding pairs should be protected from rats.

Fatuhiva Monarch
Pomarea whitneyi

Population: 274 ⬇	REASON FOR CR-LISTING		
	DECLINE	POPULATION	RANGE

THREATS
Invasives

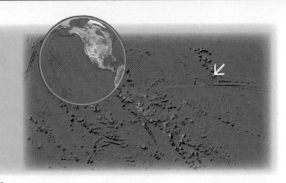

Painting: © Douglas H. Pratt / Oxford University Press

This large flycatcher only occurs on Fatu Hiva, Marquesas Islands, French Polynesia. In 1990 it was still considered common, but a major decrease has been noted in accessible areas on Fatu Hiva and the decline is now over 30% from lower estimates in 2000. Forty four individuals were found in a survey in 2007. Unoccupied, suitable habitat and few observations of adults with immatures support this decline. It occurs in dense, native forest from 50 m to 700 m, with some non-breeding birds found higher in native wet forest.

It feeds on insects (e.g. *Coleoptera*), spiders and seeds. Fatu Hiva is a well-forested island with a low rate of destruction from grazing and fire. Rats are suspected to be correlated to the decline of Fatuhiva Monarch. Rats were observed on Fatu Hiva for the first time in 2000 and rat control is ongoing within four valleys and this work is being extended gradually to additional areas. A feasibility study is underway to assess the suitability of other islands for translocation. Future conservation measures include continuing rat control, conduct surveys elsewhere on the island, continued monitoring of the known population, conduct a more thorough study over several months into the species's ecology and the threat that rats pose and continue a public awareness programme.

Manu

Banggai Crow
Corvus unicolor

Population: < 50 ?	REASON FOR CR-LISTING		
	DECLINE	POPULATION	RANGE

THREATS
Agriculture

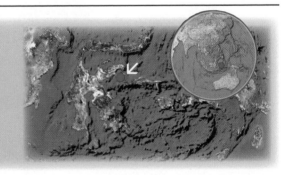

Painting: © Hilary Burn

This crow is only known from two specimens taken on an unspecified island in the Banggai archipelago, Indonesia. Since 2004, a crow smaller than the confusion species Slender-billed Crow *C. enca* has been observed, trapped and photographed, most recently in 2008 in Banggai but its identity is not proven beyond doubt. It appears to occur at 500-900 metres altitude in limestone forests. Little more is known about its habits, habitats or preferences.

As this species is so little known, it is impossible to specify threats, but extensive deforestation is assumed to be a major threat.
There are sacred sites in the forests where it occurs and talks with local religious leaders and villagers have been held regarding its conservation and the possibilities connected with its survival. At these sites, which comprise 300 ha, use of the forest for purposes such as logging is forbidden.
A 965,000 yen grant has been awarded by Nagao Natural Environment Organisation for a search in 2008. Media and local government have been informed about the species.
Future conservation measures include conducting a comprehensive search for the species throughout the archipelago and continuing working with religious leaders and local villagers to protect it.

Mariana Crow
Corvus kubaryi

Ten Mariana Crows were captured in the early 90s and kept at US zoos in order to develop protocols for captive-breeding. Six of the birds were released on Guam in 1997 in order to augment the dwindling population there.

Rota, Northern Mariana Islands, 2007

Photo © Emily Weiser

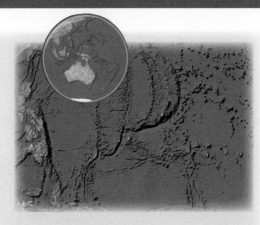

History

1885 – Anton Reichenow (1847-1941) describes the species.

1981 – 250 birds estimated on Guam.

1982 – 1,318 birds on Rota.

1993 – a National Wildlife Refuge is established on Guam.

1995 – less than 40 birds estimated on Guam, and 592 on Rota.

1999 – seven birds on Guam.

2001 – 16 birds on Guam after introduction of birds from Rota.

2007 – c.50 confirmed pairs on Rota.

his, the only corvid in Micronesia, inhabits Guam
d Rota in the Northern Mariana Islands, USA. It
es in mature and second growth forest and coastal
rand vegetation but probably only nests in native
rest. It forages in the forest canopy, understorey
d occasionally on the forest floor for seeds, fruit,
thropods and lizards. The usual clutch size is one or
vo and the young depend on the parents for up to a
ar, which is a long time for a passerine.

n Guam, its decline is due to predation by the
troduced Brown Tree Snake *Boiga irregularis*.
n Rota, recent typhoons have devastated forest
abitat and forest has been cleared for homestead
evelopment, resort and golf-course construction
d agricultural settlement; activities which are
ten accompanied by direct persecution (shooting).
dditional threats include nest-predation/disturbance
introduced rats *Rattus spp.* and monitor lizard
aranus indicus*, competition with introduced Black
rongo *Dicrurus macrocercus* and disease. The recent
troduction of Brown Tree Snake on Rota is likely
lead to an even more serious decline if the snake
opulation becomes firmly established.

rds are being translocated from Rota in an effort
maintain the wild population on the island. A
ha snake-free area created on North-west field
available for the introduction of crows, and
adjacent larger area is being readied for the
anslocation of Rota crows. A predation control
periment will soon be starting on Rota, which may
clude demographic work in the future. A grant has

been obtained for a Habitat Conservation Plan for
Rota's Agricultural Homesteads, which will increase
the amount of land in protected areas. Biological
control for the Brown Tree Snake is also being
investigated. On Rota, life history studies are currently
being conducted and there are proposals to protect
vital tracts of forest under a Habitat Conservation
Plan. Three birds are held in captivity.

Future conservation measures required include the
implementation of stringent measures to prevent
the spread of Brown Tree Snake from Guam to Rota,
continue research including study of population
biology and health of marked birds, conduct annual
censuses using standardised methodology, continue
nest protection and increase trapping of rats and
monitor lizards efforts in adjacent areas, begin control
of Black Drongo, facilitate the enactment of the
proposed Habitat Conservation Plan, conduct a public
education programme to reduce persecution and
introduce more stringent controls for construction
projects.

Mariana Islands, 1998

Photo: © Jack Jeffrey

Mariana Islands, 1998

Photo: © Jack Jeffrey

Raso Lark
Alauda razae

Raso, Cape Verde Islands 2007

Population: ↕ 130	REASON FOR CR-LISTING		
	DECLINE	POPULATION	RANGE

THREATS
Invasives, climate change

History

1898 – English ornithologist Boyd Alexander (1873-1910) describes the species.

1955 – Raso Lark is protected according to Cape Verde law.

1985 – a survey shows at least 150 birds to be present.

1986 – number is 75-100 pairs.

1989 – 200 birds are counted.

1990 and 1992 – surveys based on day visits produce 250 birds.

1990 – Raso is declared a National Park.

2003 – a complete survey produces 98 birds.

2004 – following rains, the population is up to 130 individuals.

This lark is only found on the uninhabited island of Raso, Cape Verde Islands, although it may have formerly occurred on Branco, Santa Luzia and Sao Vicente. It is found on level plains with volcanic soil and is associated with small vegetated patches along dry stream beds in which it feeds and breeds. There are considerable differences in feeding habits between males and females, males spend more time digging for food while females spend more time taking food from the surface. Breeding is erratic and governed by the slight and irregular rains. Adult survival appears to be high and the species is thought to be relatively long-lived.

Drought over successive breeding seasons is undoubtedly the cause of the present extremely small population and long-term desertification, as an effect of global climate change is clearly a major threat. In addition, nest-predation (probably by a near-endemic gecko) is high. Ground-nesting makes it extremely vulnerable to the potential accidental introduction of rats, cats and dogs brought by fishermen visiting the islet to collect seabirds' eggs and young. The island is currently considered to be mammal-free.

The species is protected and Raso is a National Park. An annual population monitoring and a research project are underway.

Future conservation actions include conducting research into potential nest-predators, investigate the suitability of Santa Luzia in order to establish a second population, raise awareness amongst tourists and tour operators visiting Raso to ensure precautions are taken to avoid accidental introduction of alien species, maintain good relations with fishermen using the island and engage them in conservation activities and continue regular monitoring of the population and the status of introduced predators.

Taita Apalis
Apalis fuscigularis

Population: ⬇ 600-930	REASON FOR CR-LISTING		
	DECLINE	POPULATION	RANGE

THREATS
Agriculture, plantations

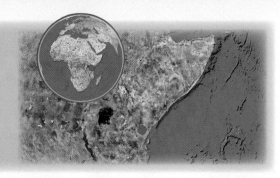

Ngangao Forest Reserve, Kenya, April 2001

Photo: © Ken Norris

his species is restricted to tiny forest fragments in e Taita Hills, Kenya. It inhabits the understory of ontane forest, mostly in gaps and forest edges with ick undergrowth. It feeds by gleaning insects and arching leaves, twigs, branches and tree-trunks, metimes descending to the ground and only casionally ascending to the mid-canopy.

Little is understood about threats, but deforestation may be involved.

Reforestation work has commenced through the local communities around the Taita Hills which formed Environmental Committees and have initiated extensive tree nurseries combining both indigenous and a few (environmental- and agriculture-friendly) exotic species. The indigenous trees will be planted so they can enhance connectivity of the landscape. The exotic, fast-growing species will be planted on farms to reduce the pressure on the natural forest. A few income-generating activities, including bee-keeping and butterfly-rearing have been initiated and farmers are taught about best-practices. These activities will improve the perceptions of the local community concerning natural resources and conservation as well as providing some income to individual farmers. Future conservation measures include the formation of a Community Forest Association to enable local community engagement.

Long-billed Tailorbird
Artisornis moreaui

Population: ⬇ 50-249	REASON FOR CR-LISTING		
	DECLINE	POPULATION	RANGE

THREATS
Logging

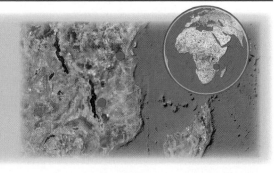

Amani, Tanzania, 2007

Photo: © Nik Borrow

his tailorbird occurs in two widely separated rests; in the East Usumbaras in Tanzania (nominate bspecies) and the Njesi Plateau in Mozambique bspecies *sousae*). The nominate subspecies is the tter known; its primary habitat is forest edge and rge canopy gaps. It is apparently territorial; one obable male, colour-ringed in 2000, has maintained e same territory at the headquarters of Amani ature Reserve up to 2007. Its breeding ecology mains unknown.

Despite being found in forest-edge habitats, forest destruction is the main threat and remaining unprotected forest in the East Usumbaras is under heavy pressure. Nothing is known of the status of the Mozambique population.

Two current projects in the East Usumbaras are working to increase the amount of forest in protected areas. A Darwin Initiative funded project run by the Mulanje Mountain Conservation Trust and working in the mountains of northern Mozambique may visit the Njesi plateau in the future.

Future conservation actions include revisiting the Njesi Plateau in Mozambique, searching for the species in intermediate areas, engage stakeholders on the Amani Plateau in forest management and raise awareness of this species's status, conduct ecological surveys to understand why it is apparently so rare and thinly distributed and concentrate searches in new areas using the newly understood habitat requirements.

Blue-crowned Laughingthrush

Garrulax courtoisi

A delicate balance must be maintained when promoting local awareness of this splendid species; on one hand the realisation of its rareness could fuel the bird trade, on the other hand ignorance about it could lead to other threats which could reduce numbers.

Jersey Zoo

Photo: Gregory Guida / www.pgvida.com

Population: 50-249 ↓	REASON FOR CR-LISTING		
	DECLINE	POPULATION	RANGE

THREATS
Infrastructure development, transport, persecution

History

1919 – French missionary Père A. Riviere collects two specimens, probably in Wuyuan County, Jiangxi Province in September which are forwarded by Père F. Courtois.

1923 – French biologist Henri Auguste Ménégaux (1857-1937) describes the species as *Garrulax courtoisi* in honour of Père F. Courtois.

1956 – three specimens are collected near Simao, Yunnan Province and constitute the only wild record of the subspecies *simaoensis*.

1982 - Chinese ornithologists Professors Cheng Tso-hsin and Tang Rui-chang describe the subspecies *simaoensis* based on the 1956 specimens.

1988 – birds of Chinese origin appear in wild bird trade in Europe.

1997 – the species is rediscovered in the wild in November by Professor He Fen-qi of the Institute of Zoology of Academia Sinica, Beijing.

2000 – the species is rediscovered in Wuyuan county, 80-90 birds are found in two breeding flocks 40 km apart. Chester Zoo and Leeds Castle contribute financial support.

2001 – a census finds 150-160 individuals in four flocks.

Over 20 nests are found. Leeds Castle and Chester Zoo join ZGAP and CEPA to form consortium of European partners funding in-situ conservation.

2004 - Chester Zoo accepts co-ordination role of field conservation project for European partners.

2006 – European Partners and He Fen-qi organise searches for the species in Jiangxi, Yunnan and Guangxi provinces.

2007 – Memorandum of Agreement (MOA) is renewed between European partners and Wuyuan Forestry Bureau to enact local protection of Blue-crowned Laughing-thrush and their breeding sites

2008 – four breeding sites with five colonies holding c. 200 birds are present. A bird ringed in 2004 is still alive. A Conservation Action Plan for the species is established in October 2007 and reviewed in June 2008.

s species is confined to a few breeding locations in ngxi Province, China. The wintering grounds are not own, but are thought to be near the breeding sites. tarts breeding in April in trees adjacent to villages d human habitation in habitat which has been med fung shui wood and birds will visit gardens. It ages in trees and on the ground in vocal groups. e threat picture is relatively unknown, but road struction and urban development have been olicated in destroying nesting sites. The western *oanesis* populations have not been seen for some e and hunting pressure may lie behind their appearance. The bird trade could also pose a eat as captive birds have turned up in Europe, and omoting awareness among locals of the presence of e of the worlds rarest birds in their gardens must tactically done as local, national and international e bird trade could pose a threat.

A number of small Special Protected Areas were established by Wuyuan County, Jiangxi Province, local government and supported by the German NGO ZGAP and WWF – China. There are 110 individuals in captivity in the USA, Europe and Hong Kong and a European studbook exists. A DNA study is underway concerning the relationships between this species and the closely related Yellow-throated Laughingthrush *Garrulax galbanus*.

Future conservation actions include conducting further surveys in an attempt to identify the wintering range and additional breeding sub-populations in Jiangxi as well as continuing searches to ascertain if the western populations around Simao, southern Yunnan, still exist. It is also necessary to establish formal protection for the species against infrastructure development as well as raising awareness of the species in general.

Jersey Zoo

Millerbird
Acrocephalus familiaris

Nihoa, 2007

Population: ↓ 250-450	REASON FOR CR-LISTING
	DECLINE | POPULATION | RANGE

THREATS
Invasives, climate change

History

1892 – Baron Lionel Walter Rotschild (1868-1937) describes the species.

1903 – rabbits are introduced to Nihoa.

1909 – The Hawaiian Islands National Wildlife Refuge is created and includes Nihoa.

1916 – 1,500 Millerbirds estimated on Laysan.

1923 – extinct from Laysan, but discovered on Nihoa.

1996 – 155 birds are counted in July.

2007 – 85 Millerbirds are colour-marked to allow for mapping their activities.

This warbler, with only the subspecies *kingi* remaining, is endemic to the island of Nihoa in the north-western Hawaiian Islands, USA. It prefers dense cover near the ground, and feeds on small beetles, spiders, roaches and larvae. The name stems from Laysan birds´ feeding on miller moths. Pairs show year-to-year fidelity in specific territories, with nesting occurring in the winter, but possibly throughout the year and probably associated with the onset of the rainy season. Nests are located in dense shrubs and two eggs are generally laid.

It disappeared from Laysan due to rabbits which denuded the island of vegetation and thereby caused food shortage. On Nihoa, the population size is probably regulated primarily by the weather, apparently being linked to precipitation levels, with droughts, storms and hurricanes inevitably having a negative impact. Variations in insect-supply also affect the population. Fire is a past and potential threat and

introduction of detrimental non-native species is a permanent possibility.

Nihoa is part of the Hawaiian Islands National Wildl Refuge, and legal access is controlled by a permit system that is restricted largely to biologists and oth researchers. Strict protocols are followed to ensure that legal permit holders do not accidentally introdu new species via seeds, eggs or insects travelling on clothes and equipment. Visiting scientists make effo to control alien plants by hand weeding. A planning document identifying candidate translocation site h been produced, identifying Laysan, Kure and Lisians as the most suitable islands. This has involved study occurrence of predators, island size and elevation at prospective introduction sites.

Future conservation actions include ensuring strict protocols to prevent further accidental introduction of alien species and to translocate birds to start new populations.

Mauritius Olive White-eye
Zosterops chloronothus

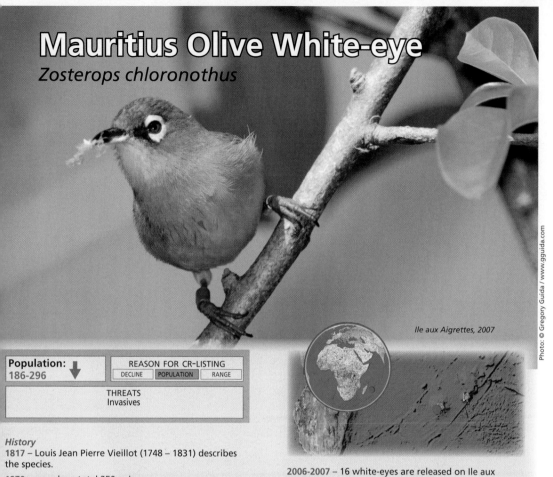

Ile aux Aigrettes, 2007

Population: ↓ 186-296	REASON FOR CR-LISTING		
	DECLINE	POPULATION	RANGE
	THREATS Invasives		

History

1817 – Louis Jean Pierre Vieillot (1748 – 1831) describes the species.

1970s – numbers total 350 pairs.

1980s – numbers total 275 pairs.

2001 – around 100 pairs remain.

2005 – a species recovery programme is initiated by the Mauritian Wildlife Foundation.

2006-2007 – 16 white-eyes are released on Ile aux Aigrettes.

2007 – 18 birds are released on Ile aux Aigrettes on 20th December.

2008 – two to five breeding pairs are recorded on Ile aux Aigrettes in July.

This white-eye is endemic to Mauritius where it occurs a small area of the south-west island. Birds have so been translocated to Ile aux Aigrettes. It is re-ricted to the wettest native upland forests where it eds on both nectar and insects, and travels conside-ble distances to productive flowers. High densities ay be associated with mosaics of small plantations of otic trees, where nest-predation may be low, inter-ersed with native vegetation for foraging. It has rge non-exclusive home ranges but aggressively de-nds a territory around a favoured flower or nest-site th against conspecifics and Mauritius Grey White-es *Z. borbonicus mauritianus*. In recent decades pairs ve not fledged more than one offspring per nesting tempt and productivity has been low. Recently (2005-08) productivity has been higher and pairs have ten been recorded to fledge two chicks per nesting tempt. The clutch-size is one to three eggs. st predation by introduced mammals and birds and bitat deterioration due to introduced plants are the ain threats.

It is protected by law and occurs within a National Park. Rehabilitation of small plots of native vegetation has been initiated and there is ongoing research to assess benefits of this to native birds. Over the past three seasons (2005-2008) an intensive management plan has been applied, involving wild population monitoring, predator control at nest sites, rescue/harvest of wild nests, artificial incubation and hand-rearing of offspring. It also includes releases of birds to the predator-free, restored offshore islet Ile aux Aigrettes where they receive supplementary food. Two breeding pairs have already been identified on Ile aux Aigrettes. It is thought that release into the wild is a more efficient way of increasing numbers than captive breeding, which has been tried unsuccessfully for the related Mascarene Grey White-eye *Zosterops barbonicus*.

Future conservation actions include acquiring habitat around Bassin Blanc, rehabilitation of native forest and releases on Ile aux Aigrettes and initiation of studies to investigate habitat requirements.

Golden White-eye
Antilophia bokermanni

This is the most numerous species featured in the book, yet it is threatened as it occurs on just two islands, Saipan and Aguijan. The population on the inhabited Saipan is decreasing and an alien, potentially predating, snake has become established there.

Saipan, North Mariana Islands, 2006

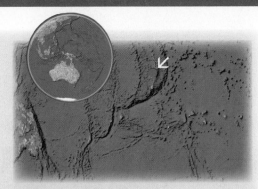

Population: ↓ 57,522	REASON FOR CR-LISTING
	DECLINE | POPULATION | RANGE

THREATS
Invasives

History

1889 – French zoologist Jean-Frédéric Émile Oustalet (1844-1905) describes the species.

1978 – the first Green Tree Skink is collected on Saipan.

1982 – 55,522 individuals are estimated on Saipan and 2,000 in Aguijan.

1996 – a Brown Tree Snake control plan is published.

1997 – a survey on Saipan indicates that the population may be in decline.

2002 – second survey on Aguijan indicates that the population has risen to over 9,000.

2007 – 23 birds are brought into captivity.

2008 – 23 more birds are taken into captivity.

eviously thought to be a honeycreeper, this white-
ve is endemic to the Northern Mariana Islands (to
SA) where it occurs on Saipan and the uninhabited
land Aguijan. Prehistorically, it probably occurred
n Rota and Tinian as well. The population density
n Saipan is at 2,095 birds/km² which is amongst the
ghest for any bird and indicates that the island
ay be at its carrying capacity. The population on
aipan seems to be declining, while the Aguijan
opulations are apparently on the increase. On
aipan, it occurs in all wooded habitats and also in
rban areas but the highest nesting densities are
corded in limestone forest. It forages in small
roups, presumably consisting of family parties
redominantly in the foliage of trees feeding on
vertebrates, flying insects, nectar, fruit and flowers
nd also taking insects from tree bark. The Rufous
antail *Rhipidura rufifrons* often follows Golden
Vhite-eyes taking advantage of insects unsettled by
e white-eyes' movement in the vegetation. The nest
 a cup situated two to four metres above ground.
esting occurs all year round, but peaks in March
 July with both males and females incubating.
 is strongly territorial against its own species as
ell as (Endangered) Bridled White-eyes *Zosterops*
nspicillatus and (Least Concern) Rufous Fantails.
his is the most numerous species featured in the
ook, but as the Brown Tree Snake has become
stablished on Saipan, with over 75 sightings
cluding 11 captures since 1986, it could be under
onsiderable threat even if there so far are no

documented cases of predation by this snake. Aguijan is difficult to get to and it is unlikely that snakes could be accidentally introduced there. The Golden White-eye's ability to utilise different habitats may help to explain its persistence despite periodic typhoon damage and extensive, human-caused habitat change. Introduced Green Tree Skinks *Lamprolepis smaragdina* and Micronesian Starlings *Aplonis opaca* have also been observed predating nests.

Although not directed solely at the conservation of this species, extensive efforts are underway to determine the status of Brown Tree Snake and begin relevant control measures. This agile and mildly venomous climbing snake originates in the Phillippines and has been transported via Guam by US military cargo vessels. Efforts are also underway to develop captive breeding techniques for the White-eye and to explore the potential of establishing populations on additional islands. The birds that have recently been collected for captive breeding have been distributed to six zoos and the first breeding attempts are expected to take place within two years. This will eventually lead to reintroductions on new islands.

Future conservation actions include monitor population trends through detailed censuses, continue to control Brown Tree Snakes by trapping at ports and monitor its spread, develop and implement techniques to control small incipient populations of Brown Tree Snakes.

Saipan, North Mariana Islands, 1997

Photo: © Jack Jeffrey

Rota Bridled White-eye
Zosterops rotensis

Population: ↓ 1,100	REASON FOR CR-LISTING
	DECLINE	POPULATION	RANGE

THREATS
Agriculture, invasives, pollution, climate change

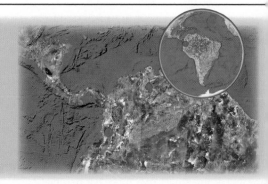

Rota, 2006

Photo: © Lainie Berry

This white-eye is restricted to Rota in the Northern Mariana Islands. It may favour native, mature, wet lime-stone forest where it feeds on insects, seeds, and fruit, and perhaps nectar. Nesting has been recorded from December to August and clutch-size is one to two eggs. The rapid decline rate equivalent to 74% over ten years and localised distribution are most likely to be primarily a result of habitat loss and degradation owing to agricultural activities and development and typhoons. Brown Tree Snake *Boiga irregularis*

is believed to be established on Saipan which can be another source, besides from Guam, for introducing this Philippine species on Rota. Predation by introduced rats and Black Drongo *Dicrurus macrocercus* has also been implicated in its decline. Habitat is now protected and a recovery plan has been published. Quarterly monitoring of the species is ongoing but there has been no population estimates since the late 1990s. A foraging ecology study to help determine reasons for its limited distribution has begun. Funding for a snake barrier at the Rota port has also been provided but planning and construction are still in early phases. The draft Recovery Plan presents a long-term goal of restoring the population to a stable 10,000 individuals.

Future actions include monitoring population trends and monitor Brown Tree Snake and other possible predators. Establishing a captive population will become a priority as an insurance measure if Brown Tree Snake becomes established on Rota.

Munchique Wood-wren
Henicorhina negreti

Population: ↓ 250-999	REASON FOR CR-LISTING
	DECLINE	POPULATION	RANGE

THREATS
Agriculture, logging, altered fire regimes

Colombia, 2008

Photo: © Juan Pablo Lopez /Fundación ProAves www.proaves.org

This wood-wren is restricted to two small areas in western Colombia. It occurs in extremely wet, stunted cloud forest where it is common in naturally disturbed forest on steep slopes between 2,250 m and 2,640 m. Nothing is known about its breeding.

This extremely small bird is at extreme risk from global

warming in conjunction with regional deforestation. The increasing severity of dry seasons in the Chocó region has facilitated many man-induced fires in otherwise extremely wet forests and human pressure is escalating. This will allow congeners to colonise the mountain peaks where Munchique Wood-wrens currently occur in isolation placing the species at serious risk of extinction.

It occurs in two protected areas - Munchique National Natural Park and Tambito Nature Reserve. Fundación ProAves, with the support of the American Bird Conservancy and Swarovski Optik were able to purchase five key properties that encompassed the majority of the species's range in 2004.

Future conservation actions include survey new areas for additional subpopulations, lobby the government to adequately protect known sites by directing resources more effectively and support organisations seeking to protect key sites.

White-chested White-eye
Zosterops albogularis

Population: ↓	REASON FOR CR-LISTING		
< 50	DECLINE	POPULATION	RANGE

THREATS
Invasives

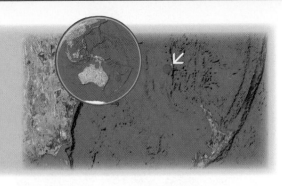

Painting: © Lyn Wells / BirdLife International

his white-eye is endemic to Norfolk Island, Australia where only scattered observations of up to four irds have been made since the 70s. The most recent ecords are from 2005. It seems to occur in weed-free ndigenous forest and feeds high in shrubs and trees. Iack rats are believed to have been introduced in he 1940s and pose the primary threat. Clearance of

native forest and invasion of weeds, as well as possible competition from the self-introduced Silvereye *Z. lateralis* have exacerbated the decline.

Rat baiting, cat trapping and control of other invasive plants and animals takes place in Norfolk Island National Park. Responsible cat ownership is being encouraged on the island, through the sponsorship of cat neutering clinics. Captive breeding is considered an unlikely measure as the associated risks of catching what are perhaps the last wild birds is high, especially as nothing is known about feeding regimes and habitat parameters. The Australian Government has recently rated Norfolk Island very high on its list of the Australian islands where they are considering the eradication of exotic rodents.

Future measures include determining a method for finding the birds reliably and conduct thorough surveys to estimate the remaining population size.

Faichuk White-eye
Rukia ruki

Population: ↓	REASON FOR CR-LISTING		
526	DECLINE	POPULATION	RANGE

THREATS
Invasives, climate change

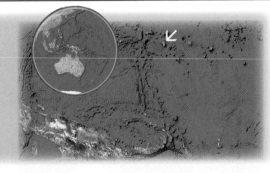

Photo: © Chris Collins

Tol Island, Chuuk, Federated States of Micronesia, 2005

his species occurs on four small islands (Tol South, Vonei, Pata, and Polle) in the Faichuk Group of the Chuuk (Truk) lagoon, Federated States of Micronesia. he endemic poison tree *Semecarpus kraemeri* possibly plays an important ecological role in the pecies' survival. It feeds from insects in the foliage nd is territorial. Breeding has been observed in April, nd the only recorded nest was in a *S. kraemeri* tree,

supporting the premise that a commensal and possibly mutual relationship exists between the two species. The potential introduction of alien species to the islands is a concern, particularly Brown Tree Snake *Boiga irregularis*. Deforestation has occurred across much of Chuuk Archipelago, but forests on the plateau of Tol South where this species lives are apparently old-growth and relatively undisturbed. Access to the plateau is difficult, therefore this threat is low.

No conservation actions are known but a stamp depicting the species was issued by the Republic of Naurau in 2005.

Future conservation measures include conserve native forest above 250 m on Mt. Winipot, identify and protect native forest on Polle, promote local awareness of this endemic species through an education programme, re-visit the islands to establish the current population size and trends.

Iquitos Gnatcatcher
Polioptila clementsi

Population: ↓
50-249

REASON FOR CR-LISTING
| DECLINE | POPULATION | RANGE |

THREATS
Agriculture, logging

Allpahuayo-Mishana national Reserve, Peru

Photo: © José Alvarez Alonso

This species was discovered in 2005 in the Reserva Nacio-nal Allpahuayo-Mishana west of Iquitos, Loreto, Peru. Only 15 pairs have been located in the reserve and it has become increasingly more difficult to locate. It is rare within white-sand forest with a variable canopy height between 15 and 30 m and consistently found in tall, humid varillal forest. It sings for approximately two months during August-October, but very little is known of its ecology. Available habitat continues to be threatened by clear-ance for agriculture facilitated by government incentives to encourage colonisation of land surrounding Iquitos, also logging of forest within a national reserve, for construction, fire wood and charcoal. The entire known population occurs within the boundaries of the recently established Reserva Nacional Allpahuayo-Mishana. There is now increased awareness of the bird in villages surrounding its known range. It has been adopted as the official bird of Iquitos; 'La Perlita de Iquitos'.

Future conservation actions include attempt to purchase land within and outside the Allpahuayo-Mishana reserve in appropriate habitat, natural history research (especially foraging flock dynamics, micro habitat requirements and breeding behaviour) which would be essential to improve survey methods and protection actions, conduct further surveys during its vocal period and enforce protection of remaining habitat within the Reserva Nacional Allpahuayo-Mishana.

Socorro Mockingbird
Mimus graysoni

Population: ↔
285-420

REASON FOR CR-LISTING
| DECLINE | POPULATION | RANGE |

THREATS
Invasives

Isla Socorro, Mexico, 1993

Photo: © Robert L. Curry

This mockingbird is endemic to Socorro, in the Revillagigedo islands, Mexico. In summer 2008, the breeding population was believed to be smaller than previously thought. It occurs principally in moist dwarf forest and ravines with a mixture of shrubs and trees at elevations above 600 m. Fig groves may act as regeneration nuclei for the species, supporting birds when a suitable understorey is present. It is reluctant to fly, preferring to hop away from danger instead. It lives alone or in couples, but shows a social hierarchy when feeding with conspecifics. Nesting may occur from November-July with a peak in March-April. Food includes crab remains, small invertebrates and fruit. The main threat is grazing by sheep which had affected almost one third of the island by 1990. The Revillagigedo Islands were declared a biosphere reserve in 1994 and the organisation Endémicos Insulares A. C. is active in studying the species. Future conservation actions include eradication of cats and sheep, implementation of a vegetation and soil restoration plan and establishment of a research monitoring station.

www.endemicos.org

Floreana Mockingbird
Mimus trifasciatus

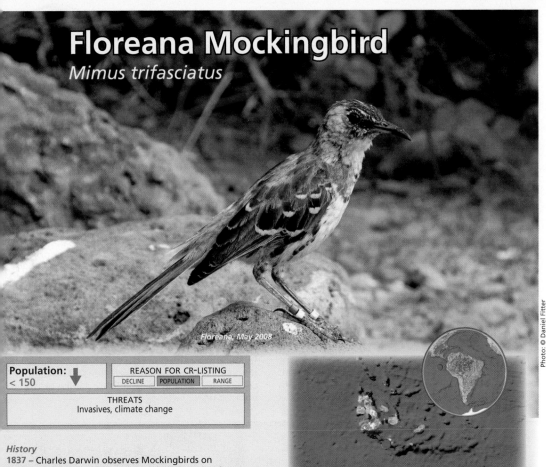

Floreana, May 2008

Photo: © Daniel Fitter

Population: ↓	REASON FOR CR-LISTING		
< 150	DECLINE	POPULATION	RANGE

THREATS
Invasives, climate change

History

1837 – Charles Darwin observes Mockingbirds on Galapagos which triggers his ideas on the origin of species.

1837 – English ornithologist John Gould (1804-1881) describes the species.

1888 – it becomes extinct on Floreana.

1966 – in total 150 birds are estimated.

1979 – the Galápagos Islands are designated a World Heritage Site.

2006 – the population is estimated to 69 birds. Twenty birds are seen on Champion in December.

2007 – The Gardner population is possibly around 100. An Action Plan is developed.

2008 – 45 individuals are counted before the breeding season on Floreana.

This is one of four endemic mockingbird species and survives in small numbers on the islets of Champion and Gardner-by-Floreana in the Galápagos Islands, Ecuador. It inhabits large cactus and other stands of vegetation. It feeds mostly on terrestrial insects, but also arboreal insects, fruit, nectar, pollen, centipedes, crabs, lizards and regurgitated food of boobies *Sula* spp. It is a co-operative breeder, with a variable mating system.

The extinction from Floreana was probably caused by the introduction of Black Rat *Rattus rattus*, which could also be accidentally introduced to other islands. The current decline is being thought to be driven by La Niña events, whereby an unusually dry climate kills adults. Smooth-billed Ani *Crotophaga ani* that has colonised the breeding islets is known to predate other bird species on the archipelago and needs to be monitored. Avian Pox virus is thought to have been responsible for increased mortality on Champion

during 1982-1983. Potential threats include the introduction of fire ants.

A ten-year action plan has been developed, with plans to take active measures to safeguard existing populations, and to create suitable conditions for reintroduction to Floreana. The Galápagos National Park was gazetted in 1959, and includes almost all the land area of the islands.

Future conservation measures include annual monitoring of populations and environmental conditions on both islands, assessing the stability and viability of both populations, using computer modelling of population demography, eradicate Smooth-billed Ani from the two islets, minimise chance introductions of predators and disease, eradicate goats, pigs and donkeys and, if technology allows, Black Rat from Floreana, investigate reintroduction to Floreana if rat eradication is successful and suitable habitat can be created.

Puaiohi
Myadestes palmeri

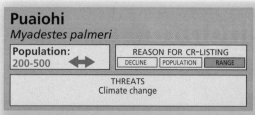

Population: 200-500 ⟷	REASON FOR CR-LISTING
	DECLINE | POPULATION | **RANGE**

THREATS
Climate change

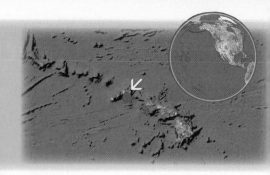

Photo: © Jack Jeffrey

Alakai Swamp, Kauai, Hawaii, 1997

This species is endemic to the island Kaua`i, Hawaii islands, USA. Up until 2007, 132 captive-bred individuals were released and have been breeding successfully. It is now restricted to high-elevation `ohi`a forests . It is primarily frugivorous, with arthropods (particularly insects) forming an important dietary component. Breeding peaks in April-June and helpers (second-year birds) take part. It has potentially high but variable productivity, with pairs producing 0.4 to 4.9 young per year during the three years

of observation. It is now the sole native frugivore on Kauai, and probably plays a major role in seed dispersal within its range.

Pig-destroyed understory, diseases (although some birds may be malaria-resistant), predation by Short-eared Owls *Asio flammeus* and alien mammals hampering reproductivity and competing for food may be causes of decline.

It is protected in the Alaka`i Wilderness Preserve. Rat poison, bait stations and rodent-resistant nest-boxes have been installed. A captive population has been established and breeding has occurred in the wild between released and wild birds. Over 200 young have hatched in captivity.

Future conservation measures include regular surveys to monitor population trends, research to determine the impacts of predation and habitat degradation by alien species and to establish a disease-resistant population.

São Tomé Grosbeak
Neospiza concolor

Population: < 50 ⟷	REASON FOR CR-LISTING
	DECLINE | **POPULATION** | RANGE

THREATS
No high/medium-impact threats

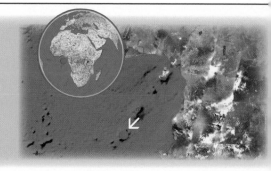

Photo: © Tasso Leventis

São Tomé

This species was rediscovered in 1991, having been known only from a 19th century specimen, in São Tomé e Príncipe. It moves in pairs or alone and comes to the forest understory to feed on seeds that it crushes with its bill. It is reportedly quite silent but vocalisations have recently been recorded.

Large areas of lowland forest have been cleared to give way to cocoa plantations while land privatisation is leading to increased on habitat. Road development along the east and west coasts are increasing access t previously remote areas and introduced mammals are potential predators.

Pressure on the habitat within Obe National Park seems low although feral pigs, rats, stoats and civets occur there. A training course, sponsored by the A. P. Leventis Conservation Foundation took place in summer 2008 aiming at involving locals in carrying their own monitoring and research projects on local, endemic birds, including this species.

Future conservation measures include researching population size, distribution, ecological requirements and key threats in order to produce conservation recommendations, and ensuring that designated protected areas are actively protected and to list it as a protected species under National law.

Bali Starling

Leucopsar rothschildi

Hong Kong Park Sir Edward Youde Aviary

This snow-white bird with blue spectacles is appreciated as a cagebird and has a price tag of several thousand dollars to it. So sought after is it that its whole future existence was severely jeopardised in a burglary in 1999.

Population: ↓ 24	REASON FOR CR-LISTING		
	DECLINE	POPULATION	RANGE

THREATS
Persecution

History

1911 – German ornithologist Erwin Stresemann (1889-1972) collects the holotype and describes it the year after.

1970 – the species becomes protected under Indonesian law.

1975 – 200 birds are estimated in September.

1983 – the Bali Starling project is established.

1990 – wild population estimated at c.15 birds.

1999 – an estimated 3,000 birds are in captivity, of which a third are registered in a studbook.

2001 – six birds are found.

2005 – 24 individuals are found, following releases.

2006 – 37 birds are released in Nusa Penida and offered to the gods in religious ceremonies performed by Hindu priests.

2007 – 12 birds released in Nusa Penida. Ten birds bred in Japan are prepared for release in the West Bali National Park in May.

2008 – 56 adults and 39 young in the Penida Nusa population, with around 50 birds in West Bali National Park.

his species is endemic to the island of Bali, Indonesia. second population has become established on earby Nusa Penida and there are about 1,000 birds captivity. In the breeding season, which is usually etween October-November, it inhabits fire-induced pen shrub, tree and palm-savannah plus adjacent osed-canopy monsoon-forest below 175 m. In the on-breeding season, birds disperse into open forest dge and flooded savannah woodland. In the past ey also occurred, and even nested, in coconut roves near villages. Previously thought to rely on vities excavated and vacated by other birds, released dividuals on Nusa Penida have nested in sugar palm, oconut and fig trees.

he main cause of its marked decline is unsustainable, egal trapping for the cage-bird trade. In 1999, while lack-market prices soared (US $2,000 per bird in mid-990s), an armed gang stole almost all the 39 captive dividuals in the park while awaiting release into the ild.

his threat continues despite the fact that the whole population now confined within a national ark on Bali is protected by the local population n Nusa Penida and has been the subject of a pecific conservation programme. The park and rogramme have, however, suffered from repeated nismanagement and corruption. These serious roblems are compounded by habitat loss. With the opulation now at such a critically low level, other hreats may include genetic erosion, inter-specific ompetition, natural predation and disease.

ince 1983, the Bali Starling Project has helped to nprove the guarding of the National Park, bolstered he wild population through release of captive-red birds, and provided the foundation for the evelopment of the Bali Starling Recovery Plan. It lso appears to be benefiting from efforts within the usa Penida Bird Sanctuary. In addition, the Wildlife onservation Society continues to operate wildlife rime market/trade surveillance and enforcement at ey trading hubs in Indonesia.

Future actions include legalising breeding and trading of Bali Starling to open up the market and undermine illegal trade, continue to monitor population trends closely, commence strict implementation of the Bali Starling Recovery Plan and continue to monitor the success of the release on Nusa Penida, in particular investigating interactions with Black-winged Starling *Sturnus melanopterus*.

Photo: © Marvin Hyett

Reid Park, Tucson, Arizona, USA, 2004

Mauritius Fody
Foudia rubra

Mauritius Fody may be safer from predation by nesting in exotic, introduced trees than if it uses decreasing, native trees but probably also faces competition from the introduced Madagascar Fody.

Mauritius, 2007

Photo: © Lucy Garrett

Population: ↓ 210-250	REASON FOR CR-LISTING		
	DECLINE	POPULATION	RANGE
THREATS Invasives			

History

1789 – Johann Friedrich Gmelin (1748-1804) describes the species.

1975 – 247-260 pairs are estimated.

2001 – 108-122 pairs.

2005 – 47 individuals were produced in captivity and 45 hand-reared chicks were released on Ile aux Aigrettes.

2006 – 40 young fledged on Ile aux Aigrettes and the total population there is now 135 individuals.

2007 – wild pairs produce 37 fledglings; 13,000 visitors make it to Ile aux Aigrettes.

2008 – 142 birds are present on Ile aux Aigrettes and a translocation project to Round Island has been given government permission with at least 20 birds planned for release there at the end of the year.

This fody has a small range on Mauritius, where it occurs in three areas. The rate of decline has slowed in the last 15 years, but was 55% between 1975 and 1993. It holds territories in all types of native forest, including degraded forest invaded by exotics, and increasingly uses non-native forests. In fact its use of exotic vegetation increased markedly during the recent increase in range between 1994 and 2003. Paradoxically, it seems likely that the exotic *Cryptomeria* nesting habitat may provide some respite from the high levels of nest predation experienced in native habitats on the island. Its diet is comprised primarily of insects, but also of fruit and nectar. Introduced predators, notably rats and macaques, have caused almost total breeding failure in most areas and nest-predation is regarded as the major cause of the present-day decline in this species. It is thought that introduced Madagascar Red Fody *F. madagascariensis* may compete with Mauritius Fody. Clearance of upland forest, especially in the 1970s, also affected this species severely. In addition to that, it also suffers from the general degradation of native habitats on Mauritius caused by introduced animals and plants. Over 90% of the present global population exists as a single subpopulation, exacerbating its susceptibility to stochastic factors. The Bassin Blanc area is suffering from accelerated invasion of invasive species.

Rats and macaques are controlled as part of a programme to rehabilitate plots of native vegetation and a captive-rearing programme implemented by the Mauritian Wildlife Foundation, the Gerald Durrell Endemic Wildlife Sanctuary and the National Parks and Conservation Service is proving highly effective. Protocols for captive husbandry and artificial propagation are being developed to facilitate the translocation objectives. The Black River National Park partly covers its range, and the habitat around Bassin Blanc, not originally included within the boundary, may be bought by compulsory purchase in the future. Research into the species's ecology is ongoing and prospective surveys to assess the suitability of Round Island for translocation have been conducted. Future conservation actions include studying fecundity differences between non-native and native forest, developing a Conservation Management Area at Combo which is stocked with favoured nectar-producing plants and has predator control, increasing breeding productivity by supplemental feeding, double clutching and captive-rearing of harvested wild clutches, continuing releases on offshore islands and monitoring the population on Ile aux Aigrettes and releasing birds onto Round Island for at least the next three years.

Ile aux Aigrettes, 2007

Photo: © Gregory Guida / www.gguida.com

Taita Thrush

Turdus helleri

Population: ↓ 1,350	REASON FOR CR-LISTING
	DECLINE | POPULATION | **RANGE**

THREATS
Agriculture, plantations

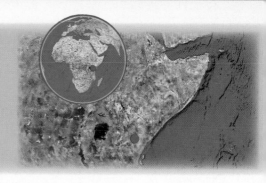

Taita Hills, Kenya, 2006

Photo: ©Tom Callens

Taita Thrush is a forest specialist, only occurring in good quality montane cloud-forest with adequate canopy cover, understorey and litter cover in Taita Hills, Kenya. The diet is is composed of both insects and fruit. It is (apparently) monogamous and mostly breeds between September and March.

Most indigenous forest has been cleared in the Taita Hills. A highly male-biased sex ratio coupled with a bottleneck in Chawia might have significant negative consequences for the long-term survival of that subpopulation.

Considerable conservation work has been commenced in cooperation with local communities. Some reforestation using indigenous tree species is underway and planned which will help both create new habitats as well as enhance connectivity between patches. Income-generating activities, such as bee-keeping and butterfly-rearing, have been initiated and farmers taught on best-practices which will lead to improved perceptions of natural resources and conservation as well as some income to individual farmers.

Future conservation measures include sustaining and expanding these income-generating ventures and formation of Community Forest Associations to enable engagement of the local community in forest management. A translocation experiment aimed at reinforcing the population at Chawia is also planned but needs adequate ground-work to ensure high chances of success.

Cebu Flowerpecker

Dicaeum quadricolor

Population: ↓ 85-105	REASON FOR CR-LISTING
	DECLINE | **POPULATION** | RANGE

THREATS
Agriculture, energy

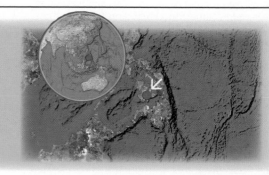

Painting: © Melinda Bitting

This flowerpecker is endemic to the island of Cebu, Philippines where it was refound in 1992. Recent observations clearly indicate an association with the tallest remaining forest patches up to c.500 m, most of which are on karst limestone. It has been observed feeding on mistletoe-like plants and small, ripe *Ficus* fruits. Breeding is presumed to take place in February to August.

The remaining forest on Cebu was rapidly cleared in the 1890s. One hundred years later, only 15 km², or 0.03%, of original cover remained. Competition with Red-striped Flowerpecker *D. australe* may have increased.

Establishment of corridors has been initiated to link up different areas holding Cebu Flowerpecker, especially in the region of the Alcoy forest. Malabuyoc, which may hold this species, is within the borders of a cement company reserve. A Protected Area Management Board for Mt. Lamoy has been created and manages the 7,265 ha protected area. Future conservations action include identify remnant forest tracts on Cebu and survey them for remaining populations, research the species's ecology with particular emphasis on interactions with Red-striped Flowerpecker and habitat rehabilitation by replanting native trees.

Azores Bullfinch
Pyrrhula murina

São Miguel, 2002

Photo: © Leo J. R. Boon / www.cursorius.com

Population: ↓ 203-331	REASON FOR CR-LISTING		
	DECLINE	POPULATION	RANGE

THREATS
Invasives

History

1866 – Frederick DuCane Godman (1834-1919) describes the species.

1933 – it is split as a species from Eurasian Bullfinch *Pyrrhula pyrrhula*.

1995 – habitat management begins.

1996 – a species action plan is published.

2005 – Pico da Vara is extended to comprise 6,067 ha. 36 birds are colour-ringed.

2006 – 68 individuals are colour-ringed.

2008 – a simultaneous count in June gave 78 birds, suggesting the species numbers several hundred birds. Records outside its core range indicate a larger distribution than previously thought.

This bullfinch is endemic to the Azores and confined to the eastern part of the island São Miguel. During the winter and spring (January-April), it appears to depend on the native laurissilva forest. In the summer and autumn (May-November), its habitat use is more catholic; birds utilise bare ground, inhabit vegetation less than two metres high and forest margins. It has also been seen using exotic vegetation in the summer. The birds breed from mid-June to end of August, apparently in Japanese Red Cedar trees.

It was formerly considered a pest of fruit orchards and became rare after c.1920 due to hunting and forest clearance. The historical decline and its extremely small range are believed to be consequences of the widespread clearance of native forest for forestry plantations and agriculture. The spread of alien invasive plant species, which have largely overrun the remaining patches of natural vegetation, suppress the natural fruit, seed and bud food supply of this species. Food shortages are potentially a problem throughout the year, but are most severe in late winter. Random environmental and demographic factors can affect such small populations and inbreeding may reduce reproductive output. Predation by introduced rats

may also be affecting nesting success. It is protected under Portuguese law. The sole occurrence area Pico da Vara/Ribeira do Guilherme has been designated as a Special Protected Area (SPA). Ecological research was conducted during 1991-1993 and a short booklet on the species has been distributed to schools in São Miguel. A number of actions as part of an ongoing EU LIFE-Nature include the development of a management plan for the SPA, the clearance of invasive plant species and replanting with native species in over 70 ha in the core range and the planting of traditional fruit trees at lower altitudes. Future actions include continuation and expansion of the population monitoring scheme, investigate the possibility of breeding at another site, continue the removal and exclusion of exotic flora, continue the replanting of native vegetation (particularly key food plants), monitor the species's response to ongoing habitat restoration, promote land use changes in the buffer areas around the SPA and investigate the impact of rat predation on nesting success.

Birdwatch
The home of birding

Nihoa Finch
Telespiza ultima

Nihoa, Hawaiian Islands, 1996

Population:	REASON FOR CR-LISTING		
2,060-2,550	DECLINE	POPULATION	RANGE

THREATS
Altered fire regimes, invasives, climate change

History

1916 – Lieut. W. H. Munter collects a specimen on 12th February.

1917 – American ornithologist William Alanson Bryan (1875-1942) describes the species.

1968 – 6,686 individuals are estimated.

1985 – 3,200 birds are estimated.

1987 – 946 individuals are estimated. An attempted introduction of 42 birds to French Frigate Shoals fails.

2007 – 2,807 individuals are estimated.

This finch only occurs on Nihoa, north-western Hawaii islands, USA. It occurred on Molokai in the main Hawaiian islands, but was extirpated from there in prehistory, probably by a combination of introduced mammals and habitat loss. The population fluctuates. It occurs in low shrubs and grasses and feeds on seeds, invertebrates other plant parts and eggs. It nests in cavities in cliffs, rock crevices or in piles of loose rock from February to July and the average clutch size is three. Males defend the nest sites and feed females on the nest while females construct the nests and incubate.

It is thought that the presence of an introduced grasshopper on Nihoa, and its periodic irruptions which lead to the virtual defoliation of the island, may be a significant threat. Other potential threats include the introduction of detrimental non-native species and diseases and stochastic events. Fire is a past and still potential threat.

Nihoa is part of the Hawaiian Islands National Wildlife Refuge and the Papahânaumokuâkea Marine National Monument, and legal access is controlled by a permit system that is restricted largely to biologists, researchers, and cultural practitioners. Strict protocols are followed to ensure that permitted visitors do not accidentally introduce new species via seeds, eggs or insects travelling on clothes and equipment. Visiting scientists make regular efforts to control one of the three species of alien plant on Nihoa by hand weeding. A process of evaluatation and prioritisation of potential translocation sites throughout the archipelago for this species (and the other two north-western Hawaiian islands passerines) is currently underway. Disease susceptibility may preclude reintroduction of the Nihoa Finch to the main Hawaiian Islands, and translocation efforts may focus on the north-western Islands.

Future conservation actions include continue monitoring, ensure that strict protocols prevent further accidental introductions of alien species, introduction of a population to Kure atoll and (following removal of mice and mosquitoes) Midway atoll plus restoration of a high island for future translocations.

Maui Parrotbill
Pseudonestor xanthophrys

Photo: © Jack Jeffrey

Waikamoi, Maui, Hawaii, 2003

Population: ↓	REASON FOR CR-LISTING		
500	DECLINE	POPULATION	RANGE

THREATS
Invasives

History

1893 – Lord Rotschild (1868-1937) describes the species.

1945 – feral pigs are introduced and start devastating habitat.

1950 – the species is rediscovered.

1997 – the first chick, a male, is hatched in captivity.

1999 – two collected eggs hatch in captivity and result in two females.

2000 – the first captive breeding takes place.

2008 – a detailed nest-study takes place in January to May and shows a higher nesting success rate than in previous years.

This honeycreeper is endemic to Maui, Hawaii Islands, USA where there only remains 35km² of suitable habitat. It is now restricted to montane, well-developed mesic and wet forest at 1,200-2,150 m and is absent from adjacent areas dominated by exotic trees. It feeds mainly on invertebrates. The range size is c.2.26 ha and territories are defended year-round. The cup-shaped nest is placed in the outer canopy forks of mature ohia *Metrosideros polymorph* - a situation that may afford some protection from introduced predators. During the breeding season in November to June, one chick is usually raised and young are dependent on the parents for five to eight months.

Feral pigs on Haleakala caused chronic habitat degradation and facilitated the spread of disease-carrying mosquitoes. Most of the species's range is now fenced. Weather influences the survival of young and thus potential recruitment rates. Other limiting factors include predation and competition from exotic birds and insects and rats.

The East Maui watershed is cooperatively managed with fencing and removal of feral ungulates. In the Waikamoi Preserve, Hanawi Natural Area Reserve and Haleakala National Park, conservation practices have resulted in the forest understorey recovering well and non-native plant invasions have slowed. Rats are being poisoned in a tiny area. A small population exists in captivity and now numbers three males and seven females. Progeny from this flock will be used for a pilot release programme in the mesic forests of leeward East Maui where weather conditions may result in higher productivity.

Future conservation actions include carrying out surveys to obtain up-to-date estimates of the population, monitoring population trends through regular surveys, assessment of ungulates' occurrence, controlling alien plants, including outside the three wildlife protection areas, continue to replant koa forest in areas adjacent to its current distribution and improving techniques for successful captive-breeding and release so a second population can be established.

Akikiki
Oreomystis bairdi

Kauai's Alakai Swamp, 2004

Population: ↓
780-1,840

REASON FOR CR-LISTING		
DECLINE	POPULATION	RANGE

THREATS
Invasives, climate change

History

1887 – Norwegian zoologist Leonhard Hess Stejneger (1851-1943) describes the species.

1890s-1900s – early naturalists consider the Akikiki common at elevations as low as 300 m.

1973-1981 – population confined to Alaka'i swamp and estimated at about 6,800.

1983 and 1992 – hurricanes Iwa and Iniki, respectively, devastate forests throughout Kaua'i affecting all bird populations.

2000 – population estimated at 1,500 and confined to 36 km² area.

2005 – the US Fish and Wildlife Service announces that the Akikiki should be officially designated an Endangered species.

2007 – surveys in April and May indicate a population of 1,300 birds +/- 500.

2008 – captive breeding of Akikiki starts.

This bird was common and widely distributed on Kaua'i, Hawaii Islands, USA in the 1890s but has declined dramatically and is now restricted to the Alaka'i region. The population has declined by 64% in the thirty years between 1970 and 2000. It is found in high-elevation 'ohi'a and koa-'ohi'a forest. The Alaka'i stronghold is at 1,000-1,600 m. Previous surveys found it distributed at lower altitudes in a few areas, and it may not occur above 1,500 m. It feeds on invertebrates. The clearance of lowland forests for timber and agriculture, feral livestock and feral pigs' spreading of plants and mosquitoes and their associated diseases are major causes for the decline. Predation by introduced animals and competition among introduced birds and insects for arthropods are other factors. Rising temperatures could cause mosquitoes to survive at higher altitudes and thereby spread avian malaria and avian pox.

It occurs within the Alaka'i Wilderness Preserve. The Zoological Society of San Diego is developing techniques for rearing creepers from eggs and breeding them in captivity at the Keauhou Bird Conservation Centre. The Kaua'i Watershed Alliance and The Nature Conservancy are considering fencing (to exclude herbivores and possibly other predators) the north-eastern section of the Alakai Plateau on Kaua'i where the species was last recorded. Future measures include protecting the Alaka'i Wilderness Preserve from the invasion of introduced plants and feral ungulates and restore degraded areas, continue to monitor its population's status and distribution and develop the programme for captive-rearing and release, before the population falls to a critical level.

Akekee
Loxops caeruleirostris

Kauai, 2007

Photo: © Jim Denny

Population: ↓	REASON FOR CR-LISTING		
2,506-4,566	DECLINE	POPULATION	RANGE
	THREATS		
	Invasives		

History

1890 – Scott Barchard Wilson (1865-1923) describes the species.

2000 – a survey finds around 8,000 birds. Previously thought to number around 20,000 and being stable.

2005 – around 6,000 are estimated.

2007 – around 4,000 birds are estimated in a survey in April by the Hawaii Department of Land and Natural Resources in response to anecdotal evidence of a crash in numbers. A petition is filed by the American Bird Conservancy to the US Fish and Wildlife Service requesting protection of Akekee under the Endangered Species Act.

is species is endemic to Kaua`I, Hawaii Islands, USA. inhabits wet and diverse mesic forest from 600 - 600 m, appearing to tolerate considerable habitat sturbance if sufficient `ohi`a trees remain. It feeds imarily on spiders and insects, taking nectar very rely. Breeding occurs in March and April, possibly bruary to June, and all known nests have been in hi`a trees.

evelopment is reducing habitat availability in the oke`e region, while the spread of exotic plants and ral ungulates is degrading remaining areas. Avian ox and malaria are thought to cause mortality ecause introduced mosquitoes are now common at 00 m and appear to be encroaching on the Alaka`i ateau, facilitated by pigs´ opening up of the forest, here this species has its highest density. There is ncern that rising average temperatures could low mosquitoes to survive at higher elevations nd increase the exposure of birds to disease. ood resources may be limited by alien wasps and ants which greatly reduce populations of native arthropods. Introduced birds may be competitors and introduced predators, especially rats, probably cause some mortality. Adverse weather may be a significant limiting factor, e.g. prolonged, heavy rains which can result in nesting failure and cause massive mortality among fledglings and juveniles. Two recent hurricanes resulted in serious damage to Kaua`i's forests. Much of the current range is protected by Alaka`i Wilderness Preserve and, to some extent, by Koke`e State Park. Future conservation actions include to continue population surveys, research basic ecology, prevent further habitat degradation and restore habitat, control and prevent further introductions of alien species, fence out and remove invasive species, identify and translocate disease-resistant birds to parts of the historical range that are affected by disease-carrying mosquitoes, initiate a captive-breeding programme and list under the Endangered Species Act as a matter of emergency.

Akohekohe
Palmeria dolei

Waikamoi, Hawaii, 1991

Population: ↓ 2,750	REASON FOR CR-LISTING
	DECLINE | POPULATION | RANGE
THREATS Invasives	

History

1891 – Scott Barchard Wilson (1865-1923) describes the species.

1907 – the last confirmed observation from Koloka`i is made.

1967 – it is declared an Endangered species.

1980 – 3,800 birds are estimated.

1996 – 2,000 acres are fenced off in the Hanawi Natural Area Reserve.

1997 – the first Akohekohe is reared in captivity.

2008 – capture techniques, in order to colour band birds for studying the Frisbee Meadows population, are successfully developed in May.

This bird, which has received its name from its call, lives on Maui, Hawaii Islands, USA where it occurs in mesic and wet forest at 1,100-2,300 m. It feeds primarily on `ohi`a nectar and also invertebrates, especially caterpillars, and is an important pollinator of `ohi`a. When `ohi`a bloom is at its seasonal low, it feeds on sub-canopy and understorey flowers and fruit. All known nests have been in `ohi`a trees and it raises one to two young per nest, usually nesting twice seasonally between November to June. Habitat destruction and modification and the rapid spread of disease-carrying mosquitoes in the lowlands, are thought to be responsible for past declines. It may be particularly vulnerable to mosquito-borne diseases as it migrates in altitude in response to varying `ohi`a flowering physiology, and thus is at a potentially increasing risk of exposure to mosquitoes at lower elevations. A 473% increase in feral pig activity in one reserve during 1970-1997 reduced alternative food sources to `ohi`a bloom. Predation by introduced rats, cats and Barn Owl *Tyto alba* and possibly small Indian Mongoose *Herpestes auropunctatus* occurs. Conservation practices include combating the establishment of alien plants in two protected areas and, from the late 1980s, feral pigs have been under control. Research into captive breeding is underway, and six individuals have been hatched from late-stage wild eggs. Captive breeding is difficult and expensive as the species is aggressive and requires single-occupancy cages.

Future conservation measures include surveys to obtain an up-to-date estimate of the population size, colour-banding of a two-digit number of birds, monitor population trends, preserve remote and ecologically diverse areas, extend plant control to areas outside reserves complete and routinely monitor the East Maui watershed habitat conservation programme, establish a population in historically occupied habitat to reduce the threat from catastrophes that could wipe out a single population and continue monitoring of captive-breeding efforts.

Belding´s Yellowthroat
Geothlypis beldingi

San José del Cabo, Baja California Sur, Mexico, 2008

Photo: © Javier Lascurain

Population: 1,000-2,499 ⬇

REASON FOR CR-LISTING		
DECLINE	POPULATION	RANGE

THREATS
Infrastructure development, agriculture

History

1883 – American ornithologist Robert Ridgway (1850-1929) describes the species and names it after Lyman Belding, a Californian naturalist.

1917 – the subspecies *goldmani* is described by Harry C. Oberholser.

1928 – the species is known from 11 sites.

2006 – the species is found in May in an apparently newly established marsh in a hotel district at Cabo San Lucas. A highest single-day count of 85 individuals is made at Estero San José on 23rd May.

This species has a fragmented distribution on the Baja California peninsula, Mexico where the two subspecies *beldingi* and *goldmani* are recognised. The former occurs south of 25° N at 20 localities and the latter north of 26° N at 12 localities. It is common at most sites and is closely associated with freshwater habitats but dispersive birds have been recorded up to 400 km from their ranges, also in drier habitats, suggesting it is capable of dispersing over reasonably large distances perhaps as a response to the appearance and disappearance of small marshes. Eggs are laid between March and May.

The oases of Baja California are under high human pressure, especially in the south. Accidental and induced fires, reed-cutting, and drainage for agriculture and cattle-ranching have decreased suitable habitat, although the species occurs in at least one newly created marsh in a hotel district and near active agriculture which suggests that human activities may be beneficial.

None of the known sites are currently protected and conservation focus must be on sharing the scarce water resources between humans and wildlife. Damming of waterways could for example, benefit this species. Angeles del Estero and Agrupación Ciudadana Ecologista - two small local NGOs in the town of San José del Cabo have a history of involvement in the conservation of an IBA that incorporates breeding habitat. The reporting system of North American Birds has provided much new data on this species's distribution since 2000.

Future conservation actions include standardized surveys of all populations and potential areas between the two subspecies, habitat restoration and creation in connection with development projects, develop a Species Action plan, initiate a public awareness programme, promote bird tourism to generate income for protecting key sites, banding to study dispersal and to evaluate the two subspecies genetically.

213

Montserrat Oriole
Icterus oberi

The national bird of Montserrat, the Montserrat Oriole, is dependent on the national plant, the *Heliconia*, from which it suspends its woven basket-nest.

Population: ↓ 520-5,200	REASON FOR CR-LISTING		
	DECLINE	POPULATION	RANGE

THREATS
Invasives, geological events, climate change

History

1880 – George Newbold Lawrence (1806-1895) describes the species and names it after American zoologist Fred Oberi.

1995-1997 – volcanic activity destroys two thirds of its remaining habitat.

1997 – the estimated population is c.4,000 birds in December.

1999 – eight birds are taken to Jersey Zoo for development of husbandry techniques.

2000 – the first captive-bred chick hatches in Jersey Zoo.

2001 and 2003 – drought appears to reduce laying frequency and clutch-size.

2005 – surveys indicate that the downward trend from

1997-2003 may have become reversed. A Species Action Plan is published.

2006 – experimental rat control starts in one area, the Centre Hills.

2008 – colour-ringed birds are used to compare nesting success in areas with rat control versus those without.

his oriole inhabits a very small area on Montserrat, esser Antilles (to UK). It occurs in most forest types etween c.150-900 m with highest densities in wetter, gh-altitude forest. It can also be found at the edges cultivated areas and banana plantations. It is the ational bird of Montserrat and is strongly associated ith the *Heliconia* plant, which is the National plant. e basket nest is suspended from a broad-leaved ee and a typical clutch contains two or three eggs. ccessful pairs can rear up to three clutches in a ason. The food consists mainly of insects but also uit and possibly nectar.

olcanic eruptions are the main threat, with follow-on fects of low insect availability and health problems the birds. Nest cameras have recorded predation rats and native Pearly-eyed Thrashers *Margarops scatus*. Drought is thought to reduce laying equency and clutch-size, while excessive rainfall can so have a negative impact.

comprehensive programme to monitor the

population and breeding success is in place. In 2003, preliminary tests of management interventions were made, aimed at boosting reproductive success. One site where it occurs, the Centre Hills, has been designated a protected area and development is not permitted within its marked boundaries. An environmental awareness programme has recently been initiated. A successful captive population, remaining the property of the Government of Montserrat, is held in the UK at Durrell, Edinburgh and Chester. At the moment, there are no plans for augmenting the wild population with birds from captive stock.

Future conservation measures include continuing the existing programme and research into the causes of the decline, developing potential management interventions to boost reproductive success, continuing the close monitoring of the population and investigating the reasons for the high densities of nest predators in the Centre Hills.

Montserrat, 2001

Photo: © Chris Bowden / RSPB

Montserrat, 2007

Photo: © Geoff Hilton / RSPB

Gough Bunting
Rowettia goughensis

This is one of the world's largest finches and it requires several years to attain its adult plumage. Its main threats are competition with and predation from introduced, giant mice.

Gough Island, 2007

| Population: ↓ | REASON FOR CR-LISTING | | |
| 1,500 | DECLINE | POPULATION | RANGE |

| THREATS |
| Invasives |

History

1904 – British zoologist William Eagle Clarke (1853-1938) describes the species.

1972-1974 – 200 pairs are thought to exist.

1983 – an unconfirmed sighting of a rat on Gough Island is reported.

1991 – 1,500 pairs are thought to exist.

2000 – the population is thought to be 400-500 pairs.

2007 – densities are found to be very low in some low-lying areas, having halved since the 1990s, which is thought to be caused by mice predation. Mice eradication is found feasible in a study in September.

2008 – the RSPB calls for a large-scale mice eradication project, involving dropping bait from helicopters.

his bunting is endemic to Gough Island, Tristan da unha, St Helena (to UK) in the South Atlantic where was considered much more common in the 1920s an today. It derived from vagrant South American nches and is today one of the largest finches in the orld. Indications are that the density of territorial airs roughly halved between 1990 and 2007. It is ost common in tussock-grassland, wet heath and eld-mark up to 800 m, and occurs at lower densities fern-bush and peat bogs. It feeds primarily on vertebrates (80% of foraging time), but also eats uit and grass seeds as well as scavenges broken eggs nd dead birds. The nest lies on the ground amongst r under vegetation, but mostly on steep slopes or iffs, and it usually lays two eggs. Different plumage pes suggest that it takes at least three years to cquire full adult plumage.

he introduced House Mouse *Mus musculus* poses the reatest threat through competition and predation. lice are known to have substantially altered vertebrate populations on other sub-Antarctic lands and Gough Bunting is much less abundant n Gough than other bunting species feeding on vertebrates on nearby, mouse-free islands. n the mice-free, offshore stack Penguin island, ough Buntings have denser populations. Recent esearch from Gough Island has shown that mice are significant predator of breeding seabirds (see e. g. ristan Albatross on pp 94-95) and the probability that unting nests are depredated is high. Furthermore, ough Buntings are found at low density in the owlands where mice are abundant on Gough land, and predation rates of dummy eggs are up thirty times higher in these areas. The proportion f juveniles in the population has declined from 0% to 20% over the last 15 years, suggesting that ecruitment is too low to sustain the population. The ccidental introduction of the Black Rat *Rattus rattus* om Tristan is a potential threat.

ough is a nature reserve and World Heritage te and is uninhabited apart from staff that runs meteorological station. Territory mapping to vestigate pair density in different habitats was onducted in 2000-2001, in addition to an assessment of the potential role of mice as nest-predators. Further investigation of diet overlap with mice, and predation by mice has been undertaken during 2003 to 2006. Future conservation measures include carrying out regular surveys to monitor the population, eradicate mice from Gough Island, and minimise the risk of other alien species becoming established on the island, particularly any rat species.

Photo: © Ross Wanless

Gough Island, 2004

Mangrove Finch

Camarhynchus heliobates

Isabela, Galapagos, 2007

Photo: © Greg Lasley

Mangrove Finch was one of the peculiar finches Charles Darwin encountered in the Galápagos and which affected his thoughts on evolution. It has a strong bill and uses tools to extract food.

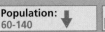

Population: ↓	REASON FOR CR-LISTING		
60-140	DECLINE	POPULATION	RANGE

THREATS
No high/medium-impact threats

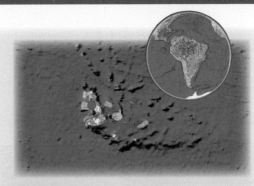

History

1898/99 – the Hopkins-Stanford Expedition collects 34 Mangrove Finches from Isabela and Fernandina.

1901 – zoologists Robert Evans Snodgrass (1875-1962) and Edmund Heller (1875-1939) describe the species.

1962 – Curio and Kramer estimate the population at Playa Tortuga Negra at 20 pairs at most.

1974 – three birds seen on Fernandina are the last ones from that island.

1979 – the Galápagos Islands are classified a World Heritage Site.

1997 and 1998 – surveys on Isabela finds breeding populations in only two areas, estimated at 37 and 21 pairs respectively. Fire ants are believed to have been eliminated.

1999 – the populations are estimated at 36 and 16 pairs.

2006 – a follow up of the breeding biology study in 1999 commences.

2007 – territory mapping reveal a maximum of 24 and 14 pairs respectively. 35% of nests failed, including the first documented case of a nestling succumbing to the *Philornis* parasite. Six young fledged.

2008 – breeding success increased with 17 fledglings. Several historic sites are surveyed in spring and four to five finches are found in February at Carthago Bay, Isabela, but fail to respond to playback of calls from the other population at Playa Tortuga Negra which has different-sounding calls.

is, the most endangered of "Darwin's finches" is stricted to Isabela (at two sites) in the Galápagos ands, Ecuador. It inhabits dense mangrove swamps, here it feeds on insects, larvae, spiders and some getable matter. The bill is strong and can strip rk from dead wood as well as use cactus spines twigs to pierce worms or grubs. The onset of eeding coincides with the rainy season in December January and finishes in May. Its preferred feeding bstrate is among abundant leaf litter and dead ood that has not been washed out to sea.

is not fully known why the species is declining but edation and competition with introduced animals em to be the main threats. The abundance of rats high at both breeding sites and is believed to be a ajor reason for high nesting failure. Other possible troduced predators include feral cats, Smooth-billed ni *Crotophaga ani* and possibly fire ants *Solenopsis* p although they are believed to have been terminated a decade ago. The blood-sucking nest arasite *Philornis downsi* is present in all nests and festation is high.

The habitat of this species is protected within the Galápagos National Park. Botanists are monitoring the mangrove habitat and acting to control invasive species. Research by the Charles Darwin Research Institute is underway to determine if rats are having an effect on its breeding success. A project funded by the Darwin Initiative and coordinated by Durrell Wildlife Conservation Trust and Charles Darwin Foundation is established. Predator control is ongoing and a pilot study of control of *Philornis* started with the 2007-2008 breeding season. Captive breeding of Woodpecker Finches *Camarhynchus pallidus* is expected to develop husbandry techniques and provide breeders with experience for breeding Mangrove Finches.

Required conservation actions include completing a survey of distribution and numbers, establishing yearly monitoring, continuing control measures for rats, wasps, anis, cats and fire ants at Playa Tortuga Negra and Caleta Black and establish new sites through remote mapping of mangroves and field visits to reintroduce the species.

Galápagos, 2008

Photo: © Roger Ahlman

Isabela, Galápagos, 2007

Photo: © Birgit Fessl

Carrizal Seedeater
Amaurospiza carrizalensis

Population: < 50 ↓	REASON FOR CR-LISTING		
	DECLINE	POPULATION	RANGE

THREATS
Dams & water use

Photo: © Miguel Lentino

Isla Carrizal, Venezuela, 2001

This bamboo specialist was recently described from an underexplored area in Venezuela. It was discovered on an island, Isla Carrizal, which has since been destroyed. It has only been found in stands of spiny bamboo forest and three new sites holding both males and females were discovered in April 2008. Its bill shows some degree of specialisation for feeding and analysis shows that it feeds on weevil species

which could be specific to its spiny forest habitat. Habitat at the original locality was all destroyed during the development of the Guri Dam. It continues to be a focus for research by the Colección Ornitológica Phelps, Conservation International, and the Venezuelan Audubon Society funded by hydro electric company Edelca. The spiny bamboo habitat from which the species was described is not only extremely challenging/dangerous to survey in, much of it also lies beneath the forest canopy and hence aerial survey methods cannot be used to detect habitat. Samples of tall grasses and seeding bamboo have been collected and feeding observations made. Required conservation actions include surveying potentially suitable habitat along the Caroni and Orinoco rivers in Venezuela and Colombia, monitor the loss and degradation of potentially suitable habitat and designate areas of potentially suitable habitat as protected.

Pale-headed Brush-finch
Atlapetes pallidiceps

Population: 162-166 ↑	REASON FOR CR-LISTING		
	DECLINE	POPULATION	RANGE

THREATS
Agriculture, altered fire regimes

Photo: © Mery Juiña

Yunguilla, Ecuador, 2006

Brood parasitism by Shiny Cowbird *Molothrus bonariensis* has a significant impact on breeding success. The population has increased in recent years thanks to intensive management, but further increases may be constrained by high land-prices and the difficulty of exercising cowbird control.
The Yunguilla reserve, created in 1999, now encompasses 150 ha and holds 98% of the known brush-finch territories. Management for this species has been extremely successful and has very probably saved it from extinction.
There are plans to establish a second reserve and move some birds there, once the present population has reached 200 pairs.
Required conservation actions include maintaining fences to exclude cattle and goats, establish environmental education programmes, protect the second known area and establish a fire break at the northern boundary of Yungilla Reserve.

This finch occurs in the rio Jubones drainage in south Ecuador. It was unrecorded between 1969 and 1998. In 2008 110–120 pairs were estimated in the Yunguilla Reserve. Nests are placed within dense thickets of small bushes or bamboo and a single clutch is laid in February-April, sometimes exceptionally until as late as in May.

Cone-billed Tanager
Conothraupis mesoleuca

Population: ↓ 50-249	REASON FOR CR-LISTING		
	DECLINE	POPULATION	RANGE

THREATS
No high/medium-impact threats

Parque Nacional das Emas, Mineiros, Goiás, Brazil, 2004

Photo: © Dante Buzzetti

is rarely seen tanager occurs in Mato Grosso, Brazil.
may be nomadic and probably favours gallery forest
d is strongly associated with water.
e rarity of this bird suggests that some unknown
ctors have affected its status. Until at least recently,
ere appears to have been extensive areas of

the various possible habitats. The spread of soya
cultivation in particular poses a serious threat
outside of Emas National Park where it occurs and an
impending hydroelectric project may have detrimental
impact.
The Emas National Park park is reportedly well
protected. A proposal has been submitted to survey
the population in the Bacia do Alto Juruena area, and
Noel Kempff national Park in Bolivia is surveyed in
2008.
Required conservation actions include research the
status, distribution, ecology and habitat requirements,
survey by using tape-recordings of the song in other
areas, including the Noel Kempff Mercado National
Park in Bolivia, conduct surveys in deciduous and semi-
deciduous woodland, increase the area of suitable
habitat that has protected status and lobby against
the proposed hydroelectric project.

Cherry-throated Tanager
Nemosia rourei

Population: ↓ 50-249	REASON FOR CR-LISTING		
	DECLINE	POPULATION	RANGE

THREATS
Infrastructure development, agriculture, plantations

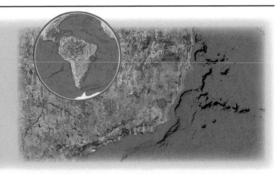

Vargem Alta, Espírito Santo State, August 2006

Photo: © Andre de Luca

is species is known from Espírito Santo, Brazil
d is assumed to have a patchy distribution and be
credibly rare. It occurs primarily in the canopy of
umid montane forest at elevations of 900-1,100 m.
titudinal movements are likely but the species is
parently resident at one site, Fazenda Pindobas
. Birds forage in the interior of the crowns of tall
ees, occasionally lower towards the forest edge, and
ppear to favour moss and lichen-encrusted branches.

Individual birds have been observed apparently
acting as sentries for conspecifics within a flock. The
diet is reportedly arthropods. Nest-building has been
observed in late November and it has been recorded
as living to over six years of age.
Extensive deforestation within its range must have
had an impact on this species; the forest within
Itarana where the species was first recorded in
1941 has since been reduced to a number of small
fragments.
It is protected under Brazilian law. There is a probable
record in one reserve, Augusto Ruschi Biological
Reserve, but it is unlikely that the area supports a
population. There are two other protected areas within its conceivable range which may support the species,
although one almost entirely consists of secondary
forest. Required conservation actions include performing surveys, research ecology and seasonal
abundance and promote the creation of a Reserva
Particular do Patrimônio Natural at private farms.

Critically Endangered Species

that are not covered in the directory 2009

THE FOLLOWING 60 CRITICALLY ENDANGERED SPECIES are not covered in detail in Rare Birds Yearbook 2009. The reasons therefore are that new information about them has not been forthcoming and/or they have not been recorded since the publication of Rare Birds Yearbook 2008. They are listed here with their main country/countries of occurrence as well as a page reference to Rare Birds Yearbook 2008 where they are illustrated and covered in more detail.

Himalayan Quail (Ophrysia superciliosa), Painting by Paschalis Dougalis

Kinglet Calyptura (Calyptura cristata), Painting by Tomasz Cofta

Name	Latin name	Country/region	page in Rare Birds Yearbook 2008
Himalayan Quail	Ophrysia superciliosa	India	87
Crested Shelduck	Tadorna cristata	East Asia	90
Pink-headed Duck	Rhodonessa caryophyllacea	South Asia	90
Jamaica Petrel	Pterodroma caribbaea	Jamaica	100
Mascarene Petrel	Pseudobulweria aterrima	Réunion	103
Guadalupe Storm-petrel	Oceanodroma macrodactyla	Guadelupe	106
Alaotra Grebe	Tachybaptus rufolavatus	Madagascar	106
Cuban Kite	Chondrohierax wilsonii	Cuba	118
New Caledonian Rail	Gallirallus lafresnayanus	New Caledonia	134
Samoan Moorhen	Gallinula pacifica	Samoa	133
Makira Moorhen	Gallinula silvestris	Solomon Islands	133
Javan Lapwing	Vanellus macropterus	Indonesia	134
Eskimo Curlew	Numenius borealis	Americas	140
Slender-billed Curlew	Numenius tenuirostris	Eurasia	139
Jerdon's Courser	Rhinoptilus bitorquatus	India	140
Silvery Wood-pigeon	Columba argentina	Indonesia, Malaysia	144
Blue-eyed Ground-dove	Columbina cyanopis	Brazil	144
Sulu Bleeding-heart	Gallicolumba menagei	Philippines	148
Negros Fruit-dove	Ptilinopus arcanus	Philippines	149
Blue-fronted Lorikeet	Charmosyna toxopei	Indonesia	153
New Caledonian Lorikeet	Charmosyna diadema	New Caledonia	154
Red-throated Lorikeet	Charmosyna amabilis	Fiji	154
Night Parrot	Pezoporus occidentalis	Australia	158
Glaucous Macaw	Anadorhynchus glaucus	South America	159
Siau Scops-owl	Otus siaoensis	Indonesia	166
Anjouan Scops-owl	Otus capnodes	Comoro Islands	166
Moheli Scops-owl	Otus moheliensis	Comoro Islands	167
Grand Comoro Scops-owl	Otus pauliani	Comoro Islands	167
Pernambuco Pygmy-owl	Glaucidium mooreorum	Brazil	170
Jamaican Pauraque	Siphonorhis americana	Jamaica	171
New Caledonian Owlet-nightjar	Aegotheles savesi	Jamaica	171
Short-crested Coquette	Lophornis brachylophus	Mexico	174
Sapphire-bellied Hummingbird	Lepidopyga lilliae	Colombia	174
Dusky Starfrontlet	Coeligena orina	Colombia	176
Turquoise-throated Puffleg	Eriocnemis godini	Ecuador, possibly Colombia	182
Colourful Puffleg	Eriocnemis mirabilis	Colombia	182
Sulu Hornbill	Anthracoceros montani	Philippines	183
Imperial Woodpecker	Campephilus imperialis	Mexico	187
Ivory-billed Woodpecker	Campephilus principalis	USA and Cuba	189
Kinglet Calyptura	Calyptura cristata	Brazil	194
Alagoas Antwren	Myrmotherula snowi	Brazil	196
Bulo Burti Boubou	Laniarius liberatus	Somalia	202
Black-chinned Monarch	Monarcha boanensis	Indonesia	207
White-eyed River-martin	Eurochelidon sirintarae	South-east Asia	208
Archer's Lark	Heteromirafra archeri	Somalia	208
Liberian Greenbul	Phyllastrephus leucolepis	Liberia	211
Sangihe White-eye	Zosterops nehrkorni	Indonesia	216
Niceforo's Wren	Thryothorus nicefori	Colombia	220
Cozumel Thrasher	Toxostoma guttatum	Mexico	222
Pohnpei Starling	Aplonis pelzelni	Micronesia	224
Olomao	Myadestes lanaiensis	USA	224
Rueck's Blue-flycatcher	Cyornis ruckii	Indonesia	227
Ou	Psittirostra psittacea	USA	231
Nukupuu	Hemignathus lucidus	USA	232
Oahu Alauahio	Paroreomyza maculate	USA	235
Poo-uli	Melamprosops phaeosoma	USA	234
Bachman's Warbler	Vermivora bachmanii	USA and Cuba	236
Semper's Warbler	Leucopeza semperi	St. Lucia	236
Hooded Seedeater	Sporophila melanops	Brazil	239
Entre Rios Seedeater	Sporophila zelichi	South America	240

Endangered Species
- the ones to look out for

Moravia, Czech Republic, 20[...]
Photo: © Petr Mückstein

THE CATEGORY JUST BELOW CRITICALLY ENDANGERED is Endangered (see pp. 80-81 for an explanation of IUCN's classification). Almost twice as many species as those that are Critically Endangered, around 350, are classified as Endangered. In the following pages some of these beautiful birds will be presented. Perhaps, but hopefully not, a few of them will be unfortunate enough to be upgraded and treated in full in future editions of *Rare Birds Yearbook*.

More information concerning these birds may be obtained in *Handbook of the Birds of the World* and the BirdLife fact sheets,www.birdlife.org, where full references can also be found.

Saker Falcon
Falco cherrug
7,200-8,800 decreasing

This is a Palaearctic breeding species which is found from Austria in the west to China in the east. It is also the classical falcon used by the Bedu of Arabia when hunting Houbara Bustards. Traditionally, migrating falcons were caught on the Arabian Peninsula on their southward migration, trained in early winter, used for hunting for a few months and then released in spring so they could migrate north again. The wintering range encompasses Tunisia in the west east to China, with the southernmost records from Kenya, but if prey is available some adult birds may stay at the breeding sites in winter. It breeds in other birds' nests and lays up to six eggs. It specialises in diurnal, mid-sized rodents and is physically adapted to hunt and manoeuvre at high speed close to open ground. At some sites it may take other birds.

The threats vary over its range. Degradation of steppe habitat is one main threat in the breeding range in Europe, often in connection with agricultural changes, while trapping for falconry purposes is another in the Middle East. It has been calculated that thousands of Sakers are trapped annually in Arabia. The females, being larger, are more sought after, which may affect the wild population's sex ratios. Captive hybrids of this and other large falcons have been created for the purpose of producing hunting falcons with desired characters and features, which would threaten genetic purity if they were to be released or escape. Persecution and hunting still occurs in its Asian range.

The species is listed in CITES Appendix II and captive breeding has been developed in some countries to substitute for wild captures. Wardening and management programmes have been implemented in East European countries which has led to an improved situation there.

Golden-cheeked Warbler
Centrocercus minimus
21,000 decreasing

Balcones Canyonlands National Wildlife Refuge, Texas, 2007

This wood warbler is a local breeder in southern Texas, USA. It winters in southern Mexico, Guatemala, El Salvador, Nicaragua and Honduras, with records from Costa Rica and Panama. It breeds in juniper-oak woodlands, where it depends on juniper bark for nesting material and lays eggs around late March to mid May. In July it heads south to the wintering sites. The nest is made of long strips of bark and spider webs and it lays three to four eggs. In winter, it occurs in mixed-species flocks, foraging at sites with a high density of "encino" oaks at 1,500-3,000 m.

Breeding habitat is under clearance for land development and agriculture. Fragmentation impairs gene flow and nest survival decreases with increasing forest edge density. However, the main cause of decline may be logging and firewood-extraction, and agricultural conversion for cattle reducing pine-oak habitats in southern Mexico, Guatemala and Honduras. Cowbirds may predate on breeding birds.

There is a recovery plan in the USA. Various small reserves are managed for the species in Texas. There is currently an ongoing effort involving Pronatura Sur, Defensores de la Naturaleza, and Salva Natura to gather information on the warbler south of the US, including details on its wintering habitat, and a community education initiative is underway. Surveys to monitor breeding populations are ongoing. The Leon River Restoration Project in central Texas is working on a habitat restoration project with Golden-cheeked Warbler and Black-capped Vireo as the primary focus.

Ethiopian Bush-crow
Zavattariornis stresemanni
2,500-9,999 decreasing

Yabello, Ethiopia, 2005

This species is confined to extreme southern Ethiopia, where its stronghold is the Yabello Wildlife Sanctuary. It lives in semi-arid areas of short-grass savannah with scattered low Acacia bushes at approximately 1,700 m and can be found near human habitation. Its food includes larvae and pupae, arthropods, cattle parasites and flying insects. Breeding takes place in February/March, and can involve cooperation with usually one, but possibly up to four, extra-pair individuals, which may each help more than one nesting pair. The nest is usually in the top of an acacia bush and it lays up to six eggs and has en extended breeding season or double broods.

Being an open-habitat species, the encroachment of bushes, probably as a result of increased grazing pressure from livestock, the enforcement of fire suppression in the sanctuary and the disappearance of wild herbivores, threatens its habitat at the Yabello reserve. Maize cultivation is encouraged for economic reasons and may also change habitat. Old acacia trees cleared for firewood or establishing more grazing land can create a dearth of suitable nest sites. Human population growth has an impact as well.

The Yabello Sanctuary comprises approximately 2,500 km² and was designated in 1985 to protect this species and White-tailed Swallow, but it has not yet been gazetted and management for ranching has taken place in the sanctuary. Although tree clearance for firewood is prohibited in the sanctuary, this is difficult to enforce, and clearance for cultivation is apparently acceptable. Responsibility for protected areas is with Regional Government and collaboration with Zonal Government and local communities may result in more substantive protection.

Red-breasted Goose
Branta ruficollis
37,300 decreasing

Photo: © Dimiter Georgiev

Bulgaria, 1996

This beautiful goose breeds in the high Arctic of Russia and winters mainly around the Black and Caspian Seas. As many as 80-90% of the population can be found in five winter roosts in Bulgaria and Romania, with some variation in the choice of wintering sites depending on weather and food availability. There are five known migration staging areas in Kazakhstan and the Ukraine but small numbers regularly winter in the Netherlands and are seen in the Baltic region on migration, often with Barnacle *Branta leucopsis* or White-fronted Geese *Anser albifrons*. It breeds for the first time at three to four years of age and lays six to seven eggs.

The threat picture on the breeding grounds is not well-known and it is possible that the fluctuating numbers are normal for a species living in Arctic conditions. It associates with Snowy Owls *Bubo scandiaca* and Peregrine Falcon *Falco peregrinus* for predator protection. Nesting and success seems to be greatest in years when lemmings are abundant and predators do not depend on goose chicks for food. Long-term climate change is likely to affect availability of breeding habitat, and one model predicts a nearly 70% reduction in habitat by 2070. At the wintering and staging sites habitat changes forced by building for industry and tourism, change of agricultural practices, disturbance by fishermen at important feeding sites and hunting, both recreational and for subsistence, are threats.
In 1996 a European Action Plan was published.

Kagu
Rhynochetos jubatus
250-999 stable

Photo: © Tony Wilson/Manu Tours www.nzbirding.co.nz

Blue River Park, New Caledonia, 2005

This terrestrial bird is alone in its genus, and can weigh up to one kg. It lives in both dry and wet forests in New Caledonia where it feeds on worms, snails and lizards. It lays one egg between June and August, sometimes later, in a nest made of leaves directly on the ground. The pair takes turns at incubation, shifting duties at noon and being away for 24 hours foraging. Wild birds can live up to 15 years, with captive individuals reaching 30. It is usually sedentary and requires a territory of up to 28 ha. The extent of movements is individual, with pairs mostly remaining in their territories but young birds or birds with partners that disappear may wander for kilometres. There is even one case of a young bird returning after a year.

Its main threat is from introduced cats and rats, and dogs have also been known to take birds. Feral pigs destroy the ground making food difficult to find and human activities in the forests facilitate access. Trade has also been a threat as the bird became fashionable in the 19th century, but all captive birds are ringed and the species has become a symbol of New Caledonia having been depicted on bank notes and attracting tourists.

Captive-bred birds are used for reintroductions and in 2008-2009 a new survey of the wild population will be carried out.

Spotted Greenshank
Tringa guttifer

500-1,000 decreasing

Mai Po Nature Reserve, Hong Kong, 2004

Photo: © John & Jemi Holmes

This wader breeds around the Sea of Okhotsk and Sakhalin in eastern Russia and winters in Bangladesh, Myanmar, Thailand, Cambodia, Vietnam and Malaysia with winter and passage records from China, South and North Korea, Japan, India, Sri Lanka, Singapore, Indonesia, Philippines and Australia. Its breeding habitat consists of larch forest, wet coastal meadows and coastal mudflats. It breeds in June and builds a nest from twigs, lichens and moss in larch trees several metres up in which it lays four eggs. It breeds in scattered pairs or lose colonies of up to ten pairs. Wintering birds usually frequent estuaries, coastal mudflats and lowland swamps, and sometimes damp meadows, saltpans and rice-fields. In the vicinity of their breeding grounds, the food consists primarily of sticklebacks, worms, small crustaceans and insects. In the non-breeding range, its prey also includes fish, larvae and small molluscs.

Being a coastal species living in a part of the world which is facing strong industrial development, it is threatened by land-filling, reclamation of wetlands, industrial development, pollution and human disturbance. The breeding sites are threatened by overgrazing by reindeer.

It is included in CITES appendix 1 and protected areas have been established within its breeding range in Russia. There are also several key protected areas along its migration routes where hunting is prohibited.

New Zealand Plover
Thinornis novaeseelandiae

156-166 stable

Manawatu Estuary, New Zealand, 2008

Photo: © Alex L. Scott

This plover was widespread on the coasts of South Island, New Zealand but was exterminated by the 1870s and numbers were down to 72 pairs in 1937. It has been reintroduced with varying success to offshore islands; unsuccessfully on Motuora Island, Haruaki Gulf, successfully on an island off the North Island where 100 birds now live and on an island in the Chatham Islands where six pairs live. At another site releases had to be halted when the birds caught avian pox. A five-year release programme is also underway on Mana Island, near Wellington. It nests at the head of rock wave-platforms, on salt meadows and on sandy and boulder beaches and feeds on small crustaceans, molluscs and invertebrates. Two or three eggs are laid. The average age of the population in the 1990s was determined to be six years with the oldest known individual being a male aged 21.

Cats and rats caused its extinction from South Island and removal of sheep from South Island since 1961 has converted its short-grass breeding habitat into forest. Other threats include fire, expansion of fur seal colonies, disease, large seas and storms and predation by Brown Skua *Catharacta lonnbergi*. Losses from trans-located populations have largely been the result of dispersal to the mainland and predation by birds of prey such as Southern Boobook *Ninox novaeseelandiae* and Swamp Harrier *Circus approximans* has been recorded.

All trans-located populations are monitored continuously and two captive populations exist. One population exists on a privately-owned, undisclosed island. Transferred birds to Rangatira and Mangere have some interchange between them.

Socorro Parakeet
Aratinga brevipes

300 decreasing

Photo: © Juan Martinez

This parakeet is endemic to Socorro Island in the Revillagigedo Islands, Mexico. It lives in forests and nests in natural cavities from November. Three birds attend the nests and large flocks of up to a 100 birds may gather after breeding.

The spread of erosion and lack of forest regeneration caused by heavy sheep-grazing has presumably had a severe effect on the availability of suitable habitat. Although its remains have not been found in cat scats, there is a threat of cat predation as it is a tame parakeet. Since 1994 there have been locust outbreaks twice annually which have resulted in damaged vegetation and defoliage of forests, the habitat degradation by introduced species may have facilitated this. The risk of rat introduction to the island is high as no prevention measures are in place.

It is listed in CITES appendix II and the Revillagigedo Islands are a biosphere reserve. A captive-breeding programme has been instigated and sheep have been reduced to 300, with an eradication being planned for 2008-2009. A cat eradication programme will also take place and pilot programme of nest-box provision has been initiated.

Mariana Fruit-dove
Ptilinopus roseicapilla

2,500-9,999 decreasing

Photo: © Shelley Kremer

This species is confined to Rota, Saipan, Tinian and Aguijan in the Mariana islands (to USA). It is the official bird of the Northern Mariana Islands. It is occasionally seen on Guam, from where it is extirpated, presumably involving dispersing birds from Rota to the north. It is found in different types of forest, both native and non-native and also in heavily grazed forest and feeds on fruit from forest canopy but may also feed in bushes and on the ground. It breeds all year round, peaking in April-July, and lays one egg in a nest in a fork of a tree branch.

The Brown Tree Snake is the reason behind its extermination from Guam and is a potential threat on Tinian and Rota where it has been observed but so far not yet established. Tourism development in Tinian requires imports of construction material which could act as a vehicle to introduce the snake there. Introduced plants, hunting and habitat destruction also threaten it.

It is legally protected from hunting and trapping on Rota, and snake barriers are being constructed on Tinian and Rota. It has also featured in a campaign "Promoting Protection through Pride". Since 1993 there has been a captive population in the St. Louis Zoo for breeding purposes

Sharpe's Longclaw
Macronyx sharpie
10,000-19,999 decreasing

Photo: © Philip Briggs

Kenya, 2008

This pipit is endemic to Kenya where it occurs in three main sites; the Kinangop Plateau, Mau Narok and Uasin Gishu grasslands. It is a sedentary species restricted to high-altitude grassland below 2,800 metres. It requires tussocks for nesting, prefers short grass before long and avoids cultivation or woodlots. It apparently co-exists with livestock as long as adequate tussock-cover remains.

The greatest threat is the replacement of its habitat by cultivation and woodlots, driven by the settlement of small-scale farmers. Cultivation is becoming more attractive than live-stock rearing in the Kinangop Plateaus, with farmers converting pastoral lands to arable. Only 50% of the plateau is covered by grasslands today, and only 30% of these are tussock grasslands and these tussock grasslands are fragmented.

Most of the population occurs on private farm-lands outside protected areas. Local volunteers are organised and embarked on awareness campaigns. Proposals to develop milk-cooling facilities to promote live-stock rearing are being discussed and acquisition of private lands may be necessary to stop its decline. A 90-acre reserve was instated by Nature Kenya in 2004/05 and a few pairs are resident there now.

Fuerteventura Stonechat
Saxicola dacotiae
1,000-2,499 decreasing

Photo: © Lasse Olsson

Fuerteventura, 2003

This Stonechat is endemic to the Canary Islands, Spain. It occurs on Fuerteventura and occasionally on Lanzarote, but is extinct from Algranze and Montaña Clara. It occurs mainly on rocky hillsides and a ravine habitat with shrubby vegetation known locally as barranco, but can also be found in other habitats such as cultivated areas and gardens. It feeds on arthropods and individuals show strong site fidelity. It breeds in January to March and lays its nest on the ground, rarely above half a metre. Sometimes a third bird is present helping with breeding.

The Canary Islands are under heavy pressure from tourism and increases in infrastructural development, such as tourist and residential centres, road building, industrial plants, mineral operations and golf courses, are destroying the habitat of this species. Additional threats include excessive grazing by extensively-ranched, semi-feral "coastal" goats and nest predation by feral cats and other introduced mammals, such as rats. High fidelity to particular sites may exacerbate the problem of the destruction and degradation of optimal habitats.

An Action Plan was published in 1999 and several studies of the species are ongoing.

Yellow Cardinal

Gubernatrix cristata

1,500-3,000 decreasing

Estancia El Socorro, province of Corrientes, 2007

Photo: © Roberto Güller

This cardinal was previously common and widespread throughout Argentina and Uruguay with a few records from southern Brazil. It is rare and local in Argentina and now only occurs in four departments in Uruguay. An old record from Paraguay probably refers to escaped cage-birds. It lives in open woodland, savannah, scrub and shrubby steppe up to approximately 700 metres. It breeds in the austral spring, with eggs found in November.

Constant and chronic exploitation as a songbird for the cage-bird market remains the most significant threat. It presumably suffers from timber extraction for firewood and furniture and, especially, rapid afforestation with Eucalyptus plantations. Conversion to cattle pasture may be another potential threat. Hybridisation with Common Diuca-finch *Diuca diuca* has been recorded.

It occurs in CITES Appendix II. There are some occurrences in Argentinian parks and reserves and captive-breeding programmes are established in Uruguay and Brazil, in the latter country using birds seized from poachers.

Flame-templed Babbler

Dasycrotapha speciosa

2,500-9,999 decreasing

Mount Kanlaon, Negros, 2007

Photo: © Leif Gabrielsen

This babbler is endemic to Negros (18 sites) and was also discovered on Panay (five sites) in the Philippines in 1987. Its distribution on Panay is patchy and it is seemingly uncommon there. It lives in lowland forest, forest edge and secondary growth below 1,000 metres with occasional records to 1,280 metres where it feeds on insects and forages in small parties or together with other forest birds such as fantails and leaf-warblers. The highest densities have been recorded in the thick undergrowth of degraded secondary forest and observations invariably come from the lower strata where birds stay in deep cover and are consequently unobtrusive unless singing.

Continuing forest destruction is the main threat, as for other species in this region. Habitat degradation, particularly selective logging of large trees, continues to pose a serious threat to remaining fragments throughout its limited range. Very little lowland forest remains at Mt Canlaon, a key site for the species.

It occurs in Mt Canlaon Natural Park (Negros) and the North Negros Forest Reserve, which only receives nominal protection. It also occurs in the proposed Central Panay Mountains National Park, which reportedly contains the largest block of remaining forest in the Western Visayas, and Mt Talinis/Twin Lakes (Negros). Both sites benefit from conservation funding.

Yellow-eyed Penguin
Megadyptes antipodes

4,840 decreasing

Otago Peninsula, Dunedin, New Zealand

This New Zealand penguin requires its nest to be concealed from neighbouring Yellow-eyed penguins in order to breed successfully. It breeds in forests on islands and in scrub remnants on South Island. Juveniles disperse as far as 500 km from the colony while adults remain year-round. It has been recorded diving for prey to a depth of 100 metres, which befits its latin name meaning "big diver from the southern lands". The local Maori name is Hoiho, meaning "noise shouter". One parent stays with the chicks when they hatch whilst the other collects food at sea and about half of surviving juveniles return to their hatching place.

Deteriorating habitat threatens breeding sites even if some of the changes have been halted. Population crashes have also been brought about due to other reasons such as diphtheria or blood parasites. Introduced predators like ferret, stoat and cats are problematic in some places, though not on Campbell Island. Predation by sea lions has also been recorded. Climate change is likely to cause food shortages as sea temperatures rise and tourism and other human disturbances can affect fledgling weight. There have also been cases of drowning caused by fishing nets.

A five year study of the colonies on Stewart Island was completed in 2008 and breeding success in 2007/08 was much better than the previous year when no penguins fledged. Three sites had a success of 19, 59 and 76% respectively. Chick deaths were caused by starvation and disease, but no predation was recorded.

Photo: © Denis Paterson / www.yellow-eyedpenguin.org.nz

Storm's Stork
Ciconia stormi

200-500 decreasing

Kinabatangan Riverbasin, Sabah, Malaysia, 2006

This solitary stork is found in South-East Asia. It is known from southern Thailand, Malaysia, Indonesia and Brunei. It was thought extinct from Thailand but rediscovered there in April 2004 and is thought to breed in the Klong Saeng-Khao Sok Forest Complex. Sumatra, Kalimantan and Brunei are considered to hold the core population.

It prefers undisturbed lowland forest, especially freshwater and peat-swamp forests on the flood-plains of large rivers. It has also been recorded in disturbed, recently burned and logged areas and places subjected to tidal movements. Little is known about its food preferences, but fish and probably reptiles and amphibians are included in its diet. Very few nests have been found, and as far as is known from those found it breeds in trees in April-July in Sumatra with hatched young in October in Thailand. It is a solitary breeder and lays at least two eggs with chicks able to fly after 90 days.

The main threats are deforestation as a result of logging, dam construction and conversion of habitat to oil palm plantations combined with disturbance. Hunting and trade are minor threats and there is one case of a Storm's Stork being rescued from entanglement in a fisherman's net. It has legal protection in Thailand, Malaysia and Indonesia and has been recorded from a number of protected areas. More surveys are needed to confirm its distribution, habitat and population numbers and logging in swamp-forests should cease.

Photo: © Markus Rehnberg

White-browed Nuthatch
Sitta victoriae
2,500-9,999 decreasing

This nuthatch is restricted to the Mt. Victoria range in Myanmar where it inhabits oak and rhododendron forest at 2,300-3,000 metres. It appears to be most common beneath 2,500 metres and feeds in mixed flocks mostly in the outer branches of large trees.

Forest habitat between 2,000-2,500 m has been heavily degraded in Mt. Victoria. Significant threats therefore include habitat loss from logging (both commercial and small-scale), shifting cultivation, and potentially also hunting.

Mt. Victoria lies within Natma Taung National Park, although no management activities have yet been initiated and it is unclear how effective protection is likely to be.

Natmataung National Park (Mt Victoria), Myanmar, 2005

Photo: © John and Jemi Holmes

Tuamotu Kingfisher Photo: © Simon Hu

The BirdLife International Partnership

The BirdLife International Partnership is unique in that 112 member organisations across the globe belong to it. Some are big, counting their membership in the million, while other are small and only have a few hundred of members or even fewer. Regardless of size, they are all dedicated to conserving the world's birds and build on the often unpaid work of bird enthusiasts.

To present all partner organisations would require a book of its own, but we present 11 partner organisations on the following pages and hope to run through a similar number in Rare Birds Yearbook 2010. The presentation is intended to give a current snapshot of a special activity in the organisation, not a complete picture of it.

An overview of names and addresses of the BirdLife International Partnership can be found on pages 22-27 or at www.birdlife.org/worldwide/national/index.html

Using the BirdLife partnership to save the Sociable Lapwing

Photo: © Maxim Koshkin, ACBK

Researchers colour-ringing an adult Sociable Lapwing to help determine adult survival and gather data on migration routes and wintering areas.

HE POPULATION DECLINE of the Sociable Lapwing *Vanellus gregarius* (see pp 134-135) has been large n recent years. Research on Sociable Lapwing was nitiated in 2005 in Kazakhstan by The Association or the Biodiversity Protection in Kazakhstan (ACBK) working in partnership with a team from the RSPB. In 2006, the team secured funding through the UK overnment's Darwin Initiative. The international eam has been undertaking detailed research work in he Korgalzhyn region of central Kazakhstan, as well s rapid surveys of other parts of the known breeding rounds. Survey work in Russia by the Birdlife artner there, RBCU, suggests that very few reeding colonies remain in that country nd that the world breeding population is ow largely confined to Kazakhstan.

Breeding success appears to be generally high. However, there is a low return rate of colour-ringed irds back on the breeding grounds in subsequent ears, suggesting that adult birds might suffer igh winter mortality. The project team has been working with a number of Birdlife partners in Turkey Doga Dernegi), Syria (Syrian Society for Wildlife Conservation), Sudan (Sudanese Wildlife Society) and raq (Nature Iraq) amongst others to undertake survey work on know migration staging sites.

The partners have been able to mobilise survey teams at short notice to look for satellite-tagged birds as they move along their migration routes. The collaboration has been hugely successful and large flocks of birds have been located in Syria, Turkey and Sudan. Teams of ornithologists in Syria and Iraq have reported incidents of hunting of Sociable Lapwing and this could be a key threat to the species on the wintering grounds or migration routes.

Conservationists will be re-focusing efforts away from the breeding grounds in the next few years and are looking to undertake increased survey effort and educational work with local people in an effort to improve the conservation status of this flagship Central Asian steppe species. All of this is only possible through the collaboration of the BirdLife partnership.

RSPB

www.rspb.org.uk

Photo: © Ghulam Rasool Mughal

Volunteers Help Protect Piping Plovers in Canada

Photo: © Sue Abbott

Piping Plover nesting beach in Nova Scotia.

ON COASTAL BEACHES FROM South Carolina, U.S., to Newfoundland, Canada the Atlantic Coast Piping Plover *Charadrius melodus melodus* can be found breeding. This small shorebird winters in the Caribbean and along U.S. southeast Atlantic and Gulf coasts. It is listed as Endangered in Canada, Threatened in the U.S., and globally Near Threatened on the IUCN Red List. Elsewhere in North America, the subspecies *C. m. circumcinctus* breeds along parts of the Great Lakes and in the Great Plains.

Results from the 2006 International Piping Plover Census estimate that 200 plover pairs breed in eastern Canada and Saint-Pierre et Miquelon (France). Nova Scotia, Canada now supports just 37 pairs, a decline of 27% since 1991. Threats faced by Piping Plovers also affect beach-nesting species globally: loss of habitat due to shoreline development, human disturbance, high levels of nest predation, and flooding of nests.

Across North America, non-governmental organizations like Bird Studies Canada (birdscanada.org) are actively involved in regional recovery programs. Because Piping Plovers have specific habitat requirements, suitable breeding sites are scattered. Localized challenges and opportunities are best met through a network of government and non-governmental partners, and dedicated volunteers. Engaging people from communities that rely on beaches for tourism is vital.

On the Atlantic Coast, we are taking a leadership role to recover Piping Plovers in Nova Scotia. Over 60 trained volunteers help biologists cordon nesting habitat; sandbag around nests to prevent flooding; monitor nests and chicks; and educate beachgoers. We also conduct outreach with stakeholders such as coastal landowners and recreation groups, to improve management and protection of plover habitat.

Although intensive population monitoring, conservation, and stewardship actions on the Piping Plover's breeding grounds are critical to its survival, recovery also hinges upon effective conservation of key migration and wintering areas. Cooperation of several BirdLife partners in the Americas will be an essential part of the story.

Photo: © Ron Ridout

BIRD STUDIES
ÉTUDES D'OISEAUX CANADA   www.birdscanada.org

he Regent Honeyeater as a Flagship or Threatened Australian Woodland Species Conservation

Photo: © Dean Ingwersen

Regent Honeyeater project staff monitor the released birds

A THIRD OF AUSTRALIA WAS ONCE VEGETATED with woodland, but in the face of widespread clearance, mostly for agriculture, only a fraction remains. Many remnant woodlands are highly fragmented and severely degraded, with their complex structure becoming simplified. As a result, wood-land communities are the most threatened in the nation: one in every five woodland birds is threatened. An example of this is the endangered Regent Honeyeater *Anthochaera phrygia*. This striking, yellow-and-black honeyeater once roamed the temperate eucalypt woodlands of south-eastern Australia in its thousands, and sometimes good numbers even visited suburbs of the larger cities. It has, however, not been recorded in South Australia since the mid-1970s, and it is probably also extinct in western Victoria. Within its remaining, reduced range, the population nosedived to fewer than 1,500 birds, and records from anywhere now generate a degree of excitement.

The Regent Honeyeater has been earmarked as a flagship species, as work to assist its recovery should achieve positive outcomes for other threatened fauna, endangered ecological communities, and numerous threatened plants. Birds Australia is actively involved in the recovery of the Regent Honeyeater through a number of volunteer-based programs, coordinated by its Threatened Bird Network. One of the most important of these is restoring and expanding degraded habitat through extensive revegetation at key sites in the species' breeding range on the inland slopes of the Great Dividing Range. This has been complemented with a captive-breeding program, which saw the successful release of 27 birds into the wild in 2008. Almost immediately, captive-bred birds sought out and interacted with wild birds, and breeding behaviour was observed. Each bird was fitted with a radio-transmitter, so ongoing monitoring will allow researchers to track their movements and behaviour, thus augmenting the vast body of data already gathered by Birds Australia's long-running volunteer-based monitoring program. The future seems brighter.

One of the captive-bred Regent Honeyeaters thriving after release

Birds Australia
CONSERVATION THROUGH KNOWLEDGE

www.birdsaustralia.com

Caretaking IBAs With Heart and Mind

Caretaker group members in IBA/SPA Orlické Záhoří are focused both on Corncrake research and agri-environmental schemes.

THE CZECH SOCIETY FOR ORNITHOLOGY (CSO), established in 1926, has always been a gathering place for top experts in ornithology as well as for nature lovers. The slogan "With Heart and Mind" thus became the main motto of the 80th anniversary celebrations in 2006.

This long history of connecting ornithologists was extremely useful when joining one of the fundamental programmes of BirdLife International – the Important Bird Areas (IBA) Programme. The selection of sites in the Czech Republic was just a starting point that brought the idea of using the large number of regional members for monitoring the situation in IBAs. This way, the unique system of so-called caretaker groups composed of professional and amateur ornithologists working together on a voluntary basis came to

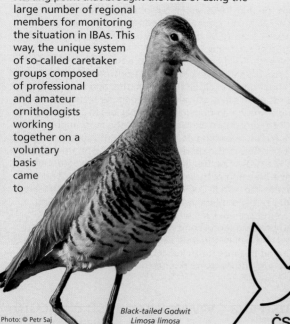

being. The members play important roles in "their" localities as they are involved in research activities, monitoring schemes and ringing programmes. They also take part in practical conservation measures aimed at bird species and their habitats, information campaigns for wider public and cooperate with foresters, hunters, fishers, farmers and other stakeholders. The concept of caretaker groups, now used by many BirdLife Partners all over the world, is a Czech contribution to the approaches of protection o birds and their habitats.

In 2000-2002, CSO, together with the state Agency for Nature Conservation and Landscape Protection of the Czech Republic, elaborated on the proposal of 42 Special Protection Areas (SPAs) of the Natura 2000 network in the Czech Republic. CSO helped with targeted actions in designating 39 of those areas. Practically all the SPAs are also IBAs – the overlap is 96.7%. Since the entry of the Czech Republic into the European Union in 2004, the caretaker groups play an indispensable role in taking care of the sites, in the required monitoring of the sites and in management planning.

The concept of caretaker groups thus gained a new dimension and with the new spectrum of activities, they are an important tool for ensuring the adequate protection of designated SPAs. The combination of expert knowledge and know-how of the members and the action power of the locally based caretaker groups contributes to the favourable status of the SPAs, and, more importantly, to the prosperity of thei criteria bird species.

Black-tailed Godwit
Limosa limosa

ČSO   www.birdlife.cz

The goal is to restore one
million hectares of the
Philippine rainforests by 2020!

Photo: © Haribon Foundation

Haribon biologists gathering baseline data in one of the Philippines largest remaining rainforests,
the Sierra Madre mountains in the province of Quezon in Luzon island.

HARIBON FOUNDATION FOR THE CONSERVATION OF NATURAL RESOURCES is a membership
organization dedicated to the conservation of Philippine biodiversity. It started in 1972 as a
small group of bird enthusiasts. Since then, Haribon has taken up the challenge to maintain
the integrity of the Philippine ecosystems from the halls of Congress to the hills of the
countryside. In its thirty years of crusade to mitigate environmental destruction, Haribon
practically gave birth to the environmental movement in the Philippines. Today, it continues to
build a constituency for environmental issues that will call for prioritizing conservation actions
on habitats and sites, based on solid scientific and socio-economic research.

The name "Haribon" was coined from "Haring Ibon" or the Philippine Eagle (see pp. 126-
127), the largest eagle in the world. It was so named because the existence of the king of birds
is a perfect barometer of the state of our forests.

The country's rich ecosystems are inhabited by a multitude of terrestrial plants and animals
of which nearly half are endemic species. From the world's largest – the Philippine Eagle,
Leatherback turtles, Golden-crowned Flying Fox; to the world's smallest – Tarsier, Sinarapan,
mouse deer, the Philippines is recognized as having the
greatest concentration of unique biological
diversity of any country in the world.
Regrettably, the Philippines also has the
greatest concentration of endangered
species of birds and mammals of any
country. Past and current deforestation
has led to unsustainable practices and
a destabilizing environment. Haribon
believes it is not too late for the
diverse and fascinating wildlife of the
Philippines.

Join our ROAD to 2020 campaign!
It aims to restore 1 million hectares of
the Philippine rainforests using native
tree species by the year 2020.

Photo: © Alejo P. Manaloto

HARIBON
FOUNDATION
protecting nature, preserving life

www.haribon.org.ph

239

Linking conservation with local communities´ livelihood

Sericulture farmers with net-bags of wild-silk moths.

THE INCOMPARABLE ARABUKO-SOKOKE FOREST in Kenya, the last large remnant of East African coastal forest, is home to abundant biodiversity – some 600 plant species, 270 birds and 52 mammals. Among these, six birds – Sokoke Scops Owl, Sokoke Pipit, East Coast Akalat, Spotted Ground Thrush, Amani Sunbird and Clarke's Weaver – and five mammals, including the distinctive Golden-rumped Sengi (Elephant-Shrew), are globally threatened. This last forest is surrounded by farming communities with some of the lowest incomes in Kenya, and is a priority site for Nature Kenya's cutting-edge programme of sustainable economic incentives for conservation. It is now recognized that local communities are likely to wisely use and protect natural resources if the link between conservation and their livelihood is clear. For the past twenty years Nature Kenya – the East Africa Natural History Society – and BirdLife International have nurtured initiatives that empower local people to effectively participate in conserving Arabuko-Sokoke Forest. These include: crafting a 25-year strategic management plan; training forest officers and communities in participatory forest management; diversification of nature-based enterprises; biodiversity and habitat monitoring; gender equity and empowerment; and NGO-Government-Community partnerships.

Today, diverse income-generating enterprises yield direct benefits to forest-adjacent communities: from the pioneering Kipepeo Project, where butterfly larvae raised by local farmers are exported as pupae to display houses worldwide, to woodlots; bee-keeping; silkworm raising; mushroom farming; cultivating Aloe vera and medicinal plants; basketry; weaving; and

expert bird guides. The National Museums of Kenya's Gedi Ruins provides market access. The enterprises are producing significant returns, and a positive attitude toward the forest, but they have a cost: more than US$5 million invested since the 1980s. To reach all forest-adjacent communities, ten times more is required. And that is only one Important Bird Area. Is the world committed to meeting the cost of conservation?

Sokoke Scops Owl
(Otus ireneae)

Photo: © Munir Virani

NatureKenya
The East Africa Natural History Society

www.naturekenya.org

240

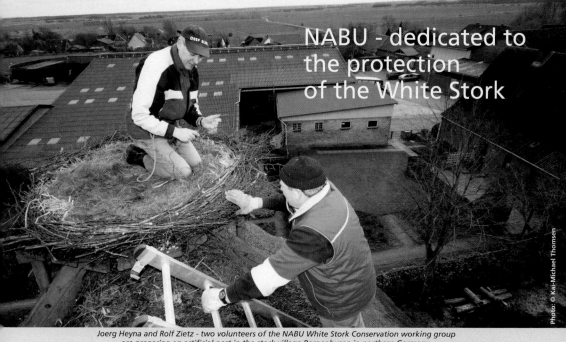

NABU - dedicated to the protection of the White Stork

Photo: © Kai-Michael Thomsen

Joerg Heyna and Rolf Zietz - two volunteers of the NABU White Stork Conservation working group are preparing an artificial nest in the stork village Bergenhusen in northern Germany.

THE MOST POPULAR BIRD IN GERMANY seems to be the White Stork (*Ciconia ciconia*). Many people anticipate the annual return of the first storks from their wintering grounds with joy, and they are highly interested in information on the number of breeding pairs and the breeding success of these birds. NABU, the BirdLife partner in Germany, cares for their protection in a particular way as it occurs on the NABU logo. The White Stork was twice chosen "Bird of the Year" (1984 and 1994), in order to make aware of the risks both for the species and its habitats.

Several hundred conservationists work together in a national White Stork Working Group of NABU. They are monitoring the German population of about 4,000 breeding pairs and look after the reproduction rate. Many conservation projects are based on these data. The volunteers also take care of injured storks, restore nest sites and register ringed birds. Moreover, the mitigation of dangerous types of electric power poles is highly important as, despite some regional progress, many storks still die from unprotected poles every year.

White Stork conservation work is also situated in the Michael-Otto-Institute, being part of the NABU. In 2000 the institute issued a national Action Plan for the birds. The plan revealed the most important breeding areas and proposed detailed measures for White Stork conservation action. In 2004/2005 NABU's institute organised the VI. International White Stork Census, taking place every ten years and supported by BirdLife International and the RSPB. 33 different countries and their national BirdLife partners took part in this bird census. Since the former census in 1994/1995 the global population of white storks increased up to 231,000 breeding pairs or 39 percent.

The last International White Stork Census coincidenced with the access of many eastern countries to the European Union. Some severe changes of agricultural policy are expected for the next years, which will influence the habitat quality of many bird species like the White Stork. The international census provides for essential knowledge about the future habitat management most favourable for those birds.

Photo: © NABU

White Stork, Ciconia ciconia

NABU www.nabu.de

Dutch Purple Herons: a flyway approach to conservation

Satellite-tagged Purple Heron ready to migrate.

AFTER A STRONG DECREASE in breeding numbers in the seventies and the eighties, Purple Heron *Ardea purpurea* numbers increased again in the Netherlands in recent years. Nowadays the Netherlands host 600-700 pairs of this colonial breeder but it is still a Red List species in the Netherlands.

The main cause of the recent upsurge is the better conditions in the wintering areas, the sub-Sahelian zone in Western Africa. After many years of drought, rainfall increased during the last two decades, resulting in better feeding conditions and lower mortality rates in e.g. the Niger Delta, one of the most important wintering areas of the Purple Heron.

Adding to the higher breeding numbers however is the conservation work on the Dutch breeding grounds. This received a boost in 2000 when the Dutch Partner of BirdLife International, Vogelbescherming Nederland, launched a Marsh Bird Conservation Plan, supported by the government. Many actions were undertaken to protect 13 species of marsh birds, including Purple Heron. Conservation however does not stop at the border, since Purple Herons are long-distance migrants. For a comprehensive conservation strategy it is necessary to know the flyways, wintering areas and migration strategies of the Dutch breeding population.

To answer these questions, Vogelbescherming started a satellite-tracking project. During 2007 and 2008 16 herons were fitted with small lightweight satellite transmitters. The results are intriguing and sometimes spectacular. Purple Herons apparently put on fat reserves in the Netherlands, undertake long distance migration flights and hardly stage in Mediterranean wetlands en route. In West Africa they stay for long periods in areas with good feeding conditions. These results help to guide conservation action along the flyway, and to forge cooperation between BirdLife partners.

The satellite-tracked birds can be followed at www.vogelbescherming.nl/purperreiger

Vogelbescherming
NEDERLAND

www.vogelbescherming.nl

The daily life of a Gyrfalcon couple revealed to the public

Creating awareness

Photo: © Anette Strand

"PEOPLE WERE AMAZED AND OVERWHELMED", says Anette Strand, the guide close to the Swedish Gyrfalcon nest, which visitors were invited to in the summer 2008.

Some 80-135 pairs of Gyrfalcon breed in the Swedish mountains. The numbers seem to be stable, although there is a consistent persecution in some areas with reindeer breeding. In 2008, a pair for the first time in many years, nested in the very southern range of the mountains. The nest was very close to a frequently used trail leading to the highest waterfall in Sweden. In cooperation with the local county administration SOF – the Swedish BirdLife-partner – decided to place volunteers near the nest with the purpose to show an extremely powerful and interesting bird but also to avoid disturbance. Binoculars and telescopes were in place.

One opinion in SOF is that awareness can be spread if you have the possibility to get closely involved with birds. That might be through feeding in wintertime, putting up nest-boxes, watching nests at a close range or taking part of migration. So showing the Gyrfalcons fitted this idea very well. Visitors who saw the nest, the young and feeding were really fascinated. At the same time there was also a kind of 'hidden' motive behind this guiding. Coming in touch with interested people, we asked for names and addresses for those who wanted a report on the outcome of the breeding. This gave the possibility to send materials about SOF and especially its conservation efforts. In this way the project was a successful part of the membership campaign.

Showing such a rare bird as a Gyrfalcon worked well at this locality. In some other, easily disturbed, areas of Sweden it might not work out as positive.

There are also other SOF-managed activities around the Gyrfalcon. Breeding pairs are counted and active nests are checked. In 2008 a satellite transmitter was attached to a nestling in another part of Sweden.

Gyrfalcon
Falco rusticolus

Photo: © Magnus Ullman

SVERIGES ORNITOLOGISKA FÖRENING

www.sofnet.org

243

El Bagual Reserve
& the Strange-tailed Tyrant:
The flags of the Chaco

Colour-banded male Strange-tailed Tyrant (Alectrurus risora).

MOST OF THE LANDSCAPES IN Argentina are in private lands. So, the owners are key stakeholders to conserve environment and protect the natural heritage. For this reason, Aves Argentinas, the partner of BirdLife International in this country, supports conservation efforts in private ranches.

One of these marvellous cases is El Bagual Reserve, in the north-east of Argentina. This private reserve, created 25 years ago, belongs to Alparamis, a company that is deeply involved in nature conservation in this part of the world. The area is 3,400 hectares in size which represents 17% of a bigger ranch. This place has become private reserve focused on research.

Since 1995 Aves Argentinas works daily with a park ranger and two assistants to convert the area in a model of nature conservation. The area contains 530 species of fishes, amphibians, reptiles, mammals and birds and almost 600 species of vascular plants. The grasslands and savannas, marshes and forests contain 350 species of birds of which 13 are globally threatened.

One of them is the Strange-tailed Tyrant. In El Bagual, Aves Argentina are leading several studies related to its natural history and mainly reproductive patterns. After twelve seasons and more than 350 active nests studied, we have found that the males defend big territories in which they produce their incredible displays. The females are in charge of the activities related to nesting and breeding. For building

the nest, they often add old skins of poisonous snake Other complex issues found in this species's biology are being under study jointly with the University of Buenos Aires. Moreover, Aves Argentinas is studying the biology of other grasslands birds, and monitoring the marsh deer populations, another endangered species among the mammals.

El Bagual Reserve is the protected area with most field studies in the American Chaco and one of the best places in the world to admire this fantastic and "strange" tyrant. So, it is an honour and a great commitment for Aves Argentinas to maintain both flags on top.

AVES ARGENTINAS®
Asociación Ornitológica del Plata

www.avesargentinas.org.ar

When will SEOR find the first-ever nest of Mascarene Petrel?

How can one find petrel burrows in these 1,000 metres high cliffs?

THERE ARE FIVE SPECIES of the genus *Pseudobulweria*. One is the now Extinct St. Helena Petrel *Pseudobulweria rupinarum* and three of the other four species are Critically Endangered: Fiji Petrel *P. macgillivrayi* (see p. 102), Beck's Petrel, *P. becki* (see 102) and Mascarene Petrel, *P. aterrima* (see p. 222 and Rare Birds Yearbook 2008 p.103). The breeding colonies of all three of these are so far undiscovered. The fourth species, the Tahiti Petrel *P. rostrata* is the only species classified as Near Threatened.

The Mascarene Petrel was first discovered by Charles Lucien Jules Laurent Bonaparte (1803-1857) who described it from two specimens in 1857. Eight more specimens were collected later in the 1890s and the species then remained unknown for 80 years, until 1970 when two specimens where finally discovered after an active research involving local people. Since 1996, things have changed though.

Mascarene Petrel is very prone to light attraction and some of the older generation on Réunion remember petrels flying close to them while walking by night with a hurricane lamp. Since 1996 SEOR has set up yearly campaigns over the island to save young petrels found on the ground due to urban light attraction. Grounded petrels are saved by the habitants who, thanks to awareness campaigns, become more and more concerned about these

birds´ fate. Besides 5,100 fledglings of Barau's Petrel *Pterodroma baraui*, an Endangered species, having been saved in this way since 1996, 22 (of which 11 were fledglings) Mascarene Petrels were rescued and 19 were healthy enough to be released back into the wild at the seashore.

The rescue of fledglings are evidence that this bird still breeds on Reunion island and shows that the fledging period extends from 1st of March until 2nd of April. We suspect that the birds are present on the island between August and April. The rescue campaigns are effective in giving us more information about this species, such as breeding phenology and biometric measurements, but are not appropriate to pin-point the exact breeding locations which are thought to be inside cliffs between 600 and 2,100 metres. We hope to be able to implement more advanced technologies such as satellite telemetry and both genetic and isotope analyses in the coming years to learn more about this enigmatic species, but the challenge of finding a petrel burrow will still remain.

Two Mascarene petrels found on the ground the same day and saved.

www.seor.fr

245

BirdLife Species Champions

Read more about the BirdLife Preventing Extinctions Programme and BirdLife Species Champions on pages 12-21

Birdfair
Global sponsor of the
BirdLife Preventing Extinctions Programme

Rio Tinto Alcan
BirdLife Species Champion
for Kakapo since September 2008

Sir David Attenborough
BirdLife Species Champion
for Araripe Manakin since August 2008

Swarovski Optik
BirdLife Species Champion
for Sociable Lapwing since August 2008

RSPB
BirdLife Species Champion
for Sociable Lapwing since August 2008

S.G. Shields (Benfleet) Ltd
BirdLife Species Champion since August 2008

The James Gibson Charitable Trust
BirdLife Species Champion
for Yellow-crested Cockatoo since August 2008

WildSounds
BirdLife Species Champion
for Spoon-billed Sandpiper since July 2008

The David & Lucile Packard Foundation
BirdLife Preventing Extinctions
Programme Supporters since July 2008

The Peter Smith Trust
BirdLife Species Champion
for Dwarf Olive Ibis since June 2008

Arbutus Images
BirdLife Species Champion since June 2008

Colin Shields
BirdLife Species Champion since June 2008

Disney Worldwide Conservation Fund
BirdLife Preventing Extinctions
Programme Supporters since June 2008

Dr. Urs-Peter Stäuble
BirdLife Species Champion
for Restinga Antwren since May 2008

Edward Keeble
BirdLife Species Champion since February 2008

Birdwatch
BirdLife Species Champion
for Azores Bullfinch since January 2008

Rare Birds Yearbook
BirdLife Species Champion since January 2008

The Reissing Family
BirdLife Species Champions
for Blue-billed Curassow since January 2008

Peter Oakley
BirdLife Species Champion since August 2007

The Olewine Family
BirdLife Species Champions since August 2007

Rockjumper Birding Tours
BirdLife Species Champion since August 2007

Porzana Ltd
BirdLife Species Champion since August 2007

Permian
BirdLife Species Champion since August 2007

NHBS
BirdLife Species Champion since August 2007

Leeds Castle
BirdLife Species Champion
for Blue-Crowned Laughingthrush since August 200

Rare Bird Alert
BirdLife Species Champion since August 2007

in focus
BirdLife Species Champion
for White-shouldered Ibis since August 2007

BirdLife Species Guardians

Read more about the BirdLife Preventing Extinctions Programme and BirdLife Species Guardians on pages 12-21

Houssein Rayaleh (Djibouti Nature)
Djibouti Francolin

Mareqeti Viti (Nature Fiji)
Fiji Petrel

SPEA & SEO
Balearic Shearwater

Kry Masphal
White-shouldered Ibis

Associação dos Biólogos Santomenses
Dwarf Olive Ibis
São Tomé Fiscal
São Tomé Grosbeak

Seng Kim Hout
Bengal Florican

Haribon Foundation
Mindoro Bleeding-heart
Black-hooded Coucal

Manu
Polynesian Ground-dove
Tahiti Monarch

Mauricio Herrera
Blue-throated Macaw

Sociedad Ornitológica Puertorriqueña, Inc
Puerto Rican Nightjar

Pingo D'água
Restinga Antwren

Isabel Gómez
Royal Cinclodes

Jasson John
Uluguru Bush-shrike

Michael Brooke (University of Cambridge) & Paul Donald (RSPB)
Raso Lark

Mwangi Githiru
Taita Apalis
Taita Thrush

Norbert Cordeiro
Long-billed Tailorbird

Pronatura Noroeste, A. C.
Belding's Yellowthroat

Nature Seychelles
Seychelles Paradise-flycatcher

SPEA
Azores Bullfinch

Belding's Yellowthroat. Photo: © Pete Morris

Critically
Endangered Birds
in the news the past year

2007
AUGUST

Bengal Florican *Houbaropsis bengalensis*
Bengal Florican, one of the world's most threatened birds, will be first to benefit from a new conservation approach that aims to save all 189 of the world's Critically Endangered birds from extinction.

Photo: © Jonathan Eames

With less than 1,000 individual birds remaining, Bengal Florican had been given just five years before disappearing forever from its stronghold, the floodplain of the Tonle Sap lake in Cambodia. The florican will benefit from the groundbreaking new 'BirdLife Species Champions' approach; whereby 'Champions' are being sought for Critically Endangered birds, to fund identified conservation programmes that will pull each species back from the brink of extinction.

The BirdLife Species Champions funding will contribute toward the government-approved 'Integrated Farming and Biodiversity Areas' programme in Cambodia, encouraging communities to favour 'low impact' traditional farming techniques over intensiv non-sustainable dry-season rice production.

First Species Champions announced
This year the British Birdwatching Fair ('Birdfair') became the first of BirdLife's Species Champions, funding conservations efforts to save not one, but four Critically Endangered birds: Belding's Yellowthroat *Geothlypis beldingi* (Mexico), Djibouti Francolin *Francolinus ochropectus* (Djibouti), Restinga Antwren *Formicivora littoralis* (Brazil) and Bengal Florican *Houbaropsis bengalensis* (Cambodia Birdfair funds will contribute to identified conservation programmes that will pull each species back from the brink of extinction.

Three other Species Champions were also announced at the Birdfair launch: *in focus* (optics) will act as Species Champions contributing to White shouldered Ibis conservation efforts; *The Leeds Cast Foundation* have stepped forward for Blue-crowned Laughingthrush; and *NHBS Environment Bookstore* will contribute much-needed core funds to the initiative.

SEPTEMBER

California Condor *Gymnogyps californianus*
Of 13 breeding attempts by Critically Endangered California Condors in the wild in southern California between 2001 and 2005, only one resulted in successful fledging. A paper published in Bird Conservation International finds that "ingested anthropogenic material" - swallowed junk - was directly responsible for the deaths of two condor nestlings, and is strongly implicated in the deaths of several more.

Four dead nestlings and two removed from the wild held substantial quantities of junk such as glass fragments, metal bottle-tops, washers, cartridge cases, electrical wiring and plastic pipes.

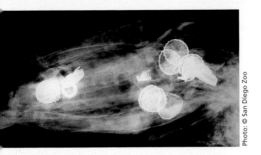
Photo: © San Diego Zoo

contrast, of nine chicks produced between 1980
d 1984, all but one fledged successfully. The US
rest Service has tried to clean up sites used by
ndors, but because of the "growing and deeper
man footprint on the environment of southern
lifornia", the task is huge.
The authors propose that as a matter of urgency,
ditional condor restaurants should be set up at
ultiple feeding sites away from problem areas.
wever, an increase in the foraging ranges of
ndors is likely to result in increased exposure to
ad. Removing the threat of lead poisoning from
e condor range would allow greater flexibility for
e management of condor populations.

ase-studies prevent extinctions
the 2007 IUCN Red List of Threatened Species
veals the scale of the escalating extinction crisis
curring across the planet, an unobtrusive parakeet
om Mauritius is showing that, with funding and
dicated fieldworkers, species can recover from the
ink of extinction. The IUCN Red List of Threatened
ecies reveals that unprecedented numbers of
ecies are now threatened with extinction.
For birds, the Red List is maintained by BirdLife
ternational, who report that 1,221 species
e considered threatened with extinction. The
verall conservation status of the world's birds has
eteriorated steadily since 1988, when they were first
mprehensively assessed. 189 birds are now listed as
itically Endangered - the highest threat category.
et even among these severely threatened birds is
small number whose survival odds are improving,
oviding case-studies to others for how species can
e successfully saved. The most encouraging recovery
en in the 2007 IUCN Red List of Threatened Species
Mauritius (Echo) Parakeet, once dubbed "the rarest
arrot on Earth".
This is the third such downlisting to occur on
auritius in recent years due to the efforts of MWF.
2000, Pink Pigeon *Nesoenas mayeri*, down to
st nine birds a decade earlier, was downlisted to
ndangered and now numbers 400 birds. Likewise,
auritius Kestrel *Falco punctatus*, went from just
ur birds in 1974 and now numbers approximately
000 individuals.

hatham Albatross *Thallassarche eremita*
n urgent call for action has been made after
ocking reports that a single longline vessel fishing
the Chatham Rise area of New Zealand was
sponsible for the deaths of 36 albatrosses globally

threatened with extinction. Twelve of the seabirds
drowned by the vessel were Critically Endangered
Chatham Albatross - a species more threatened
than the Mountain Gorilla, Giant Panda and Snow
Leopard on the IUCN's Red List. Since the incident,
Forest & Bird report that New Zealand Fisheries
Minister Jim Anderton is considering regulating to
ensure all fishing vessels adopt best practice to avoid
seabird bycatch, and that he is instructing his officials
to identify what constitutes best practice.

The Royal Forest and Bird Protection Society of
New Zealand (BirdLife in New Zealand) are now
calling on the minister to act urgently to implement
mandatory mitigation measures, rather than
voluntary measures, to prevent further disasters.

Chinese Crested Tern *Sterna bernsteini*
A study of Chinese Crested Tern highlights that
the global population has fallen to less than fifty
individuals, half what they were just three years
ago. The study believes that the main cause of
this decline is an unregulated expansion in trade
for seabird eggs, a local delicacy that has risen
in demand alongside a thriving tourist economy.
Seabird eggs are collected by local fishermen in the

Photo: © Chen Shuihua

belief that wild eggs have more nutritious value than
poultry eggs. Without urgent action conservationists
have given the bird less than five years before
disappearing completely from its two remaining
breeding areas.

The report indicates that the going rate for one
seabird egg at Juexi (nearby the Jiushan Island
breeding colony) was approximately 15 Chinese
yuans ($2USD) in 2005. In two years this price has
more than doubled: seabird eggs now sell for 35
Chinese yuans (about $4.5USD), encouraging more
people into the egg-collecting trade. In 2005 and
2006, the Chinese Crested Tern breeding colony
disappeared altogether on Jiushan Island, most likely
a sign of breeding failure caused by egg-collecting.

OCTOBER

Javan Lapwing *Vanellus macropterus*
Javan Lapwing has not been recorded with certainty
since 1940 and is currently classified as Critically

Endangered by BirdLife International. The species was confined to wide steppe-like marshes in river deltas on the Indonesian island of Java, which is now densely populated and is currently home to 124 million people. This human pressure means that there is little suitable habitat left and the situation is looking bleak for Javan Lapwings, should any remain.

In the latest issue of Bird Conservation International, a fascinating paper gives a historical insight into the life of one of the world's rarest and most poorly known species of bird, pieced together from newly translated notes by a German amateur ornithologist. In 2000, the Zoological Museum Amsterdam received a number of unpublished and previously unknown notes and manuscripts written by August Spennemann. Spennemann lived on Java from c.1915 to 1940 and among his notes was a detailed typed account of his observations of the Javan Lapwing in the late 1920s near Pamanukan, West Java province. These records come from areas with no previous reports of Javan Lapwings and suggest that these birds may have wider habitat preferences than was previously thought.

Spoon-billed Sandpiper
Eurynorhynchus pygmeus
Populations of one of the world's strangest birds have crashed over the last decade, and surveys this summer of its breeding grounds in the remote Russian province of Chukotka suggest that the situation is now critical.

Photo: © Chaiwat Chinuparawat

The charismatic, and rather aptly named, Spoon-billed Sandpiper, is now worryingly close to becoming extinct. With only 200-300 pairs left, conservationists are calling for urgent help to tackle the decline.

The reasons for these losses are complex, involving changes to habitat during migration and loss of breeding areas. What is clear is that nest predation by foxes and disturbance by people and dogs could prove to be the final nail in the coffin for the few birds left. They breed during June–July in a small strip of coastal Arctic tundra in Chukotka, NE Russia. They then migrate thousands of kilometres to winter along coasts in South and South-East Asia. Spoon-billed Sandpipers are one of several species that depend on the rich tidal coasts of the Yellow Sea in East Asia, where they stop to refuel on their way to and from their breeding grounds.

Californian Condor *Gymnogyps californianus*

Audubon (BirdLife in the US) have applauded Governor Schwarzenegger's decision to sign into law a crucial bill that will ban the use of lead ammunition for hunting big game within the range of California Condor. The newly-signed Ridley-Tree Condor Preservation Act will require the use of 'non lead centerfire' rifle and pistol ammunition when shooting big game or coyotes within specific areas of the state.

Governor Schwarzenegger ignored the objections of his own Department of Fish and Game in deciding to sign the bill (AB821) last Saturday. The accidental ingestion of lead pellets has been a key factor in California Condor declines, so much so that in 1987 the species became extinct in the wild when the last six wild individuals were captured to join a captive-breeding recovery programme. Today the wild population numbers some 70 reintroduced individuals.

Audubon California - which has long advocated on behalf of California Condor - have described the new law as the most important conservation step for the condor in years, marking a significant victory after three previous attempts to get the bill signed had failed.

Sociable Lapwing *Vanellus gregarius*
Thanks to a single satellite tag, a 3,000-strong flock of Sociable Lapwing has been discovered in Turkey - the largest seen for more than 100 years. The finding represents another significant rise in fortune for the Critically Endangered bird: almost five years ago, as few as 400 Sociable Lapwing were thought to exist globally. The birds were found in the Ceylanpinar

trict of south-eastern Turkey after a satellite
g was fitted to one of the birds migrating from
eeding grounds in Kazakhstan earlier this year. The
gged bird covered 2,000 miles, flying north of the
spian Sea, then down through the Caucasus and
uth into Turkey, where it effectively stopped.
On investigation, conservationists from Doğa
erneği found that the tagged bird was part of a
ck of 1,800 other lapwing. The following day a
aggering 3,200 Sociable Lapwing were observed at
e site. Conservationists from a number of nations
early all BirdLife Partners) have been working
conserve Sociable Lapwing in recent years, by
ordinating their actions on the ground; focusing
eir efforts to conserve wintering sites, stopover
es and breeding sites along the species' flyways.

atch out for vulture deaths in Africa
rdLife's Council for the African Partnership has
arned African BirdLife Partners that they need
be on high alert, following the discovery of the
ug diclofenac on sale at a veterinary practice in
nzania. A survey
WCST (WildLife
nservation Society
Tanzania, BirdLife in
nzania) is underway
establish the full
cts. Diclofenac, a
n-Steroidal Anti-
flammatory Drug
SAID), has been
und to cause gout
d renal failure
vultures of the
yps genus. In India,
here diclofenac
as in widespread
terinary use,
ree Gyps species,
rmerly of Least
oncern, have been
ushed to Critically
ndangered status,
sing over 99 percent of their populations in just
ver a decade. Without action by governments and
eterinary associations to ban the use of diclofenac
r veterinary purposes, the drug is likely to be very
fficult to control. Since the patent for the drug
xpired, it has been produced in generic form by
undreds of manufacturers worldwide, and is sold
nder dozens of different names.
The manufacturer of the brand found in Tanzania
xports the drug for veterinary use to 15 African
ountries spread across the continent. Governments
the Indian subcontinent have belatedly taken
ction. At a meeting of the National Wildlife Board
March 2005, the Government of India announced
at it intended to phase out the veterinary use of
clofenac within six months. In 2006, the govern-
ents of India, Pakistan and Nepal all banned
anufacture of diclofenac, sending a very clear
gnal, and it is hoped that full retail bans will
on follow. But numbers are already so low that

the future of White-rumped *Gyps bengalensis*,
Indian *Gyps indicus* and Slender-billed Vultures
Gyps tenuirostris now depends on captive breeding
programmes. Gyps vultures take several years to
reach sexual maturity, and a pair produces only
one or two young every one or two years, so it will
take decades before any of these species is likely to
come off the Critical list. Africa's vultures already
face terrible pressures, and several species formerly
of Least Concern were added to the 2007 Red List
of threatened species. In contrast, there are no
reported mortalities for Meloxicam, which has been
administered to over 700 birds from 60 species, with
safety tests carried out.

2008
JANUARY

Vulture situation in Nepal
The number of White-rumped *Gyps bengalensis*
and Slender-billed *Gyps tenuirostris* Vulture nests
recorded west of
Narayani Chitwan
National Park /
Buffer Zone Area,
Nawalparasi District,
Nepal, has doubled
in two years, as a
result of measures
taken to reduce and
replace the use of a
drug toxic to vultures.
In around a decade,
global numbers of
both species have
declined by over
95%, (over 99% in
the case of White-
rumped Vulture). The
decline is due to the
veterinary use of the
Non-Steroidal Anti-
Inflammatory Drug

Photo: © Munir Virani/The Peregrine Fund

(NSAID) diclofenac.
But a study of 11 of Nepal's 75 administrative
districts by Bird Conservation Nepal (BCN, BirdLife in
Nepal) finds that the use of diclofenac has dropped
by 90 percent since 2006, thanks to work by BCN
and its partners, notably the Nepalese government
(Department of Drug Administrative and Department
of National Parks and Wildlife Conservation). BCN
is working collaboratively for a complete phasing
out of diclofenac and other harmful NSAID drugs
from the market. Support has come not only from
conservation organisations such as RSPB (Birdlife
in the UK), Zoological Society of London and
WWF, but also from Nepal's Department of Drug
Administration, Department of Livestock Services,
local veterinary and para-veterinary practitioners,
local pharmacists, pharmaceuticals distributors
associations and local communities.
In ten districts of western Nepal including Chitwan,
BCN has replaced half a million Rupees ($8,000)

worth of diclofenac with the safe and equally effective alternative drug, meloxicam.

In a further attempt to conserve vultures, BCN has established a community-run Jatayu (Vulture) Restaurant at Pithauli, Nawalparasi District. The entire management of this restaurant, which provides vultures with cattle carcasses known to be uncontaminated with diclofenac, is done by the local community with technical support from BCN, and financial support from the UN Development Programme's Global Environment Facility and RSPB.

BCN is now identifying communities who can run similar restaurants in the Pokhara area as well as Rupandehi, Kapilvastu and Dang Districts. However, for restaurants to be effective they need to be part of a coordinated strategy of increasing conservation awareness in pharmacies, vets, and local communities, the removal of diclofenac and swapping it for meloxicam, and the provision of safe meat. However, despite this positive news from Nepal the overall trend across south Asia remains one of serious continuing decline.

Northern Bald Ibis *Geronticus eremita*
Efforts to save the Middle East's rarest bird have been boosted by two chance sightings of the species 1,500 miles apart.

Photo: © Gianluca Serra

Northern Bald Ibises were seen last month in the Jordan Valley for the first time in 13 years, and in Djibouti, east Africa, for the first time ever, raising hopes that numbers of this species are not as low as scientists fear. The bird was thought extinct in the Middle East in the 1990s before a colony of just six birds was found in Palmyra, Syria in 2002.

Since then, adult and young birds have been fitted with satellite tags by the RSPB and BirdLife Middle East, to try to discover and protect their migration routes and wintering sites. The tagged adult birds are currently in Ethiopia for the winter. Two adult Northern Bald Ibis were spotted on the Yardena cliffs on the Israel/Jordan border early last month. They were seen by a researcher surveying black storks and had disappeared when he returned the following day. Two weeks later, a young Bald Ibis was found on the beach at Tadjoura, eastern Djibouti, by a group of Swedish birdwatchers. The bird was searching for food and its appearance astonished the visitors. The Djibouti find is more significant for scientists because the bird was a juvenile and very few of the 25 birds

fledged in Syria since 2002 have returned.

Conservationists fear the missing birds are being shot on migration but until they know the young birds' migration route, they cannot alert hunters to their rarity.

Laysan Duck *Anas laysanensis*
The Critically Endangered Laysan Duck had a very successful 2007 breeding season according to U.S. Geological Survey (USGS) and U.S. Fish and Wildlife Service biologists. The year's total of adults and fledglings on the Midway Atoll National Wildlife Refuge (NWR) has now risen to about 200 individuals.

This is only the third year since this species was translocated. In 2004 and 2005, 42 individuals made 750-mile voyage across the Pacific and were released at Midway Atoll NWR, managed by the U.S. Fish and Wildlife Service, to increase the species's geographic distribution and reduce its risk of extinction. With the translocated population more than quadrupling in only three years, researchers are now optimistic that the project will help promote the conservation of this Critically Endangered species. Survival and breeding of the ducks was closely tracked. Each "founder bird" transported from Laysan carried a small transmitter so that it could be located despite dense vegetation. The post translocation monitoring revealed that the Laysan Duck is capable of flight between the small islands that comprise Midway Atoll and is able to nest in non-native vegetation.

The re-establishment of a second population at Midway Atoll reduces the risk of extinction from chance events such as hurricanes, diseases or the accidental introduction of harmful invasive plants and animals. Discussions are underway about the establishment of a third population on another predator-free island.

eventing Extinctions

e 2007 British Birdwatching Fair has provided
'ord funds of £226,000 ($445,000) for BirdLife's
al conservation work in preventing extinctions.

poon-billed Sandpipers
rynorhynchus pygmeus

ghtings of 84 Spoon-billed Sandpipers at two
astal wetland sites in Myanmar have cast new
ht on the winter distribution of this Endangered
ecies, and confirmed that these wetlands are of
ternational importance for their biodiversity.
alysis of satellite images, combined with the
perience of previous surveys in India, Bangladesh
d Thailand, and with historical records of the
ecies in Myanmar, suggested that potentially
table habitats existed in the south-western state
Arakan (Rakhine) in the Bay of Bengal, and
artaban (Mottama) Bay near the Thai border.

natham Albatross *Thalassarche eremita*

dLife International has welcomed the measures
nounced by New Zealand Fisheries Minister Jim
nderton to reduce the number of seabirds killed
New Zealand's fisheries. This follows an incident
st year where a single longline vessel fishing in the
natham Rise area of New Zealand was responsible
r the deaths of 36 albatrosses including 12 Critically
dangered Chatham Albatross. The New Zealand
inister of Fisheries acknowledged that input from
e public and sector groups, including Forest and
rd (BirdLife in New Zealand) had been useful in
lping him decide what the most effective measures
regulate would be.

ociable Lapwings *Vanellus gregarius*

Photo: © Ghulam Rasool Mughal

Two Sociable Lapwings, satellite tagged in Kazakhstan last summer, have flown more than 5,000 miles
to central Sudan, where they have spent the winter.
Satellite tagging is adding rapidly to our understanding of the distribution of this Critically Endangered
species outside the breeding season. The birds left
Korgalzhin in central Kazakhstan on August 3, 2007
and arrived at Viransehir, Turkey around October 8.
They joined a flock of over 3,000 birds –the largest
assembly of the species recorded in over a century
–before leaving Turkey in late October, arriving in
Sudan on November 3.

The tagging project began last year when scientists
from the RSPB and Association for the Conservation
of Biodiversity of Kazakhstan (ACBK) fitted satellite-
tracking devices to three birds on their breeding
grounds on the barren steppe expanses of central
Kazakhstan. Conservationists from the Sudanese
Wildlife Society, part-funded by the UK government's
Darwin Initiative, will try to locate the Sudanese
birds, count them and find out more about the sites
they are using.

Photo: © Hadoram Shirihai

MARCH

Beck's Petrel *Pseudobulweria becki*

A bird that was known only from two records
from the 1920s has been discovered in the Pacific
after a gap of 79 years. Sightings of the Critically
Endangered Beck's Petrel - published by the British
Ornithologists' Club - have finally proven the species
is still in existence, and delighted conservationists.
A voyage into the Bismarck Archipelago, north-
east of Papua New Guinea, successfully managed
to photograph more than 30 of these elusive
seabirds. This included sightings of fledged juveniles
- suggesting recent breeding. A freshly dead young
bird salvaged at sea also becomes only the third
specimen in existence.

Like other tubenoses, Beck's Petrel is potentially
threatened by introduced cats and rats at its
breeding sites, and by logging and forest clearance

for oil-palm plantations. Until the breeding sites have been identified the threats remain speculative.

Azores Bullfinch *Pyrrhula murina*
Azores Bullfinch has become the latest Critically Endangered species to find a Champion through the BirdLife Preventing Extinctions Programme. Birdwatch magazine has stepped forward to provide vital funds for the work of the Species Guardian, SPEA (BirdLife in Portugal).

Azores Bullfinch, known locally as Priolo, is confined to eastern São Miguel in the Azores, Portugal. It has suffered through widespread loss of native forest and invasion by exotic vegetation, which has largely overrun the remaining patches of natural vegetation within the species's breeding range. These funds will enable the continuation of crucial habitat restoration work to increase the core range of this species. The exact number of bullfinches is unclear. In the 1990s the population was estimated at 200-300 individuals. However, surveys since 2002 have indicated a rise to around 340 individuals, a sign that habitat restoration is already having an effect.

Extinction rate of Asian vultures
Asian vultures will be extinct in the wild within a decade without urgent action to eliminate the livestock drug that has caused their catastrophic decline, a newly published paper warns.

The new study shows that the population of White-rumped Vultures *Gyps bengalensis* is dropping by more than 40 per cent each year in India where it has plunged by 99.9% since 1992. Numbers of Indian *G. indicus* and Slender-billed Vultures *G. tenuirostris* together, have fallen by almost 97% in the same period.

Conservationists say that banning the retail sale of the veterinary drug diclofenac and constructing three more captive breeding centres is the only way to save the birds. Manufacture of the veterinary form of the drug, as an anti-inflammatory treatment for livestock, was outlawed in India in 2006 but it remains widely available. Furthermore, diclofenac formulated for humans is being used to treat livestock.

The study, published in the Journal of the Bombay Natural History Society, states that White-rumped Vulture is now in dire straits with only one thousandth of the 1992 population remaining. Scientists counted vultures in northern and central India between March and June last year. They surveyed the birds from vehicles along 18,900 kilometres of road. Their study followed four

previous counts, the last in 2003. The researchers believe that numbers of White-rumped Vultures in India could now be down to 11,000 from tens of millions in the 1980s. Populations of Indian and Slender-billed vultures have dropped to around 45,000 and 1,000 birds respectively.

APRIL

Magenta Petrel *Pterodroma magentae*
A study into one of the world's rarest seabirds provides knowledge that could help avoid extinction. Molecular analysis of the Critically Endangered Magenta Petrel (also known as the Chatham Island Taiko) discovered that 95% of non-breeding adults were male. This suggests that critically low population levels may be causing male birds difficulty in attracting a mate. Their calls are too spread out to attract the infrequent females which pass by. Conservationists are planning to increase the male Magenta Petrel's pulling power by creating a new breeding colony within a predator-proof fence.

There are now thought to be between 8 and 15 breeding pairs left in the world. Male and female Magenta Petrels look extremely similar, and are difficult to distinguish by sight alone. Scientists collected blood samples from almost the entire known living population over a 20 year period. This allowed the team to distinguish gender accurately using DNA sexing techniques. The sex-ratio of male to females was approximately even in petrel chicks and breeding adults. However, 95% of non-breeding birds were found to be male. This finding suggests that unpaired males may be having difficulty in attracting females to burrows. Scientists are hoping to use knowledge of male behaviour traits to make the plan work. By using the DNA sexing technique to slightly favour male chicks for translocation, the team hope to increase the numbers of birds returning as adult breeders to the refuge.

MAY

IUCN Red List 2008
Climate change has become firmly established as an accelerant to many of the factors which have put one in eight of the world's birds at risk of extinction today's publication of the 2008 IUCN Red List of Threatened Species of birds has found. Long term drought and sudden extreme weather are putting additional stress on the pockets

Floreana Mockingbird. Photo: © Zoological Museum of the University of Zurich

habitat that
any threatened
species depend
. This coupled
th extensive
d expanding
bitat
struction
s lead to an
rease in the
e of extinction
continents
d away from
nds, where
st historical
tinction has
curred.
The 2008 Red
t makes grim

Azores Bullfinch. Photo: © Pedro Monteiro

results were
stark. "For 79%
of threatened
bird species, the
highest priority
conservation
action in the
immediate
future is to
provide effective
safeguarding of
individual IBAs
or networks of
IBAs" said Dr
Stuart Butchart,
BirdLife's
Global Research
Coordinator
and a co-

ding with 1,226 species of bird now threatened, d eight species newly uplisted to Critically dangered, the highest threat category. In the lápagos Islands, Floreana Mockingbird *Nesomimus fasciatus* is confined to two islets off Floreana. Its pulation has declined from an estimated maximum 150 individuals in 1966 to fewer than 60, and is w at risk from extreme weather events. As a result has been uplisted to Critically Endangered.

However, there is some good news. One species ose situation has improved is Marquesan Imperial-geon *Ducula galeata*. Actions plans put in place ve resulted in the downlisting to lower threat tegories. Climate change is likely to figure more ominently in future Red List updates. Spoon-led Sandpiper *Eurynorhynchus pygmeus* has been listed from Endangered to Critically Endangered, ving to accelerating population declines, driven rtly by habitat loss and degradation of the tidal ts it depends on in its migratory and wintering nges. But climate change is expected to have increasing negative impact on this species and ners dependent on tundra for breeding. Modelling dicates that 57% of the Spoon-billed sandpiper's eeding habitat could be lost by 2070.

JNE

ving the world's most threatened birds

nat's the best way to save a species? Should we rget conservation at individual sites, or perhaps e a much broader approach - taking action at the ndscape or seascape scale?

For 99% of Globally Threatened Birds, safeguar-ng Important Bird Areas (IBAs) is a key part of e solution. Questions of scale for conservation ogrammes are the subject of a paper by scientists om BirdLife International and Conservation ternational published in the inaugural issue of nservation Letters. The study identified the most propriate spatial scale of conservation efforts for 239 species of birds, mammals, amphibians and ptiles on the IUCN Red List. Experts classified each ecies into one of four conservation strategies. The

author on the paper. In the longer term, all site-based approaches must also consider issues in the surrounding areas. For some threatened species, the need is more urgent. The scientists discovered that for 20% of birds, IBA or local-scale protection also needs to be reinforced with broader-scale action in the short term. Seabirds killed by long-line fishing, waterbirds affected by hydrological processes across a landscape, and species occurring at low population densities and impacted by hunting are just three examples.

Of all threatened birds, fewer than 1% are best conserved in the short term primarily through action at the landscape scale. As the world's leading authority on bird conservation, BirdLife maintains the list of globally threatened species on behalf of the IUCN. At present one in eight of the world's 10,000 birds are at risk of extinction, and 190 bird species are Critically Endangered.

JULY

Azores Bullfinch *Pyrrhula murina*

For the past 5 years, SPEA (Birdlife in Portugal) and the RSPB (BirdLife in the UK), together with other partners, including the Azores Regional Government, have been implementing a LIFE project to save the Critically Endangered Azores Bullfinch - or Priolo as it is known locally - from extinction.

This species is Europe's rarest songbird, and the second most globally threatened bird species in the whole continent. It occurs only in small pockets scattered in a 6,000 hectare mountain range on São Miguel island in the Azores. The species's natural habitat, which was already patchily distributed and degraded, is currently severely threatened through invasion by aggressive exotic plant species. The LIFE project has been improving the Azores Bullfinch habitat since 2003, by clearing exotic plants and planting native trees that provide the food that the birds depend on. Project staff have also been monitoring the population, which seems to be responding well to this habitat management – the population appears to be increasing fast, at least in the transects monitored by the LIFE project team. A team in Portugal and in the UK then developed a unique field experiment - a simultaneous survey of all the Azores bullfinches in the complete world range.

The event, partly funded by a generous grant of US$17,000 from the Disney Conservation Fund, attracted much interest and 50 volunteers from the UK, Holland, Brazil, Spain, France, mainland Portugal and the Azores spent several days in June being trained on Azores Bullfinch songs, habitat classification and distance sampling. Almost 200 one-kilometre squares were checked and 287 point counts took place, with eight minutes spent at each point. A total of 78 Azores Bullfinches were counted, which should result in a final estimate of several hundred birds – an increase on the 200 individuals estimated five years ago. Encouragingly, there were a number of records from outside the core range for the species, suggesting it may occur more widely than previously thought.

AUGUST

Araripe Manakin *Antilophia bokermanni*

Photo: © Jim Lawrence

Sir David Attenborough, the greatest wildlife communicator of our age, has added his weight to the BirdLife Preventing Extinctions Programme by becoming a Species Champion. Sir David chose the occasion of this year's British Birdwatching Fair to announce that he would be backing work to prevent the extinction of the Critically Endangered Araripe Manakin *Antilophia bokermanni*.

Known to science for just ten years - the bird was first described in 1998 from north-east Brazil - Araripe Manakin is at risk of making an exit as sudden as its entrance into the annals of the world's birds. A survey in 2006 led to an estimate of only 800 individuals, all confined to an area of moist forest

less than 28 km² in extent on the north-eastern slope of the Chapada do Araripe, south Ceará, Brazil. The Species Guardian for Araripe Manakin is the Brazilian conservation organization, Aquasis. As well as the work of protecting and restoring the 'gallery' forest, Sir David Attenborough will be supporting a campaign to reach rural communities, local government officials with the power to grant refuse development licences, and city schoolchildre Children from the communities around the forest a working on a puppet show telling the story of the Araripe Manakin, which will be presented to their city counterparts during the annual Arts and Cultur Festival.

Jerdon's Courser *Rhinoptilus bitorquatus*
The 270-mile Teluga Ganga Canal, from Srisailam in central Andhra Pradesh to Chennai (Madras), is to b diverted around the only remaining habitat of the Critically Endangered Jerdon's Courser.

Because of its specialised habitat requirements, Jerdon's Courser is endemic to the Eastern Ghats of Andhra Pradesh and extreme southern Madhya Pradesh, India. Believed to number no more than 5 individuals, the bird was thought to be extinct unti its rediscovery in Andhra Pradesh 22 years ago. The rediscovery led the Andhra Pradesh government to establish the Sri Lankamalleswara Wildlife Sanctuary, to protect the courser's habitat of scrub forest interspersed with bare ground in the gently rolling, rocky foothills of the Eastern Ghats. When the proposed route of the canal threatened the sanctuary, conservationists including Bombay Natur History Society (BNHS, BirdLife in India) and RSPB (BirdLife in the UK) urged the Supreme Court of India to intervene.

The Supreme Court halted the construction work, and now, three years later, a new route has been approved which avoids most of the protected sites. The Andhra Pradesh Irrigation Department has agreed, in principle, to buy 3,000 acres of scrub forest between the new canal route and the sanctuary. The state's Forest Department will mana that land to protect and enlarge the bird's habitat. Fuel wood collection and overgrazing, and more recently disturbance from the construction of the canal, may have contributed to the bird's decline, But some livestock grazing and forest management will continue in the sanctuary to maintain the open scrub.Scientists believe other nearby scrub forests could be harbouring Jerdon's coursers, and have been given permission to attach radio transmitters two birds. They will also use cameras and footprint tracking strips to find out more about the species.

Crack-down on diclofenac sellers in India
The Indian government has ordered a crackdown on companies selling the drug responsible for the near-extinction of vultures. A letter from the Drug Controller General of India, Dr Surinder Singh, has warned more than 70 drugs firms not to sell the veterinary form of diclofenac, and to mark human diclofenac containers 'not for veterinary use'. In 2004, suspicions that diclofenac was responsible

the catastrophic decline in vulture numbers were
nfirmed when the drug, present as residues in the
rcasses of cattle, was found to cause fatal renal
lure in Gyps vultures. Two years ago, following a
eeting of the Indian National Board for Wildlife
2005, chaired by the Prime Minister of India, the
nufacture of veterinary diclofenac was outlawed.
w vets are dodging the ban by using the human
rm of diclofenac for livestock, despite an effective
d safe alternative drug being available.
One major pharmaceutical company, Boehringer
gelheim, has become the first to support the work
the BNHS and RSPB to protect remaining vultures
m poisoning with diclofenac.

ji Petrel *Pseudobulweria macgillivrayi*

expedition in search of Fiji's only endemic seabird
ritically Endangered Fiji Petrel - had to be aborted.
nservation action now continues to focus upon
rking alongside local communities to locate and
otect their elusive breeding grounds. The rare
trel was previously known from just one specimen
llected in 1855 on Gau Island, Fiji. However, there
ve been more sightings in recent years from the
all island, and a bird was captured and released
ere in 1984 by Dr Dick Watling of MareqetiViti
atureFiji). The recent voyage aimed to provide
e first confirmed reports of Fiji Petrel at sea. The
entists were also keen to test the possibility of
tching and fitting adults with radio transmittors.
wever, the trip had to be abandoned after three
ys due to mechanical problems with the survey
ssel. Another expedition is planned for July 2009 to
ntinue searching for the elusive seabird.

EPTEMBER

orthern Bald Ibis *Geronticus eremita*

workshop on conservation of the Critically
dangered Northern Bald Ibis, has concluded
at the Palmyra birds should be supplemented
th juveniles taken from the expanding semi-wild
pulation at Birecik, Turkey. The meeting was
ld in Palmyra, Syria, near the site where a relict
pulation of the bird was discovered in 2002.
The workshop was organised by the Syrian Society
r the Conservation of Wildlife and Syrian Ministry
Agriculture and Agrarian Reform, the General
mmission for the Management and Development
al-Badia, with participation and funding from
dLife International's Middle East Secretariat,
e Royal Society for the Protection of Birds (RSPB,
dLife in the UK), and Germany's Hanns Seidel
undation. The proposed captive Northern Bald
s aviary will be established within the Talila
ildlife Reserve, part of the al-Badia desertic
eppe rangelands east of Palmyra, managed by the
rian government and funded by UN's Food and
griculture Organisation and others to restore to
ological health. Workshop participants included
mmunity representatives, local hunters, Bald
s Protected Area staff, and senior officials of
e General Commission for the Management and
evelopment of al-Badia.

The aim of the workshop was to identify the main
problems affecting the Bald Ibis breeding colony,
to propose practical solutions to these problems,
and, develop and endorse a national Action Plan
for Northern Bald Ibis conservation. Juvenile birds
would be taken from Birecik to form a captive
breeding colony, using adapted compounds that
were previously used for captive breeding of Arabian
Oryx (a Critically Endangered species of antelope).
The project will draw on expertise from around
the world, including Doga Dernegi (BirdLife in
Turkey), and the Konrad Lorenz Forschungsstelle
in Grünau, Austria, where a semi-wild colony has
been established. However, the Syrian government,
local Bedouins, former hunters and others are firmly
committed to the survival of the Palmyra colony.

OCTOBER

American seabirds thrown a lifeline

President George W. Bush has presented The Agreement for the Conservation of Albatrosses and Petrels
(ACAP) to the US Senate for approval. "I believe the
Agreement to be fully in the U.S. interest", wrote
President Bush. ACAP is an international treaty between nations. "Its provisions advance the U.S. goals
of protecting albatrosses and petrels. I recommend
that the Senate give early and favourable
consideration to the Agreement and give its advice
and consent to accession", stated President Bush.

The USA will join twelve countries which are
currently parties of the treaty. These are Argentina,
Australia, Brazil, Chile, France, Ecuador, New Zealand,
Norway, Peru, the Republic of South Africa, Spain
and the United Kingdom. The next steps are for the
U.S. Senate to ratifying the treaty, and produce laws
which will implement the agreement. The United
States has been an active participant in the work
of the Agreement, attending both preparatory
meetings and subsequent meetings of ACAP's
Advisory Committee and Meeting of the Parties.

Ten out of the 22 albatross species are Critically
Endangered or Endangered, and another eight are
considered to be Vulnerable to Extinction, according
to the Red List of Threatened Birds. The most
important threats to these species are accidental
deaths in longline and trawl fisheries, and loss of
eggs and chicks to introduced predators on breeding
islands. Solving these problems requires coordinated
efforts by governments, scientists, fishermen, and
conservation organisations. BirdLife's Albatross Task
Force (ATF) is a major grass-roots contribution to
meeting ACAP's goals. The ATF is the world's first
international team of mitigation instructors working
with fishermen on land and on deck, along with
government agencies, to reduce seabird bycatch.
ATF instructors routinely show that the adoption of
conservation measures are both operationally and
economically effective.

*Source: Edited BirdLife press releases, also
available in full including references and quotes at
www.birdlife.org/news/news/index.html.*

Tour Operators
that will take you to
Critically Endangered birds

NOW THAT YOU HAVE READ ABOUT THESE magnificent, rare birds, you may want to go and see them as well. Here is a listing of some tour operators which state that they see Critically Endangered birds on their trips. The listing is voluntary and even if all major tour operators have been invited to take part, some may be missing. A listing here does not imply that they have received a stamp of approval for quality by the Editor of this book nor that they operate after strict ecotourism principles. The continents visited refer to 2009.

Access Uganda Tours (Uganda)
Website: www.accessugandatours.com
Email: accessug@utlonline.co.ug,
utebihassan@yahoo.com
Phone/fax: +256 414 344 347
Phone: +256 312 284 659, +256 772 455 423,
+256 752 455 423, +256 772 588 873 or +256 752 588 873
Africa

Albatross Encounter (New Zealand)
Website: www.encounterkaikoura.co.nz
Email: info@encounterkaikoura.co.nz
Phone: +64 3319 6777, 0800 733 365
New Zealand

Andean Birding (Ecuador)
Website: www.andeanbirding.com
Email: charlie@andeanbirding.com
Fax: +593 (2) 224 4426
Phone: +593 (2) 224 4426
North & South America

ASA Wright Nature Centre (Trinidad and Tobago)
Website: www.asawright.org
Email: aright@tstt.net.tt
Fax: +868 667 4540
Phone: +868 667 4655
Trinidad & Tobago

AVESTRAVEL (Ecuador)
Website: www.avestravel.com
Email: info@avestravel.com,
robertjonsson@avestravel.com
Phone: +593 (9) 9206 628
South America

Bellavista Cloud Forest Reserve & Lodge (Ecuador)
Website: www.bellavistacloudforest.com
Email: info@bellavistacloudforest.com
Fax: +593 2 290 3165, 211 6232
Phone: +593 2 290 3166; 290 1536;
South America

Bird Treks (USA)
Website: www.birdtreks.com
Email: info@birdtreks.com
Fax: +1 717 548 3327
Phone: +1 717 548 3303
North and South America, Europe, Asia, and Africa

Bird Explorers (Australia)
Website: www.birdexplorers.com
Email: birdexplorers@surfbirder.com
Phone: +61 408 933 399
Africa, Asia, Australasia, Europe, Oceania, South Atlantic

Birdfinders (UK)
Website: www.birdfinders.co.uk
Email: info@birdfinders.co.uk
Phone: +44 1258 839066
Africa, Australasia, North and South America, Europe

Birding in Paradise Safaris (Uganda)
Website: www.birdinginparadise.com
Email: enquiries@birdinginparadise.com
Phone: +256 772 468521
Africa and Asia

Birdquest (UK)
Website: www.birdquest.co.uk
Email: birders@birdquest.co.uk
Phone: +44 1254 826317
All continents

Birdseekers (UK)
Website: www.birdseekers.co.uk
Email: info@birdseekers.co.uk
Phone: +44 1752 342001
All except Antarctic

Birdtour Asia (UK)
Website: www.birdtourasia.com
Email: info@birdtourasia.com
Phone: +44 1332 516254
Asia

DOF Travel (Denmark)
Website: www.doftravel.dk
Email: travel@dof.dk
Phone: +45 33 28 38 00
Asia, Africa, North America

Eagle-Eye Tours (Canada)
Website: www.eagle-eye.com
Email: travel@eagle-eye.com
Phone: +1 250 342 8640 or +1 800 373 5678 (toll free in North America)
North & South America, Africa, Asia, Europe, and Australasia

EcoTours Colombia (Colombia)
Website: www.ecotours.com.co
Email: info@ecotours.org
Phone: +57 12 87 65 92
South America

Fatbirder's Anytime Tours (UK)
Website: www.anytimetours.co.uk
Phone: +44 1843 298488
Africa, Asia, Australasia, South America

Field Guides Incorporated (USA)
Website: www.fieldguides.com
Email: fieldguides@fieldguides.com
Phone: +1 512 263 7295
Africa, Asia, Australasia, North & South America, Central America, Europe

Heliangelus Naturresor (Sweden)
Website: www.heliangelus.se
Email: heliangelus@telia.com
Phone: +46 140 107 44
Africa, Americas

Heritage Expeditions (New Zealand)
Website: www.heritage-expeditions.com
Email: info@heritage-expeditions.com
Fax: +64 3 365 1300
Phone: +64 3 365 3500
Asia, Western Pacific, Subantarctic Islands, Antarctic

Jenner Expeditions (UK)
Website: www.BirdingTours.info
Email: info@BirdingTours.info
Phone: +44 1342 713858 or +44 1494 721692
Africa, Asia

Jetwing Eco Holidays (Sri Lanka)
Website: www.jetwingeco.com
Email: eco@jetwing.lk
Phone: + 94 11 234 5700 (Extensions 521 or 527)
India and Sri Lanka

Kalypso Adventures (India)
Website: www.birdskerala.com
Email: info@birdskerala.com
Phone: +91 484 209 2280, 944 703 1032
Asia

KingBird Tours Inc. (USA)
Website: www.kingbirdtours.com
Email: kingbirdtours@earthlink.net
Phone: +1 212 866 7923, fax: +1 212 866 4225
Asia

Kolibri Expeditions (Peru)
Website: www.kolibriexpeditions.com
Email: kolibriexp@gmail.com
Phone: +51 1 273 7246
South America

Limosa Holidays (UK)
Website: www.limosaholidays.co.uk
Email: info@limosaholidays.co.uk
Phone: +44 1263 578143
all continents except Antarctica

Manu Expeditions (Peru)
Website: www.manuexpeditions.com,
www.birding-in-peru.com
Email: birding@manuexpeditions.com
Phone: +51 84 226671, 239974, fax +51 84 236706
South America

Manu Tours (New Zealand)
Website: www.nzbirding.co.nz
Email: Manutours@nzbirding.co.nz
Fax: +64 7 864 7475
Phone: +64 7 864 7475
New Zealand, Australia, South Pacific

Neblina Forest (Ecuador)
Wesbite: www.neblinaforest.com
Email: info@neblinaforest.com
Fax: +593 2 2267 437
Phone: +593 0808 234 1434
South America

NE Brazil Birding (Brazil)
Website: http://ciroalbano.multiply.com
Email: ciroalbano@yahoo.com.br
Phone: + 55 85 99555162, +55 85 34768136
Brazil

Neophron Tours Limited (Bulgaria)
Website: www.neophron.com
Email: office@neophron.com
Fax: +359 52 650 230
Phone: +359 52 650 230, +359 888 420 159
Bulgaria

New Zealand Land & Pelagic Bird Tours (New Zealand)
Website: www.rosssilcock.com
Email: silcock@rosssilcock.com
Fax: +64 712 374 2536

Phone: +64 712 629 5865
New Zealand

NOF-Travel (Norway)
Website: www.naturogfritid.no
Phone: +47 383 935 75
All continents

Richard Raby Eco Tours (Brazil)
Website: www.birdingbrazil.com
Email: birdingsebrazil@yahoo.co.uk
Phone: + 55 213 731 1977, +44 1223 302997
Brazil

Rockjumper Birding Tours (South Africa)
Website: www.rockjumper.co.za
Email: info@rockjumper.co.za
Fax: +27 88 033 394 0225
Phone: +27 33 394 0225
Africa

Seriema Nature Tours (Argentina)
Website: www.seriematours.com
Email: info@seriematours.com
Phone/Fax: +54 11 4312 6345
South America and Antarctica

Sunbird (UK)
Website: www.sunbirdtours.co.uk
Email: sunbird@sunbirdtours.co.uk
Phone: +44 1767 262522
Europe, Asia, Australasia, Africa, South America, North
America, Antarctica

Tropical Birding (USA)
Website: www.tropicalbirding.com
Email: info@tropicalbirding.com
Phone: +1 409 515 0514
North America, South America, Africa, Asia, Australasia

Ventures Birding and Nature Tours (USA)
Website: www.birdventures.com
Email: travel@birdventures.com
Phone: +1 828 253 4247
All continents

Wildwings (UK)
Website: www.wildwings.co.uk
Email: wildinfo@wildwings.co.uk
Fax: +44 117 937 5681
Phone: +44 117 965 8333

Wrybill Birding Tours (New Zealand)
Website: www.wrybill-tours.com
Email: info@wrybill-tours.com
Fax: +64 6 877 6300
Phone: +64 6 877 6388
New Zealand

Zambezi Safari and Travel Company (UK)
Website: www.zambezi.com, www.bushcamps.com
Email: info@zambezi.com
Phone: +44 1548 830059
Africa

Which countries hold which species?

THE CRITICALLY ENDANGERED SPECIES FOUND in the different countries of the world are listed here. This list is based on a list produced by BirdLife International, but only those species with a somewhat regular, current or historical, occurrence are mentioned. Vagrants, such as Slender-billed Curlew in the United Kingdom, are not included. Furthermore, seabirds often range over vast expanses of international, oceanic territory and they are only included here for countries where they nest or regularly occur offshore from.

Afghanistan
Indian Vulture *Gyps indicus*
Siberian Crane *Grus leucogeranus*
Sociable Lapwing *Vanellus gregarius*
Slender-billed Curlew *Numenius tenuirostris*

Albania
Slender-billed Curlew *Numenius tenuirostris*

Algeria
Balearic Shearwater *Puffinus mauretanicus*
Northern Bald Ibis *Geronticus eremita*
Slender-billed Curlew *Numenius tenuirostris*

Angola
Tristan Albatross *Diomedea dabbenena*

Argentina
Tristan Albatross *Diomedea dabbenena*
Brazilian Merganser *Mergus octosetaceus*
Eskimo Curlew *Numenius borealis*
Purple-winged Ground-dove *Claravis godefrida*
Glaucous Macaw *Anodorhynchus glaucus*
Entre Rios Seedeater *Sporophila zelichi*

Armenia
Sociable Lapwing *Vanellus gregarius*

Australia
Chatham Albatross *Thalassarche eremita*
Orange-bellied Parrot *Neophema chrysogaster*
Night Parrot *Pezoporus occidentalis*

Christmas Island (to Australia)
Christmas Frigatebird *Fregata andrewsi*

Norfolk Island (to Australia)
Chatham Albatross *Thalassarche eremita*
White-chested White-eye *Zosterops albogularis*

Azerbaijan
Siberian Crane *Grus leucogeranus*
Sociable Lapwing *Vanellus gregarius*
Slender-billed Curlew *Numenius tenuirostris*

Bangladesh
Pink-headed Duck *Rhodonessa caryophyllacea*
White-bellied Heron *Ardea insignis*
Slender-billed Vulture *Gyps tenuirostris*
Red-headed Vulture *Sarcogyps calvus*
Bengal Florican *Houbaropsis bengalensis*
Spoon-billed Sandpiper *Eurynorhynchus pygmeus*

Bhutan
White-bellied Heron *Ardea insignis*
White-rumped Vulture *Gyps bengalensis*
Red-headed Vulture *Sarcogyps calvus*

Bolivia
Blue-throated Macaw *Ara glaucogularis*
Royal Cinclodes *Cinclodes aricomae*

Brazil
Tristan Albatross *Diomedea dabbenena*
Brazilian Merganser *Mergus octosetaceus*
White-collared Kite *Leptodon forbesi*
Eskimo Curlew *Numenius borealis*

ue-eyed Ground-dove *Columbina cyanopis*
urple-winged Ground-dove *Claravis godefrida*
ear's Macaw *Anodorhynchus leari*
aucous Macaw *Anodorhynchus glaucus*
ix's Macaw *Cyanopsitta spixii*
rey-breasted Parakeet *Pyrrhura griseipectus*
ernambuco Pygmy-owl *Glaucidium mooreorum*
aempfer's Woodpecker *Celeus obrieni*
raripe Manakin *Antilophia bokermanni*
nglet Calyptura *Calyptura cristata*
inas Gerais Tyrannulet *Phylloscartes roquettei*
aempfer's Tody-tyrant *Hemitriccus kaempferi*
o de Janeiro Antwren *Myrmotherula fluminensis*
lagoas Antwren *Myrmotherula snowi*
estinga Antwren *Formicivora littoralis*
resemann's Bristlefront *Merulaxis stresemanni*
ahia Tapaculo *Scytalopus psychopompus*
lagoas Foliage-gleaner *Philydor novaesi*
ooded Seedeater *Sporophila melanops*
ne-billed Tanager *Conothraupis mesoleuca*
herry-throated Tanager *Nemosia rourei*

runei
hristmas Frigatebird *Fregata andrewsi*

ulgaria
ender-billed Curlew *Numenius tenuirostris*

ambodia
hite-shouldered Ibis *Pseudibis davisoni*
iant Ibis *Thaumatibis gigantea*
hristmas Frigatebird *Fregata andrewsi*
hite-rumped Vulture *Gyps bengalensis*
ender-billed Vulture *Gyps tenuirostris*
ed-headed Vulture *Sarcogyps calvus*
engal Florican *Houbaropsis bengalensis*

anada
kimo Curlew *Numenius borealis*
ttlitz's Murrelet *Brachyramphus brevirostris*

hile
natham Albatross *Thalassarche eremita*
skimo Curlew *Numenius borealis*
an Fernandez Firecrown *Sephanoides fernandensis*
lasafuera Rayadito *Aphrastura masafuerae*

hina
rested Shelduck *Tadorna cristata*
hite-shouldered Ibis *Pseudibis davisoni*
hristmas Frigatebird *Fregata andrewsi*
ed-headed Vulture *Sarcogyps calvus*
berian Crane *Grus leucogeranus*
oon-billed Sandpiper *Eurynorhynchus pygmeus*
ninese Crested Tern *Sterna bernsteini*
ue-crowned Laughingthrush *Garrulax courtoisi*

olombia
ue-billed Curassow *Crax alberti*
aved Albatross *Phoebastria irrorata*
alapagos Petrel *Pterodroma phaeopygia*
ellow-eared Parrot *Ognorhynchus icterotis*

Indigo-winged Parrot *Hapalopsittaca fuertesi*
Sapphire-bellied Hummingbird *Lepidopyga lilliae*
Chestnut-b. Hummingbird *Amazilia castaneiventris*
Dusky Starfrontlet *Coeligena orina*
Turquoise-throated Puffleg *Eriocnemis godini*
Colourful Puffleg *Eriocnemis mirabilis*
Niceforo's Wren *Thryothorus nicefori*
Munchique Wood-wren *Henicorhina negreti*

Comoros
Anjouan Scops-owl *Otus capnodes*
Moheli Scops-owl *Otus moheliensis*
Grand Comoro Scops-owl *Otus pauliani*

Cook Islands
Chatham Albatross *Thalassarche eremita*

Costa Rica
Galapagos Petrel *Pterodroma phaeopygia*

Croatia
Slender-billed Curlew *Numenius tenuirostris*

Cuba
Cuban Kite *Chondrohierax wilsonii*
Ivory-billed Woodpecker *Campephilus principalis*
Bachman's Warbler *Vermivora bachmanii*

Djibouti
Djibouti Francolin *Francolinus ochropectus*

Dominican Republic
Ridgway's Hawk *Buteo ridgwayi*

Ecuador
Waved Albatross *Phoebastria irrorata*
Galapagos Petrel *Pterodroma phaeopygia*
Yellow-eared Parrot *Ognorhynchus icterotis*
Black-breasted Puffleg *Eriocnemis nigrivestis*
Turquoise-throated Puffleg *Eriocnemis godini*
Floreana Mockingbird *Nesomimus trifasciatus*
Mangrove Finch *Camarhynchus heliobates*
Pale-headed Brush-finch *Atlapetes pallidiceps*

El Salvador
Galapagos Petrel *Pterodroma phaeopygia*

Eritrea
Northern Bald Ibis *Geronticus eremita*
Sociable Lapwing *Vanellus gregarius*

Ethiopia
Northern Bald Ibis *Geronticus eremita*

Fiji
Fiji Petrel *Pseudobulweria macgillivrayi*
Red-throated Lorikeet *Charmosyna amabilis*

France
Balearic Shearwater *Puffinus mauretanicus*

French Southern Territories
Amsterdam Albatross *Diomedea amsterdamensis*

French Polynesia
Chatham Albatross *Thalassarche eremita*
Polynesian Ground-dove *Gallicolumba erythroptera*
Tuamotu Kingfisher *Todiramphus gambieri*
Tahiti Monarch *Pomarea nigra*
Fatuhiva Monarch *Pomarea whitneyi*

New Caledonia (to France)
Chatham Albatross *Thalassarche eremita*
New Caledonian Rail *Gallirallus lafresnayanus*
New Caledonian Lorikeet *Charmosyna diadema*
New Caledonian Owlet-nightjar *Aegotheles savesi*

Wallis and Futuna Islands (to France)
Chatham Albatross *Thalassarche eremita*

Greece
Slender-billed Curlew *Numenius tenuirostris*

Grenada
Grenada Dove *Leptotila wellsi*

Guatemala
Galapagos Petrel *Pterodroma phaeopygia*

Haiti
Ridgway's Hawk *Buteo ridgwayi*

Honduras
Honduran Emerald *Amazilia luciae*

Hong Kong
Christmas Frigatebird *Fregata andrewsi*
Spoon-billed Sandpiper *Eurynorhynchus pygmeus*

Hungary
Slender-billed Curlew *Numenius tenuirostris*

India
Himalayan Quail *Ophrysia superciliosa*
Pink-headed Duck *Rhodonessa caryophyllacea*
White-bellied Heron *Ardea insignis*
White-rumped Vulture *Gyps bengalensis*
Indian Vulture *Gyps indicus*
Slender-billed Vulture *Gyps tenuirostris*
Red-headed Vulture *Sarcogyps calvus*
Bengal Florican *Houbaropsis bengalensis*
Siberian Crane *Grus leucogeranus*
Sociable Lapwing *Vanellus gregarius*
Spoon-billed Sandpiper *Eurynorhynchus pygmeus*
Jerdon's Courser *Rhinoptilus bitorquatus*
Forest Owlet *Heteroglaux blewitti*

Indonesia
White-shouldered Ibis *Pseudibis davisoni*
Christmas Frigatebird *Fregata andrewsi*
Javan Lapwing *Vanellus macropterus*
Chinese Crested Tern *Sterna bernsteini*
Silvery Wood-pigeon *Columba argentina*
Yellow-crested Cockatoo *Cacatua sulphurea*

Blue-fronted Lorikeet *Charmosyna toxopei*
Sumatran Ground-cuckoo *Carpococcyx viridis*
Siau Scops-owl *Otus siaoensis*
Sangihe Shrike-thrush *Colluricincla sanghirensis*
Caerulean Paradise-flycatcher *Eutrichomyias rowleyi*
Black-chinned Monarch *Monarcha boanensis*
Banggai Crow *Corvus unicolor*
Sangihe White-eye *Zosterops nehrkorni*
Bali Starling *Leucopsar rothschildi*
Rueck's Blue-flycatcher *Cyornis ruckii*

Islamic Republic of Iran
White-rumped Vulture *Gyps bengalensis*
Siberian Crane *Grus leucogeranus*
Sociable Lapwing *Vanellus gregarius*
Slender-billed Curlew *Numenius tenuirostris*

Iraq
Northern Bald Ibis *Geronticus eremita*
Sociable Lapwing *Vanellus gregarius*
Slender-billed Curlew *Numenius tenuirostris*

Ireland
Balearic Shearwater *Puffinus mauretanicus*

Jamaica
Jamaica Petrel *Pterodroma caribbaea*
Jamaican Pauraque *Siphonorhis americana*

Japan
Spoon-billed Sandpiper *Eurynorhynchus pygmeus*
Kittlitz's Murrelet *Brachyramphus brevirostris*
Okinawa Woodpecker *Dendrocopos noguchii*

Kazakhstan
Siberian Crane *Grus leucogeranus*
Sociable Lapwing *Vanellus gregarius*
Slender-billed Curlew *Numenius tenuirostris*

Kenya
Taita Apalis *Apalis fuscigularis*
Taita Thrush *Turdus helleri*

Kyrgyzstan
Sociable Lapwing *Vanellus gregarius*
Slender-billed Curlew *Numenius tenuirostris*

Laos
White-shouldered Ibis *Pseudibis davisoni*
Giant Ibis *Thaumatibis gigantea*
White-rumped Vulture *Gyps bengalensis*
Slender-billed Vulture *Gyps tenuirostris*
Red-headed Vulture *Sarcogyps calvus*

Liberia
Liberian Greenbul *Phyllastrephus leucolepis*

Libya
Slender-billed Curlew *Numenius tenuirostris*

he Former Yugoslav Republic f Macedonia
ender-billed Curlew *Numenius tenuirostris*

Madagascar
adagascar Pochard *Aythya innotata*
laotra Grebe *Tachybaptus rufolavatus*
adagascar Fish-eagle *Haliaeetus vociferoides*

Malaysia
hristmas Frigatebird *Fregata andrewsi*
ed-headed Vulture *Sarcogyps calvus*
oon-billed Sandpiper *Eurynorhynchus pygmeus*
inese Crested Tern *Sterna bernsteini*
lvery Wood-pigeon *Columba argentina*

Mauritania
orthern Bald Ibis *Geronticus eremita*

Mauritius
auritius Olive White-eye *Zosterops chloronothus*
auritius Fody *Foudia rubra*

Mediterranean and Black Sea
alearic Shearwater *Puffinus mauretanicus*

Mexico
alapagos Petrel *Pterodroma phaeopygia*
wnsend's Shearwater *Puffinus auricularis*
uadalupe Storm-petrel *Oceanodroma macrodactyla*
ort-crested Coquette *Lophornis brachylophus*
perial Woodpecker *Campephilus imperialis*
ocorro Mockingbird *Mimus graysoni*
ozumel Thrasher *Toxostoma guttatum*
elding's Yellowthroat *Geothlypis beldingi*

ederated States of Micronesia
uichuk White-eye *Rukia ruki*
ohnpei Starling *Aplonis pelzelni*

Mongolia
berian Crane *Grus leucogeranus*

Montserrat (to UK)
ontserrat Oriole *Icterus oberi*

Morocco
alearic Shearwater *Puffinus mauretanicus*
orthern Bald Ibis *Geronticus eremita*
ender-billed Curlew *Numenius tenuirostris*

Mozambique
ong-billed Tailorbird *Apalis moreaui*

Myanmar
nk-headed Duck *Rhodonessa caryophyllacea*
hite-shouldered Ibis *Pseudibis davisoni*
hite-bellied Heron *Ardea insignis*
hite-rumped Vulture *Gyps bengalensis*
ender-billed Vulture *Gyps tenuirostris*
ed-headed Vulture *Sarcogyps calvus*
oon-billed Sandpiper *Eurynorhynchus pygmeus*

Namibia
Tristan Albatross *Diomedea dabbenena*

Nepal
White-rumped Vulture *Gyps bengalensis*
Slender-billed Vulture *Gyps tenuirostris*
Red-headed Vulture *Sarcogyps calvus*
Bengal Florican *Houbaropsis bengalensis*

New Zealand
Campbell Islands Teal *Anas nesiotis*
Chatham Albatross *Thalassarche eremita*
Magenta Petrel *Pterodroma magentae*
Chatham Petrel *Pterodroma axillaris*
New Zealand Storm-petrel *Oceanites maorianus*
Chatham Islands Shag *Phalacrocorax onslowi*
Black Stilt *Himantopus novaezelandiae*
Kakapo *Strigops habroptila*
Malherbe's Parakeet *Cyanoramphus malherbi*

Niue (to New Zealand)
Chatham Albatross *Thalassarche eremita*

Nicaragua
Galapagos Petrel *Pterodroma phaeopygia*

North Korea
Spoon-billed Sandpiper *Eurynorhynchus pygmeus*

Northeast Atlantic
Balearic Shearwater *Puffinus mauretanicus*

Northern Mariana Islands (to USA)
Townsend's Shearwater *Puffinus auricularis*
Mariana Crow *Corvus kubaryi*
Rota Bridled White-eye *Zosterops rotensis*
Golden White-eye *Cleptornis marchei*

Oman
Sociable Lapwing *Vanellus gregarius*
Slender-billed Curlew *Numenius tenuirostris*

Pakistan
White-rumped Vulture *Gyps bengalensis*
Indian Vulture *Gyps indicus*
Siberian Crane *Grus leucogeranus*
Sociable Lapwing *Vanellus gregarius*

Panama
Galapagos Petrel *Pterodroma phaeopygia*

Papua New Guinea
Beck's Petrel *Pseudobulweria becki*

Paraguay
Brazilian Merganser *Mergus octosetaceus*
Purple-winged Ground-dove *Claravis godefrida*
Glaucous Macaw *Anodorhynchus glaucus*
Entre Rios Seedeater *Sporophila zelichi*

Peru
White-winged Guan *Penelope albipennis*

Waved Albatross *Phoebastria irrorata*
Chatham Albatross *Thalassarche eremita*
Galapagos Petrel *Pterodroma phaeopygia*
Junin Grebe *Podiceps taczanowskii*
Royal Cinclodes *Cinclodes aricomae*
Iquitos Gnatcatcher *Polioptila clementsi*

Philippines
Philippine Eagle *Pithecophaga jefferyi*
Spoon-billed Sandpiper *Eurynorhynchus pygmeus*
Chinese Crested Tern *Sterna bernsteini*
Mindoro Bleeding-heart *Gallicolumba platenae*
Negros Bleeding-heart *Gallicolumba keayi*
Sulu Bleeding-heart *Gallicolumba menagei*
Negros Fruit-dove *Ptilinopus arcanus*
Philippine Cockatoo *Cacatua haematuropygia*
Black-hooded Coucal *Centropus steerii*
Sulu Hornbill *Anthracoceros montani*
Rufous-headed Hornbill *Aceros waldeni*
Isabela Oriole *Oriolus isabellae*
Cebu Flowerpecker *Dicaeum quadricolor*

Pitcairn Islands (to UK)
Chatham Albatross *Thalassarche eremita*

Portugal
Balearic Shearwater *Puffinus mauretanicus*
Azores Bullfinch *Pyrrhula murina*

Cape Verde
Raso Lark *Alauda razae*

Puerto Rico (to USA)
Puerto Rican Amazon *Amazona vittata*
Puerto Rican Nightjar *Caprimulgus noctitherus*

Réunion (to France)
Mascarene Petrel *Pseudobulweria aterrima*
Réunion Cuckoo-shrike *Coracina tenuirostris*

Romania
Slender-billed Curlew *Numenius tenuirostris*

Russia
Crested Shelduck *Tadorna cristata*
Siberian Crane *Grus leucogeranus*
Spoon-billed Sandpiper *Eurynorhynchus pygmeus*
Kittlitz's Murrelet *Brachyramphus brevirostris*
Sociable Lapwing *Vanellus gregarius*
Slender-billed Curlew *Numenius tenuirostris*

Samoa
Samoan Moorhen *Gallinula pacifica*

Sâo Tomé e Principe
Dwarf Olive Ibis *Bostrychia bocagei*
Sao Tome Fiscal *Lanius newtoni*
Sao Tome Grosbeak *Neospiza concolor*

Saudi Arabia
Northern Bald Ibis *Geronticus eremita*
Sociable Lapwing *Vanellus gregarius*
Slender-billed Curlew *Numenius tenuirostris*

Serbia and Montenegro
Slender-billed Curlew *Numenius tenuirostris*

Seychelles
Seychelles Paradise-flycatcher *Terpsiphone corvina*

Singapore
Christmas Frigatebird *Fregata andrewsi*
Spoon-billed Sandpiper *Eurynorhynchus pygmeus*

Solomon Islands
Beck's Petrel *Pseudobulweria becki*
Makira Moorhen *Gallinula silvestris*

Somalia
Bulo Burti Boubou *Laniarius liberatus*
Archer's Lark *Heteromirafra archeri*

South Africa
Tristan Albatross *Diomedea dabbenena*

South Korea
Crested Shelduck *Tadorna cristata*
Siberian Crane *Grus leucogeranus*
Spoon-billed Sandpiper *Eurynorhynchus pygmeus*

Spain
Balearic Shearwater *Puffinus mauretanicus*

Sri Lanka
Christmas Frigatebird *Fregata andrewsi*
Spoon-billed Sandpiper *Eurynorhynchus pygmeus*

St Lucia
Semper's Warbler *Leucopeza semperi*

Sudan
Sociable Lapwing *Vanellus gregarius*

Syria
Northern Bald Ibis *Geronticus eremita*
Sociable Lapwing *Vanellus gregarius*

Taiwan
Spoon-billed Sandpiper *Eurynorhynchus pygmeus*
Chinese Crested Tern *Sterna bernsteini*

Tajikistan
Sociable Lapwing *Vanellus gregarius*

Tanzania
Uluguru Bush-shrike *Malaconotus alius*
Long-billed Tailorbird *Apalis moreaui*

Thailand
Christmas Frigatebird *Fregata andrewsi*
White-rumped Vulture *Gyps bengalensis*
Red-headed Vulture *Sarcogyps calvus*
Spoon-billed Sandpiper *Eurynorhynchus pygmeus*
Chinese Crested Tern *Sterna bernsteini*
White-eyed River-martin *Eurochelidon sirintarae*

Timor-Leste
Christmas Frigatebird *Fregata andrewsi*
Yellow-crested Cockatoo *Cacatua sulphurea*

Trinidad and Tobago
Trinidad Piping-guan *Pipile pipile*

Tunisia
Slender-billed Curlew *Numenius tenuirostris*

Turkey
Northern Bald Ibis *Geronticus eremita*
Sociable Lapwing *Vanellus gregarius*
Slender-billed Curlew *Numenius tenuirostris*

Turkmenistan
Siberian Crane *Grus leucogeranus*
Sociable Lapwing *Vanellus gregarius*
Slender-billed Curlew *Numenius tenuirostris*

Ukraine
Slender-billed Curlew *Numenius tenuirostris*

United Kingdom
Balearic Shearwater *Puffinus mauretanicus*

Gibraltar (to UK)
Balearic Shearwater *Puffinus mauretanicus*

St Helena (to UK)
St Helena Plover *Charadrius sanctaehelenae*
Tristan Albatross *Diomedea dabbenena*
Gough Bunting *Rowettia goughensis*

Uruguay
Tristan Albatross *Diomedea dabbenena*
Glaucous Macaw *Anodorhynchus glaucus*
Entre Rios Seedeater *Sporophila zelichi*

USA
Laysan Duck *Anas laysanensis*
California Condor *Gymnogyps californianus*
Eskimo Curlew *Numenius borealis*
Kittlitz's Murrelet *Brachyramphus brevirostris*

Ivory-billed Woodpecker *Campephilus principalis*
Millerbird *Acrocephalus familiaris*
Olomao *Myadestes lanaiensis*
Puaiohi *Myadestes palmeri*
Nihoa Finch *Telespiza ultima*
Ou *Psittirostra psittacea*
Maui Parrotbill *Pseudonestor xanthophrys*
Nukupuu *Hemignathus lucidus*
Akikiki *Oreomystis bairdi*
Oahu Alauahio *Paroreomyza maculata*
Akohekohe *Palmeria dolei*
Poo-uli *Melamprosops phaeosoma*
Bachman's Warbler *Vermivora bachmanii*
Akekee *Loxops caeruleiostris*

American Samoa
Chatham Albatross *Thalassarche eremita*

Guam (to USA)
Townsend's Shearwater *Puffinus auricularis*
Mariana Crow *Corvus kubaryi*

Northern Mariana Islands (to USA)
Mariana Crow *Corvus kubaryi*

United States Minor Outlying Islands (to USA)
Townsend's Shearwater *Puffinus auricularis*

Uzbekistan
Sociable Lapwing *Vanellus gregarius*
Slender-billed Curlew *Numenius tenuirostris*

Venezuela
Tachira Antpitta *Grallaria chthonia*
Carrizal Seedeater *Amaurospiza carrizalensis*

Vietnam
White-shouldered Ibis *Pseudibis davisoni*
White-rumped Vulture Gyps bengalensis
Red-headed Vulture *Sarcogyps calvus*
Bengal Florican *Houbaropsis bengalensis*
Spoon-billed Sandpiper *Eurynorhynchus pygmeus*

Yemen
Northern Bald Ibis *Geronticus eremita*
Slender-billed Curlew *Numenius tenuirostris*

Red-headed Vulture Photo: © René Pop

Checklist

- [ ] White-winged Guan *Penelope albipennis*
- [ ] Trinidad Piping-guan *Pipile pipile*
- [ ] Blue-billed Curassow *Crax alberti*
- [ ] Djibouti Francolin *Francolinus ochropectus*
- [ ] Himalayan Quail *Ophrysia superciliosa*
- [ ] Crested Shelduck *Tadorna cristata*
- [ ] Laysan Duck *Anas laysanensis*
- [ ] Campbell Islands Teal *Anas nesiotis*
- [ ] Pink-headed Duck *Rhodonessa caryophyllacea*
- [ ] Madagascar Pochard *Aythya innotata*
- [ ] Brazilian Merganser *Mergus octosetaceus*
- [ ] Amsterdam Albatross *Diomedea amsterdamensis*
- [ ] Tristan Albatross *Diomedea dabbenena*
- [ ] Waved Albatross *Phoebastria irrorata*
- [ ] Chatham Albatross *Thalassarche eremita*
- [ ] Galapagos Petrel *Pterodroma phaeopygia*
- [ ] Jamaica Petrel *Pterodroma caribbaea*
- [ ] Magenta Petrel *Pterodroma magentae*
- [ ] Chatham Petrel *Pterodroma axillaris*
- [ ] Fiji Petrel *Pseudobulweria macgillivrayi*
- [ ] Beck's Petrel *Pseudobulweria becki*
- [ ] Mascarene Petrel *Pseudobulweria aterrima*
- [ ] Balearic Shearwater *Puffinus mauretanicus*
- [ ] Townsend's Shearwater *Puffinus auricularis*
- [ ] New Zealand Storm-petrel *Oceanites maorianus*
- [ ] Guadalupe Storm-petrel *Oceanodroma macrodactyla*
- [ ] Alaotra Grebe *Tachybaptus rufolavatus*
- [ ] Junin Grebe *Podiceps taczanowskii*
- [ ] White-bellied Heron *Ardea insignis*
- [ ] White-shouldered Ibis *Pseudibis davisoni*
- [ ] Giant Ibis *Thaumatibis gigantea*
- [ ] Northern Bald Ibis *Geronticus eremita*
- [ ] Dwarf Olive Ibis *Bostrychia bocagei*
- [ ] Christmas Island Frigatebird *Fregata andrewsi*
- [ ] Chatham Islands Shag *Phalacrocorax onslowi*
- [ ] California Condor *Gymnogyps californianus*
- [ ] White-collared Kite *Leptodon forbesi*
- [ ] Cuban Kite *Chondrohierax wilsonii*
- [ ] Madagascar Fish-eagle *Haliaeetus vociferoides*
- [ ] White-rumped Vulture *Gyps bengalensis*
- [ ] Indian Vulture *Gyps indicus*
- [ ] Slender-billed Vulture *Gyps tenuirostris*
- [ ] Red-headed Vulture *Sarcogyps calvus*
- [ ] Ridgway's Hawk *Buteo ridgwayi*
- [ ] Philippine Eagle *Pithecophaga jefferyi*

- [ ] Bengal Florican *Houbaropsis bengalensis*
- [ ] New Caledonian Rail *Gallirallus lafresnayanus*
- [ ] Samoan Moorhen *Gallinula pacifica*
- [ ] Makira Moorhen *Gallinula silvestris*
- [ ] Siberian Crane *Grus leucogeranus*
- [ ] Black Stilt *Himantopus novaezelandiae*
- [ ] Javan Lapwing *Vanellus macropterus*
- [ ] Sociable Lapwing *Vanellus gregarius*
- [ ] St Helena Plover *Charadrius sanctaehelenae*
- [ ] Eskimo Curlew *Numenius borealis*
- [ ] Slender-billed Curlew *Numenius tenuirostris*
- [ ] Spoon-billed Sandpiper *Eurynorhynchus pygmeus*
- [ ] Jerdon's Courser *Rhinoptilus bitorquatus*
- [ ] Chinese Crested Tern *Sterna bernsteini*
- [ ] Kittlitz's Murrelet *Brachyramphus brevirostris*
- [ ] Silvery Wood-pigeon *Columba argentina*
- [ ] Blue-eyed Ground-dove *Columbina cyanopis*
- [ ] Purple-winged Ground-dove *Claravis godefrida*
- [ ] Grenada Dove *Leptotila wellsi*
- [ ] Mindoro Bleeding-heart *Gallicolumba platenae*
- [ ] Negros Bleeding-heart *Gallicolumba keayi*
- [ ] Sulu Bleeding-heart *Gallicolumba menagei*
- [ ] Polynesian Ground-dove *Gallicolumba erythroptera*
- [ ] Negros Fruit-dove *Ptilinopus arcanus*
- [ ] Kakapo *Strigops habroptila*
- [ ] Yellow-crested Cockatoo *Cacatua sulphurea*
- [ ] Philippine Cockatoo *Cacatua haematuropygia*
- [ ] Blue-fronted Lorikeet *Charmosyna toxopei*
- [ ] New Caledonian Lorikeet *Charmosyna diadema*
- [ ] Red-throated Lorikeet *Charmosyna amabilis*
- [ ] Malherbe's Parakeet *Cyanoramphus malherbi*
- [ ] Orange-bellied Parrot *Neophema chrysogaster*
- [ ] Night Parrot *Pezoporus occidentalis*
- [ ] Lear's Macaw *Anodorhynchus leari*
- [ ] Glaucous Macaw *Anodorhynchus glaucus*
- [ ] Spix's Macaw *Cyanopsitta spixii*
- [ ] Blue-throated Macaw *Ara glaucogularis*
- [ ] Yellow-eared Parrot *Ognorhynchus icterotis*
- [ ] Grey-breasted Parakeet *Pyrrhura griseipectus*
- [ ] Indigo-winged Parrot *Hapalopsittaca fuertesi*
- [ ] Puerto Rican Amazon *Amazona vittata*
- [ ] Sumatran Ground-cuckoo *Carpococcyx viridis*
- [ ] Black-hooded Coucal *Centropus steerii*
- [ ] Siau Scops-owl *Otus siaoensis*
- [ ] Anjouan Scops-owl *Otus capnodes*

Moheli Scops-owl *Otus moheliensis*

Grand Comoro Scops-owl *Otus pauliani*

Pernambuco Pygmy-owl *Glaucidium mooreorum*

Forest Owlet *Heteroglaux blewitti*

Jamaican Pauraque *Siphonorhis americana*

Puerto Rican Nightjar *Caprimulgus noctitherus*

New Caledonian Owlet-nightjar *Aegotheles savesi*

Short-crested Coquette *Lophornis brachylophus*

Sapphire-bellied Hummingbird *Lepidopyga lilliae*

Honduran Emerald *Amazilia luciae*

Chestnut-bellied Hummingbird *Amazilia castaneiventris*

Dusky Starfrontlet *Coeligena orina*

Juan Fernandez Firecrown *Sephanoides fernandensis*

Black-breasted Puffleg *Eriocnemis nigrivestis*

Turquoise-throated Puffleg *Eriocnemis godini*

Colourful Puffleg *Eriocnemis mirabilis*

Tuamotu Kingfisher *Todiramphus gambieri*

Sulu Hornbill *Anthracoceros montani*

Rufous-headed Hornbill *Aceros waldeni*

Okinawa Woodpecker *Dendrocopos noguchii*

Imperial Woodpecker *Campephilus imperialis*

Ivory-billed Woodpecker *Campephilus principalis*

Kaempfer´s Woodpecker *Celeus obrieni*

Araripe Manakin *Antilophia bokermanni*

Kinglet Calyptura *Calyptura cristata*

Minas Gerais Tyrannulet *Phylloscartes roquettei*

Kaempfer's Tody-tyrant *Hemitriccus kaempferi*

Rio de Janeiro Antwren *Myrmotherula fluminensis*

Alagoas Antwren *Myrmotherula snowi*

Restinga Antwren *Formicivora littoralis*

Stresemann's Bristlefront *Merulaxis stresemanni*

Bahia Tapaculo *Scytalopus psychopompus*

Royal Cinclodes *Cinclodes aricomae*

Tachira Antpitta *Grallaria chthonia*

Masafuera Rayadito *Aphrastura masafuerae*

Alagoas Foliage-gleaner *Philydor novaesi*

Uluguru Bush-shrike *Malaconotus alius*

Bulo Burti Boubou *Laniarius liberatus*

Réunion Cuckoo-shrike *Coracina newtoni*

Sao Tome Fiscal *Lanius newtoni*

Isabela Oriole *Oriolus isabellae*

Sangihe Shrike-thrush *Colluricincla sanghirensis*

Caerulean Paradise-flycatcher *Eutrichomyias rowleyi*

Seychelles Paradise-flycatcher *Terpsiphone corvina*

Tahiti Monarch *Pomarea nigra*

Fatuhiva Monarch *Pomarea whitneyi*

Black-chinned Monarch *Monarcha boanensis*

Banggai Crow *Corvus unicolor*

Mariana Crow *Corvus kubaryi*

White-eyed River-martin *Eurochelidon sirintarae*

☐ Archer's Lark *Heteromirafra archeri*

☐ Raso Lark *Alauda razae*

☐ Taita Apalis *Apalis fuscigularis*

☐ Long-billed Tailorbird *Apalis moreaui*

☐ Liberian Greenbul *Phyllastrephus leucolepis*

☐ Millerbird *Acrocephalus familiaris*

☐ Blue-crowned Laughingthrush *Garrulax courtoisi*

☐ Mauritius Olive White-eye *Zosterops chloronothus*

☐ Rota Bridled White-eye *Zosterops rotensis*

☐ Sangihe White-eye *Zosterops nehrkorni*

☐ White-chested White-eye *Zosterops albogularis*

☐ Faichuk White-eye *Rukia ruki*

☐ Golden White-eye *Cleptornis marchei*

☐ Niceforo's Wren *Thryothorus nicefori*

☐ Munchique Wood-Wren *Henicorhina negreti*

☐ Iquitos Gnatcatcher *Polioptila clementsi*

☐ Socorro Mockingbird *Mimus graysoni*

☐ Floreana Mockingbird *Nesomimus trifasciatus*

☐ Cozumel Thrasher *Toxostoma guttatum*

☐ Pohnpei Starling *Aplonis pelzelni*

☐ Bali Starling *Leucopsar rothschildi*

☐ Olomao *Myadestes lanaiensis*

☐ Puaiohi *Myadestes palmeri*

☐ Taita Thrush *Turdus helleri*

☐ Rueck's Blue-flycatcher *Cyornis ruckii*

☐ Cebu Flowerpecker *Dicaeum quadricolor*

☐ Mauritius Fody *Foudia rubra*

☐ Sao Tome Grosbeak *Neospiza concolor*

☐ Azores Bullfinch *Pyrrhula murina*

☐ Nihoa Finch *Telespiza ultima*

☐ Ou *Psittirostra psittacea*

☐ Maui Parrotbill *Pseudonestor xanthophrys*

☐ Nukupuu *Hemignathus lucidus*

☐ Akikiki *Oreomystis bairdi*

☐ Oahu Alauahio *Paroreomyza maculata*

☐ Akohekohe *Palmeria dolei*

☐ Akekee *Loxops caeruleirostris*

☐ Poo-uli *Melamprosops phaeosoma*

☐ Bachman's Warbler *Vermivora bachmanii*

☐ Belding's Yellowthroat *Geothlypis beldingi*

☐ Semper's Warbler *Leucopeza semperi*

☐ Montserrat Oriole *Icterus oberi*

☐ Gough Bunting *Rowettia goughensis*

☐ Hooded Seedeater *Sporophila melanops*

☐ Entre Rios Seedeater *Sporophila zelichi*

☐ Carrizal Blue-black Seedeater *Amaurospiza carrizalensis*

☐ Mangrove Finch *Camarhynchus heliobates*

☐ Pale-headed Brush-finch *Atlapetes pallidiceps*

☐ Cone-billed Tanager *Conothraupis mesoleuca*

☐ Cherry-throated Tanager *Nemosia rourei*

INDEX